BEHIND SUNRISE

Elsabet Ademe

BEHIND SUNRISE
Copyright © 2020 by Elsabet Ademe
All Rights Reserved

This is a work of nonfiction. Names, characters, businesses, places, events, locales, and incidents have been changed to protect the privacy of those involved.

Publisher: Absolute Author Publishing House
Editor: Dr. Melissa
Cover Designer: Rebeca @ Rebecacovers

LIBRARY OF CONGRESS CATALOGUE IN-PUBLICATION-DATA

BEHIND SUNRISE/Elsabet Ademe

   p. cm.

ISBN: 978-1-64953-042-4

   1. Nonfiction 2. Suspense 3. Thriller

ACKNOWLEDGMENT

This book wouldn't have come about without the help of many people.

First, I want to thank my God for everything: for protection, for inspiration, for sustenance, and joy.

I want to thank my other guiding light, especially my dear mother, Ager Takele. I wouldn't be here today without you, and any strength I have is because of the unconditional love and support you gave me. You are my hero.

To my father, Alubel Ademe, from the bottom of my heart, I thank you for teaching me to be myself.

And to my beautiful daughter, Yohanna Tesfalem, at all times, you are my inspiration. Thank you for your sweet words and for understanding me even at so young an age.

I'd like to thank my beloved sister Abby Ademe for continually supporting my dream.

And speaking of support, I owe a never-ending parade of thank you's to my dear friend and mentor Solomon Belay, for all your positivity and for helping me truly believe that I'm capable of doing anything I want to do.

Also, I want to offer my sincere gratitude to Negest Legesse for your uplifting words and encouragement.

Thanks to my tutor, teacher, and editor, Tim Hildebrand, for his patience and dedication. Long hours were spent together combing through the manuscript, cleaning it up, and searching for the most imaginative language.

Along those same lines, thank you to my final editor, Dr. Melissa Caudle, for the final editing and formatting this book so beautifully.

Thanks, Rebeca @Rebecacovers, for the wonderful cover art.

Finally, there's a long list of friends and family that I want to thank properly, but I'm limited by space, so I'll just quickly throw out a huge blanket thank you to these wonderful people: Alemtsehay Wodajo, Mahlet Gebre, Tsiona Aimelak, Abel Haile, Elshaday Wanna, Elsabet A Alemu, Nate Steinberg, Benny Ayele, Jibril Hussen, Kaz Hailegabriel, Kuldip Korotan, Yemane Gebregziabher, Jenni Powell, Gordon McKey, Ros Gentle, Laurel Zukowski, Christopher Chambers, my siblings, Tsega Tekle Haimanot, Benyam Geletu Oda, Fortuna Tumegzi, Tedros Mesfin, Tesfu Temelso or (Wedi Mlashey) and Filimon Gebermikael. You all know the important roles you've played in my life and work, and I love and appreciate each one of you.

TABLE OF CONTENTS

Introduction

S arah was born in Bahir Dar, Ethiopia. Bahir Dar is one of the most beautiful tourist destinations in Ethiopia. The streets have many trees, and the city is clean. Furthermore, the city is gifted with the Blue Nile and Lake Tana, where a beautiful church is located on an island. Sarah always likes going to the Nile; it's ten minutes walking distance from her home. Sarah is the second-born in her family, and she has four younger sisters and five brothers. Her favorite younger sister, Meron, likes singing, one of the other sisters loves to run, and the third wants to be a doctor. Sarah and Meron are very close; they play together, go to school together, and spend all of their time together.

Sarah likes to help her siblings, whether it's doing their homework or fixing their hair. Sarah is an extraordinarily, strong and determined girl. Her family likes her character, and they always say, "She will be successful at whatever she sets her mind to."

The neighbors also love Sarah because she likes to entertain; people like to be around her. She tells jokes and makes them laugh.

Sometimes Sarah is serious, but people still think she is joking. This makes her feel bad because nobody takes her seriously. She says to herself, "If I were dying, people would think that I was joking." She continually promises herself not to play around too much, although she can't change her nature.

When Sarah was six years old, she loved watching movies with Meron. When the film was done, Sarah got up from the couch and stood in front of the television and called out to her mom. Her mother was in the kitchen, washing dishes with the maid. "Mom, it's time for my show. Come on! Please!"

"Okay, sweetheart, we are coming," her mother, Tsehay, would reply.

As her family sat on the couch, Sarah and Meron tried their best to recreate the action of the film. When they finished, their family clapped for their performance.

Her father, Belay, asked her, "Darling, what do you want to be when you grow-up?"

Before Sarah spoke, Meron said, "She wants to be a Hollywood actress."

Sarah said, "That's right; one day, I will be there performing and acting."

"That's great," her father replied, "but first, you must focus on your school."

"Okay, I will," she said. "But I do want to be an actress."

Sarah continually thinks about how to make her dreams come true. Ethiopia doesn't have international acting for film schools, and she can't go to the USA because it's too far away. She doesn't want to leave her family, especially Meron; she doesn't even want to think about her life without her sister. Meron is not only her sister but also her best friend. Sometimes when she sleeps, she dreams about leaving her family, getting lost on the road, and feeling hungry. Sarah tells her mom, "Mom, I always have this dream."

"Sweetie, that's not a dream. That's what you're thinking about all the time."

"Ma, can I sleep with you tonight? I'm scared."

"Yes, baby."

Still, Sarah has that dream.

One day she decided to stop obsessing about going to the USA and go to church to pray. She grew up with a strong religious structure in her family, and together they always went to church every Sunday. She always asks God, "What is my destiny? Why am I on this earth? What am I doing? What is life about?" But she never gets an answer.

Sarah is a good student in class. She does her homework on time, comes to school prepared, and she participates in the class. Her teachers always give her good feedback. One of her teachers always calls her "the determined girl," because if she doesn't get what she wants, no matter how long it takes, she will make it happen!

Sarah thinks that when people start giving up, they start losing their faith, and they can't face the real world. Giving up is not an option. If we give up, we do not know how close we are to getting what we want. A lot of her friends look up to her, and she encourages them. "If we can't change our country, nobody will. The young generation, we must work hard to make it happen. Why do other countries call Ethiopia poor? I don't think so. Financial status doesn't make us poor. If we are mentally rich, we can change anything."

Chapter One

Sarah is sleeping on the bed when her mother, Tsehay, burst into her bedroom. Tsehay calls, "Sarah, wake-up! Breakfast is getting cold!"

With her eyes closed, Sarah whispers, "Okay, Ma." For a bit, she stays on the bed, stretches her arms and her legs, and then opens her eyes. Finally, she rises and sits on the bed, placing her feet on the floor. She slowly stands and strolls to the window and opens it. She mumbles, "I wish I were the sun; I could give everyone light, and I would be so beautiful."

She stands at the window for a while and has an 'Oh, my God' moment – she had forgotten about breakfast. She opens the door, rushes to the living room, says good morning, and kisses her mom on the cheek, then her father, Belay, and finally, her siblings. Ethiopians always greet each other with a kiss. After Sarah finishes greeting everyone, she takes a seat for breakfast.

The table is full of food -- quanta fit-fit, chechebsa, and quinche. Tsehay put food on her children's plates.

Sarah exclaims, "Ma, we can serve ourselves. We are old enough."

Tsehay shoots back, "Yes, but you will always be my babies no matter how old you are."

"Dad, did you hear what Mom said?"

"Your mom is right. All children are always a baby in their own family."

"Okay, but I'm not a baby. I am sixteen-years-old, and I know what is right."

Meron makes fun of her, "Okay, old lady."

"Ah, oh, someone knows how to make a joke."

"Okay, we should pray," her father Belay says, "Sarah, give a prayer today."

"Okay."

She gets up and starts praying. When she finishes, everyone says, "Amen," and they start eating. Following custom, Sarah's father begins the meal by hand-feeding his wife, and the children follow suit, feeding each other.

Sarah has morning classes, and her driver takes her to school. The driver's phone rings and he reaches his right hand into his jacket pocket and grabs his phone to answer it, placing the call through the speaker. "Hello?"

A voice says, "It's me."

"Oh, my God! Where are you?"

"Finally, I made it to Italy with God."

"I'm glad to hear that! Sorry, I'm driving. I'll call you later. Is this your number?"

"Yes, it is."

The driver turns back to Sarah, "Sorry, it was my friend. I was worried about him."

"Why?"

"He went through the Sahara Desert to go to Italy."

"Isn't it hard to cross the desert?"

"It is, but it's the easiest way for a lot of people to get to Europe because they don't need a visa."

2

The car stops in front of the gate. Sarah is reading her book, she looks up, sees the gate, turns back to her book cover, puts it into her back bag, and closes it. Then, she reaches her right hand to open the car door. She places her feet on the ground, stands, turns back to the car, bends down, and grabs her bag throwing it over her left shoulder. While she closed the car door with her right hand, "Thanks," she says, closing the car door, "I'll see you later. Bye."

During school, Sarah starts thinking about all the people who are going to Italy. She wants to know more about it, but she doesn't know how to ask her driver. She worries that he might suspect she wants to leave and will tell her family. Sarah says to herself, "I can tell him it's for my friends. No? It's just for curiosity's sake. This is a good idea. Once I know more, I'll be able to go to Italy myself. Yay! But who will I go with? It will be hard by myself. On the other hand, other people are going. Maybe they go alone? I should ask him."

After school, Sarah walks out of the classroom and runs to the gate. She sees her driver has parked the car at the corner of the street. She walks to him, taking the bag from her shoulder, opens the car, throws the bag in, and enters the vehicle taking a comfortable seat. "Hey," she says with a smile.

"Hey."

She looks around, and she scratches her head with her left hand, and then she puts the window down with her right hand. She looks over the window at the blue water wave on the edge of the street. She turns back to her driver; he is silent, and he doesn't look at her. Then she turns back to the road and watches the wind sway trees. Her eyes glance back and forth between the road and the driver. She doesn't know what to say. After a few minutes, she mentions, "How's your day? You look tired."

As he tries to answer, she doesn't stop, "I can make you a nice coffee!"

"No, thanks," he says, "I'm fine. What is wrong with you today?"

"I'm fine. I'm great."

"Alright, Okay."

"Today, in geography class, we talked about the desert. It's hot! It has a lot of sand, and nothing grows there. Nobody lives there because it's dangerous."

"Yes, it is."

"But didn't you say that people crossing the Sahara Desert could get safely to Italy?"

"Ah, well, some people don't have a choice. So, they take the risk."

"But how do they get there? To Italy?"

He turns to her, and accusingly says, "Illegally."

She stares out the window, not sure what to say next. After a minute, she turns to him. "How illegal is it?"

"Very."

"How do they get across then?"

"There is a smuggler. They pay him a lot of money, and he helps them across."

"Oh." She is happy about getting the information, but on the other hand, she's worried about how to get the money for the smugglers. Sarah doesn't have money.

***

Later at home, Sarah sits next to her mother, Tsehay, and looks at her eyes, "Ma, can I ask you something?"

"Of course, you can, sweetheart."

"You know my desire to become an actress?"

"Yes, I know. You'll never let me forget, now will you?"

"Well, we don't have any international acting for film schools here." She hugs her mother and holds her hand, "But, if I go to Italy, I can go to acting school there."

Tsehay stares at her daughter for a moment, "What? Are you leaving us?"

"No, it's not like that. I will come back as soon as I finish my studies."

"How are you going to get there?"

4

"I have good information about how to get there by going to Sudan, and then into Libya, you can travel until you get to Italy. They say it's easy to get there."

Tsehay interrupts, "Stop thinking this." She puts her two hands on her head as her eyes widen. "How dare you think about this? It cannot happen."

"Okay, sorry, Ma. Can you try to guide me to get there, legally?"

Tsehay stares at her and is quiet for a while, and then says, "Let me think about it. I need to talk to your father."

Sarah thanks Tsehay, kisses her on the cheek, and goes to her room.

Later that night, Sarah sat on her bed with her legs folded on top of each other, reading a book and wearing short pink pants and a pink T-shirt.

When Tsehay walks in, she sits on the edge of the bed, reaching her right hand into her daughter's hair, massaging slowly for a minute and then says with a smile, "How's the studying?"

Sarah answers, "Great."

Tsehay looks at her daughter. "I talked to your father. And we asked all our friends how to get the visa. They said, 'the law in Italy changed, we can't get visas right now.' We will have to wait. Maybe one day it will change. But for now, you can't go."

"Ma, when is the law going to change?"

"I don't know, sweetie."

Sarah's face drops as she squeezes it before looking at her mom, shakes her head, and her eyes feel with tears, then she looks down. Her mom puts her two hands around her daughter firmly close to her daughter's chest, then kisses her on the forehead. Sarah's tears fall on her face. They hold for a while. Sarah moves her mother as she drops her hand. Sarah jumps from the bed, walks to the outside, and sits on the balcony. She wipes her face with her hand, but her tears still fall.

Over the next few weeks, Sarah thinks about how to get money. "If they can't get a visa, I should try another way by myself. Think,

Sarah, you are so smart!" Sarah stands, holding her hands together and closes her eyes. Then, she starts walking around her room. Finally, she sits on the floor until she gets the idea. She jumps up and shouts, "Yes! That's it!"

In the evening, Sarah walks to her family's grocery store and walks inside. "Hey," she says to the employees.

"Hey, Sarah," they respond.

Sarah sneaks to Belay's office. She turns around to check if it's safe to enter the office, but one of the employees walks over to her. The employee grabs a bag near the office and leaves, and Sarah sighs with relief. "Oh my God, that was close!" She slowly opens the door, looks around, and enters quickly, shutting it behind her. She walks to the safe, enters the password, and opens it. Inside, she sees the money bag; she moves swiftly, grabs it, and opens it slowly as her hands tremble, sweat forming across her brow. She puts her hand inside the bag, and snatches one bundle of money, one hundred Ethiopia birrs, and slowly places it in her purse. Carefully wiping off fingerprints, she sets the rest of the money into the safe. She closes the safe, and little by little, she opens the door, glances up and down the hallway, closes the door behind her, and walks to the exit. "Oh, I did it!"

Sarah returns home and heads straight to bed only to wake up in the middle of the night. The house is so quiet and dark. She turns on the light as she gets out of bed, walks to her closet, and collects some of her clothes, but her body starts shaking. She lays down on the floor and silently cries.

"What am I doing?" She whispers into the night. "I'm crazy, but I must leave this country if I want to be an actress. I wish there were an acting school here."

She finishes packing, then takes off her pajamas and grabs her jeans and sweater, dressing quickly. She clutches her small backpack that contains a T-shirt, pants, underwear, and bras. She picks up her handbag and slowly walks to the door. She says, "I'm sorry, Mom," but nobody hears her. She says to herself, "All of my family, sorry, I'm leaving without saying goodbye."

Her eyes flush with tears. *Am I selfish?* She opens the door, but it's too dark outside. Then she turns to see her home for the last time. "Oh, my God! I can't do this. It's impossible, how? How can I possibly leave my home?"

She stands at the door in the dark, becomes weak, and to her, it seems she remains stuck. Her breath shallows as she puts her backpack down and sits behind the closed door. Her tears fall as she rests her head down for a moment with her eyes closed. Then she opens her eyes, but she can't see anything; it's too dark. Then slowly, she stares at the closed door. She's frightened, and she starts feeling how lonely she will be without them, especially Meron. "I'm not able to do this."

She becomes fragile. She wants to leave, but her mind and her body can't move. She decides to try another time, perhaps. She turns and opens the door and re-enters the house quietly. She unpacks her bag and puts her clothes back where they belong, then changes back into her pajamas and goes to bed. However, it's not easy to fall asleep. She rolls on her back and tosses from her left side to her right.

The next day, Sarah gets up with the sunrise, dresses, and then, without breakfast, leaves home.

The maid calls out to Tsehay, "Sarah is not in her room."

"Mom, she has work today at the store," Meron says from the living room. "She told me to tell you."

"Oh, okay."

***

Sarah goes to her family's grocery store and says, "Good morning, everyone."

"Good morning," they say to Sarah. and one of them adds, "Oh, are you working today?"

"Yeah, it's Saturday, no school," she replies. "And I want to make some money."

The employee responds, "Oh, smart."

Sarah walks through to her dad's office and puts the money back into the safe. Then she starts working at the register.

A few minutes later, Belay comes in and says, "Good morning."

7

Sarah is shocked.

"Good...... morning.... Dad."

"You okay, darling?"

"Yes, I just wasn't expecting to see you here this early."

He kisses her on the forehead and goes to his office.

Sarah is relieved and thinks, *What if he had come a little bit earlier? Oh, God, I can't imagine.*

Her dad's voice drifts from his office, "Come in. I want to talk to you."

Sarah complies, but she starts sweating all over. *Oh, God, help me. Why is he calling me into his office?*

She runs to the bathroom, but she doesn't have to pee. She looks at herself in the mirror, trying to figure out what to say. She washes her face and takes a deep breath. Then she walks to her father's office and prays that God will forgive her.

She walks into the office, swallowing hard, "Yes, Dad?"

"Have a seat." He sees something is wrong with his daughter, "Are you okay?"

"Don't worry, Dad, I'm fine. I just don't feel good. I don't know why."

"Okay, go home, have a rest."

"I can work, Dad."

"I see you are not well. Rest. And when you get up, go shopping for yourself."

She breathes deeply and follows her dad with her eyes.

He opens the safe and gets a few hundreds of Ethiopia birr.

She looks at him and takes a deep breath again and again.

He gives her the money. "This is for your shopping." Also, he grabs a half-bundle of hundreds of birr and hands it to her, saying, "This is your salary. I haven't been paying you your full amount because I was saving it for you. But you have a healthy sum here. Do you want me to put it into the bank? Or you can save it in your little piggy bank."

She whispers to herself, "Thank God." Then to her father, "Dad, it's a lot of money."

He looks at his daughter, "That's your money. You worked for it. You know why I pay you a salary, to teach you the value of hard work, and to be independent."

"Thanks, Dad. I will put it in my piggy bank, so the real bank can't steal it from me."

"That's true. That is why I leave my money here." He points his finger at the safe.

"I'm smart like my dad."

"You are my baby. I love you, sweetie." He kisses her on the forehead.

"I love you too." She hugs him, and then he gives her the money.

"I trust you are a good girl, that's why I gave you the code to the safe. You work hard and study hard. I'm immensely proud of you."

"Thanks, Dad, but it's too much money."

"No, it's not that much. It's six-thousand-five-hundred birr. That's your money; you deserve it. Save it. In the future, you can open your business when you graduate."

"I will be a good businesswoman and a great actress. Thanks, Dad!" She takes the money and leaves the store.

Now Sarah has her money. She thinks *It's my own money! I worked for it. And I have some money in the house. I don't need new clothes. Oh, thanks to God. Last night I freaked out because I stole money from my family, the people who are most proud of me. I don't want to hurt them twice. Now at least I didn't steal money. On the other hand, when I get to Italy, they will be happy. I can make them proud.*

While on her way home, she walks to one small grocery store and gives him some money and a phone number. He dialed the number, and when the phone rings, he handed it to her. She calls her friend to find out if she knows someone who has a taxi, and her friend gives her the information. Sarah thanks her friend and contacts the driver. They exchange information.

Sarah goes to her home, but she feels down; she decides she will try her best not to show her true feelings to her family. Meron is outside the house.

9

"Sarah!"

"Yes! Meron, do you want to go to the hair salon? I want my hair done."

"Yes but let me ask for some money."

"Don't worry; I have some with me."

"Oh, thanks, sis. I love you."

"Me too."

Soon they arrive at the hair salon. Meron gets her hair straightened, and Sarah gets her hair braided. Then they walk to a restaurant to have dinner.

After the meal, they go to watch a movie. As they leave the theatre, Meron asks Sarah, "What are we celebrating?"

"Nothing, I just want to spend some special and memorable time with my lovely sis-slash-best-friend."

"Oh, thanks so much! I'm so lucky to have you in my life. You're so special to me, but I don't have words to expresses my feelings." She turns to Sarah, but Sarah is crying.

"What happened, Sari? What's wrong?"

"Nothing. Your words really touched me."

"Please don't cry."

"That's the truth. I never tell you, but I think you know it."

"I know," Meron says.

Sarah cries out loud, and Meron starts to cry with her. "Please, sis, stop. If you love me, don't cry. We are together; nobody is dying. Stop."

Sarah hugs her tight and takes long breaths. Finally, she composes herself. "Let's go before it gets too late."

Later that night, Sarah is lying on her bed, watching the roof. She starts thinking about how her family will feel in the morning when they discover that she has gone. *What will they think? What Meron will feel. Have I gone crazy?* She sighs, "Whatever happens, one day, I will come back to my home."

She tries to sleep, but her mind is buzzing. She keeps checking her watch, over and over. Then she gets up and turns on the light switch on the wall. The room is bright. Slowly she goes to her closet, opens it, and bends down. She grabs her wood homemade square piggy bank that looks like a small locker. She holds it with her hand, and with her other hand, reaches into the black jacket pocket, then grabs a small wallet, and walks to her bed, slowly and sits on the bed's edge. Carefully, she places the piggy bank on the bed and opens the wallet, grabbing a small key. With a grin, she puts the key into the piggy bank and unlocks it and removes the rest of the money she saved. She quickly packs her clothes into her backpack. Not a lot, just the things she really needs. "This money will be enough. I will be fine. I will make it." She walks to the bathroom and washes her face.

At 3:00 a.m., she opens the window, and right on cue, she sees two headlights give a couple of quick flashes. She turns her room light on and off and waves her hand to show the driver she's awake. The taxi driver gets out of the car and walks to her bedroom window. Sarah climbs up onto a chair and passes her bag through it. Then she climbs onto the windowsill with his help.

"Why do you want to leave like this?" the taxi driver asks Sarah, once they're both inside the car.

"I asked my family if I could go. They wouldn't allow me."

"They did it for you. They care about you. You should think deep before it is too late."

"I know that!"

"Where are you going to go?"

"I told you, yesterday, Gondar?"

"I mean, after that?"

"Oh, I'm going to Sudan."

"Oh, you are going to Italy?"

"How do you know?"

"A lot of my friends went to Italy."

"Oh, what do they say about it?"

"They say it's not that bad."

"Oh, Okay."

The rest of the cab ride was silent. Finally, Sarah arrives at the bus station. She grabs her small backpack and opens the car door. Outside it's dark, there are few streetlights, but it's not enough. She places her feet on the ground, turns back, and grabs her handbag. "Thanks, have a blessed day."

"I wish you good luck. Stay safe."

"Thanks." She closes the door. The driver waves his hand and drives off.

She put her backpack on her back and her handbag in her right shoulder. She looks around; there is nothing moving. She starts breathing over and over as her body trembles. Her tears fall down her face as she slowly walks to the bus station.

Chapter Two

S arah sits down at the bus station. It as an hour before the bus
is scheduled to arrive. The station is outdoors, and it's cold and
dark; the lights are not bright enough to illuminate the entire
area. There are a couple of people at the station, some of whom are
homeless. Sarah has never been to this station at this time of the
morning. Her heart goes out to the homeless people lying here and
there around the station. "Wow, this is part of human life-..." she
whispers to herself. "How do they sleep here?" She finds the whole
scene overwhelming.

The bus arrives, and people start boarding it. In Ethiopia, the
men who sell and check bus tickets are seated inside the bus,
assisting the driver. This particular assistant begins checking tickets,
but Sarah must wait until everyone else gets on the bus because she
doesn't have one. Then she walks up to the assistant and asks if he
has any tickets left.

"Yes, I have two tickets left, but other people have asked me
before you."

"Oh, but I was here before everyone, I didn't know how to ask. This is my first time."

"Sorry, I can't do anything."

One of the gentlemen comes over and tells the assistant, "Yes, she was here before us. You can give her my ticket. I can wait for the next bus. It's a dangerous place for a woman to be alone."

"Thank you so much!" Sarah exclaims.

The gentleman responds, "I'm just being honest."

Sarah pays for the ticket and gives her bag to the assistant. Then she gets on the bus. She sits on a chair next to a young man who looks to be in his early thirties. He has lighter skin and short-cut dark brown hair. He glances over to Sarah and says, "Hey."

"Hey, my name is Sarah."

"Solomon. Nice to meet you."

"Nice to meet you."

"Are you from Bahir Dar?"

"Yes, what about you?"

"Addis Ababa. I love Bahir Dar. It's one of my favorite cities."

"Nice to hear that. Do you come often?"

"I do." He looks at her. She has a brown eye, individual hair braids, light blue jeans jacket; she is medium height, brown skin color.

Sarah sits next to the window; she turns her face and looks the road over the window. There is a lot of farms, trees, sheep, bulls, goats, and several shepherds with a dogs. A small river, mountain, green grass makes the view extremely comforting.

Solomon looks at her and asks, "It's your first time to travel?"

"Yes." She looks at him. "How do you know?"

"I just guess, because of the way you look at the road."

"I'm new, but I love nature. Especially in the farm area."

"Good, Ethiopia is eighty-five-percent land and is farmer area. Where are you going?"

"Gondar. What about you?"

"Metemma."

"What are you going to do there?"

14

"Are you the travel police?" he laughs. "To go to Sudan?"

"Oh, my Gosh, me too."

"Great."

Sarah suddenly realizes they've arrived in the city of Gondar. As she and Solomon talked and laughed, somehow, six hours passed in what seemed like no time at all. They get off the bus, and Solomon asks Sarah, "Do you want to go get some lunch?"

"Yes, but I don't know what time the next bus is going to Metemma."

"Don't worry; you can get that information easily enough. But where are you heading? I mean, your final destination?"

"I'm going to Italy."

"I'm so surprised. I think we are going in the same direction."

"What? Where are you going?"

"Sudan, Sahara Desert, Libya, and then to Italy."

Sarah is astonished. "Wow, I'm so happy! Yeah, we're on the same road."

"Let's go have lunch. We have about two hours before the bus comes."

"Okay."

They go together to a restaurant, and to Sarah's pleasant surprise, they talk about absolutely everything.

As they eat, Solomon asks, "Do you have a ticket?"

"No."

"Then we should leave soon."

"Okay, do you think I can find a ticket? Do you know where we can buy a ticket?"

"I come here several times. About getting a ticket, I don't know. Maybe."

"Can we go and check?"

They leave the restaurant and walk hurriedly to the bus station. Finding the driver's assistant, they ask him if there are any tickets left.

He replies, "The bus will be empty, don't worry."

"Can I get one ticket?" Sarah asks.

Solomon interrupts, "No, we need two tickets."

Sarah looks at him. "What? For whom?"

"For me."

Sarah laughs out loud, "Are you kidding me?" She looks at him suspiciously, "I thought you had one."

"No, I was messing with you."

***

Back in Sarah's home in Bahir Dar, her sister, Meron, enters the kitchen.

"Mom, where's Sarah?"

"I just got home from church; maybe she's at the store? You know your sister is a workaholic."

"I didn't see her at all today."

Tsehay laughs and says, "Oh my God! You can't live without her. You'll have to learn how to; I bet someday."

Meron covers her eyes with her hands. "No, I don't want to think about it! Mom, stop saying that!"

Tsehay takes the *injera* batter from the maid and pours some onto a hot pan.

"Next year, she will go to college; what will you do then?"

"She can go to school here, Bahir Dar. Why does she need to go to another city? The best university in the country is here!"

"Yes, but she should experience the world. Everyone must see what college life is like."

Meron looks away. "I'm not ready for that. I don't think Sarah really wants to go. She can't live without me, without all of us."

"Sarah can do anything she sets her mind to. Trust me, baby, she is very strong. She got it from her mom. I don't have any doubts about her. She is hardheaded. If she decides something, she will do it."

"When I grow-up, I want to be like her," Meron muses.

"Great, that's what I want to hear. Now, can you take lunch to your sister and your dad?"

"Yes, Mom, but Dad is not in the store. He had a meeting in the city. He told me to tell you, but I forgot."

"Okay, take this for your sister, then."

Meron happily sings as she walks to the store. Entering, she asks one of the employees, "Where's my Sarah?"

The employee responds, "I didn't see her today, but your father stopped by before he left."

"Are you sure she didn't come in to work today? Maybe she is just hiding?" Meron asks playfully.

"Yes, I'm sure," he answers. "I didn't see her."

Meron checks the entire store, but her sister is not there. She leaves the building and runs to Sarah's friend's house, but it's locked.

Then goes to their grandmother's home; it's locked. She went back to her family grocery store asks them again, but nobody has seen her since yesterday. She saunters, putting one of her fingers on top her lip and bolts to Sarah's other friend's house, knocks, but nobody is home.

She urgently storms back to her home, dashes into the house, and screams, "Ma, Sarah's not at the store!"

"What are you talking about?"

"She's not there!"

"Maybe she went to church with her friends."

Meron is clearly unsettled. "Okay, I don't think so."

"What do you mean?" Tsehay demands, suddenly worried. "Do you know anything?"

"I don't, but Sarah would have wanted me up to go with her if she went to church. And she was different yesterday."

"How?"

Meron tells her mom about her and Sarah's big day and how emotional Sarah became when they left the theatre.

Tsehay remains silent and confused. She stops making the injera but leaves the heat on. Meron calls for the maid to finish the injera while Tsehay sits on the couch, her hands folded on her chest. Meron sits on the floor next to her mom. She puts her head on her mother's legs.

17

Belay walks in. "Good afternoon." He says, but he gets no answer. Studying his wife and daughter, he sits down and asks, "What is going on?"

"I don't know where Sarah is," Tsehay responds.

"What?"

"She is not at home," Tsehay answers. "Or at the store. I don't know where she went. Do you know where she is?"

Belay says, "I thought she was at the store." He grabs his cell phone and starts making calls. One by one, he inquires at all the places he thinks she might be, but nobody has seen Sarah. Then he asks Meron, "Did you check her room?"

"Yes, but it's locked. I can't open it."

Tsehay says, "Oh God, Meron, why didn't you say that first? She is asleep! Go wake her up. Thank God."

"Mom, I tried, but she isn't answering."

"Go back and knock on the door."

Belay is deliberating. "Yesterday, she wasn't in a good mood."

"What happened to my baby?" Tsehay wonders aloud.

Meron, now standing outside Sarah's door, calls out, "Mom, she can't hear me."

Belay walks to Sarah's room and knocks loudly on the door. "Sarah? Sarah?" He calls for her several times, but nothing.

Everyone starts looking at each other. There are no words spoken as their eyes get bigger and bigger. Their mouths are slowly dropping in astonishment.

Tsehay rushes to her bedroom to grab a small key and quickly returns to Sarah's room. She tries to put the key in the hole to open the door, but her hands shake, and her eyes fill with tears. "No, I can't do this." She gives the key to her husband and closes her eyes. Her children hold her dress tightly.

Belay takes the key and opens the door: the bed is empty, and the window is open.

For several seconds, Belay can't move or take his eyes off the window. Then he turns back to the empty bed and says. "Oh no, it's not true. My God. Am I dreaming? Tsehay, where is my baby?"

18

Tsehay eyes remain closed as her tears fall. She is completely lost, not knowing what to do next.

Meron slowly walks to her sister's bedroom, opens Sarah's closet, and loudly cries out, "No!" She falls to her knees, wailing. "My Sarah's bag is not here and some of her dresses and --_where is my Sarah? I knew there was something she didn't want to tell me. She did so many things for me last night. Was it her way of saying goodbye? Was that what it was? Why? Why? Why? Please, Sari. Come back to me. I need you."

Tsehay walks in inside her daughter's room, sits on the floor, staring at the open window. She is silent, and her face full of fear.

They call the police and give them all the information; Sarah's family feels empty. The sunshine in the family goes dark. Nobody laughs, even the neighbors are somber. Everyone is talking about Sarah, but nobody has any idea what's happened.

"It's my fault," Belay says later that evening, "I gave her a lot of money yesterday. It's her money to encourage her, to show her, because she worked so hard. I trusted her, but now I don't know what happened to my baby!"

Tsehay looks up; her two hands rise to God. "Why, God? Why is this happening to me? What did I do to you? I know I'm a human, I make mistakes, but don't punish me like this. Not one of my children! If I make a mistake, you hurt me, but please God, take care of my baby! I don't know where she is, but please watch over her." Then she gets the delicate white linen garment that Ethiopian women wrap around themselves for religious meetings and decides to walk to church.

Belay looks at his wife, "it's too late to go church."

"Don't worry; I'll be back soon. I just need to go to church."

"Mom, are you going to church?" Meron asks.

"Yes."

"Mom, please pray."

"I will."

***

The bus arrives in Metemma city. Solomon touches Sarah to wake her up. Without opening her eyes, she mumbles, "Please, can I sleep a little bit more?"

"Okay, bye, then; I'm getting off."

"What?" She massages her eyes with her hands and starts to open them. "Wow, I guess I slept more than I realized." She gets up, takes her bag, and gets off the bus.

It's the middle of the night, and it's very dark, especially when they go outside the bus station. The station is quiet, silent. Nothing is moving. Metemma is the border city of Ethiopia and Sudan, a small town that is very hot and dry. Sarah wears a jacket and winter pants, thinking it would be cold, especially at night. Back in Bahir Dar, the weather is generally not that hot in the night. They get off the road to find the motel, but it's so dark they can't even see. Sarah holds Solomon tight. He holds her back.

"Are you scared?" he asks her.

"Yes."

"You should be strong. This is nothing, a piece of cake. Compared to the rest of our journey."

"What? Are you trying to scare me? Are you okay? I can't even see you."

"We have a long way to go, and things will get worse than this. Think about we are going to travel to the Sahara Desert. One of the biggest and dangerous places to be."

"Can we change the subject? Also, how do you know that? If it is that bad, why you want to travel?"

"It's a long story. I'll tell you another time. But it's hazardous."

"Oh. Maybe, but I don't know."

"We will see."

"Please don't scare me."

They see the light from far off, but they can't make out what it is. They walk toward the light, and when they get close, they see the lights of a bar.

"We can stay there until the morning," Sarah says.

Solomon agrees.

20

They walk inside the bar, and Sarah orders a nonalcoholic drink.

Solomon asks her, "You don't drink alcohol, or are you afraid of me?"

"No, I've never drunk alcohol in my life."

"Wow, that's a surprise."

"I don't have any family who drinks alcohol. I know they drink the traditional ones, but not any hard liquors."

"You come from a real high standard family."

"Yes, they are very disciplined."

Solomon orders a beer.

"Guess you'll have to say goodbye to Ethiopian beer," Sarah says with a laugh.

"Not really. You can get this stuff anywhere."

"Oh, really? How do you know that?" She looks at him suspiciously. "It looks like you have a lot of knowledge about this road?"

***

Tsehay approaches her husband. "I have a thought... maybe she went to Sudan?"

He looks at her. "But she doesn't have a visa." Belay counters.

"I know, but a couple of weeks ago she asked for our permission to go to Sudan, then she wanted to continue to Italy. I didn't tell you because I didn't want you to get angry. Also, I was sure she couldn't go anywhere without our permission."

Belay, looking at his wife, squeezes his face and reaches his hand to the table in front of him, and then hit over and over. Then slammed his head on the back of the couch. "Why didn't you tell me? Until know. Why? Why?"

"I was shocked all day. My head was all over. I just realized everything."

"Oh, I got it. We must call my sister. She lives about thirty minutes from the border." He takes his phone and -dials the number. He hears it ringing, but nobody answers. He keeps calling, but nothing.

"Let me try to my friend," Tsehay offers. She calls, and again, nobody answers. Tsehay's friend lives in Gondar.

Belay rubs his eyes. "It's the middle of the night. We can try early in the morning, maybe Sarah is still in Gondar." Belay explains to his family, "If she is planning to go to Sudan, there's no other road. First, she goes to Gondar, then Metemma."

"I certainly hope so."

Meron interjects, "I wish I knew where she is. If she told me where she was going, I would have gone with her. Maybe that's why she didn't tell me? I hope she's okay."

Sarah's family gathers, sitting on the couch. One of her younger sisters says, "Can we pray that God will help us find her?" Everyone agrees and starts praying.

***

A man comes a little too close to Sarah and asks, "Can I sit here?"

"Yes, you can."

The man asks Sarah and Solomon what they're drinking and offers to buy them another round. "No, thank you."

The man asks, "Where are you both from?"

Sarah responds, "I'm from Bahir Dar."

Solomon responds, "Addis Ababa."

The man asks, "Where are you going?"

Sarah is scared to answer and looks up at Solomon.

The man notices her apprehension and says, "Sorry, I didn't mean to scare you. It's my job. I know where you guys want to go."

Sarah is startled. "How?"

"I said it's my job. I'm a smuggler. I transfer people from here to Sudan."

Solomon's eyes widen. "Oh, that's great, *we* are going to Sudan! Are you driving?"

The man smiles. "No, I guide people across on foot. Once they cross, then they take a bus from Gallabat."

Sarah tries to warn Solomon with a look to determine how they can know whether this man is telling the truth.

22

Solomon asks the man, "Can you give me a minute to discuss it with her?"

"Yes, I will wait there." The man points to a barstool in the corner.

As the man walks away, Sarah looks at Solomon. "How can you trust him? You don't know him."

"I got all the information before I came here."

"Oh, is that right? What kind of information?"

"A lot of smugglers sit at the bar here waiting for people. You know it's illegal, right? They're not going to advertise. Trust me; this is how it works."

"I trust you. I just didn't know any of this. Ask him how much and how we can pay him."

Solomon gives her a tight hug. "Thanks, we will be fine."

"With God."

Solomon walks toward the man and sits next to him. "How much are you gonna charge us?"

"It's two hundred dollars."

Solomon looks at him and laughs. "I know this road; it doesn't even take ten minutes under the bridge. If we want, we can walk during the day with our ID." He looks around him and lowers his voice says, "I'm a smuggler, and I live in Sudan, but the girl doesn't know that so, I want to leave the earliest as possible. I can pay you a hundred dollars for both of us."

"Oh, which city you live in?"

"Khartoum."

"Can you pay a hundred-fifty-dollars?"

"As I told you, I'm a smuggler. Don't worry; I call my guys." He reaches for his cell phone and unlocks it.

"Okay. I'll take you."

"Deal, don't mention anything to her."

"Deal."

"Great, thanks. When do you want to take us?"

"We can go now. If we leave now, you will be able to catch a bus going to El-Gadarif City in Sudan."

"Okay." Solomon puts his hand into his pocket, takes out his wallet, and gives him a hundred dollars. The man takes the money and puts it in his pocket. He says, "Okay. Are you ready?"

"Yes, let me call Sarah." Solomon walks toward Sarah. "Let's go."

"Okay. Do we pay here or after?"

"I already gave it to him."

"Oh, how much?" She opens her purse, takes out some money, and looks at him for an answer.

"It's a hundred dollars for each." Then he realizes she has Ethiopian currency. "You didn't change your money?"

"No, I didn't know where to exchange it."

"You know Ethiopian money only works here. Let me ask the man if he knows where to change it for dollars." He walks over to the man and asks him.

The man tells him, "I can change it, but I don't have a lot." Then they change half of Sarah's money, and Sarah gives Solomon a hundred dollars back.

Solomon takes the money and puts it into his pocket as the smuggler looks at him and turns back.

They grab their bags and walk out of the bar.

***

Tsehay and Belay don't sleep all night. Instead, they sit on the couch, waiting for a phone call. Meron sleeps on the floor next to her mom, holding her mom's legs. The rest of the family sleeps on the couch. Tears run down Tsehay's cheeks non-stop all night, but she is silent. Nobody talks—the house phone rings.

Belay jumps up from the couch and runs to the phone. He grabs it. "Hello!"

On the other side, "Hello, I'm calling from the Police Station."

Belay's voice trembles. "Police?"

Tsehay runs to him. "Belay, tell me what happened to my baby? What happened?"

The police officer says, "Hello, hello, are you there?"

Belay's hands are shaking. "Yes."

"I was about to ask if you had any new information about your daughter?"

"No, I will tell you if I find something, but my wife has an idea. Our daughter maybe went to Sudan, but she doesn't have a visa. We are thinking maybe she's trying to cross the border illegally."

"Thanks, that's good information. I will call border patrol to check into it. Can you please send me some pictures of her?"

"Yes, I will. Thank you."

Tsehay turns back to her seat. Belay walks to the bedroom, and the house phone rings again. He runs to it, grabs it, and says, "Hello?" It's his sister Aster from Metemma city.

"Hello, my brother, are you okay? You called me over and over."

Without asking his sister how she is, Belay starts stammering, "Sis, Sarah, Sarah!"

"What happened to her? Are..."

"...I don't know where she is, but I think she's in your town."

"What is she doing here?" Aster stops, "Oh my God, don't tell me she is going to Sudan."

"I think so, but I hope not."

"No, no, No! It's the wrong decision. How come you allowed her."

"Sis, we didn't. We don't have any idea where she is. A couple of weeks ago, she asked her mom if she could go to Italy, but then she runs away from home."

"Okay, when did this happen?"

"Yesterday morning."

"Okay, let me go to the town and ask the smugglers."

"Oh, do you know them?"

"Yes, it's a small city. We know each other, and who does what."

"Okay, sis, please find them and ask them about Sarah. All my hope is in you."

Tsehay stands next to her husband, listening to the entire conversation. She says, "Please, sis, please find her. I want to know if my daughter lives. Please bring her back to me. Tell her I will die without her. I will send her legally to the United States."

"Don't worry," Aster says. "If she is here in town, I will bring her back to you. I will come with her. Let me go find out."

Belay breathes deeply. "Thank sis. Good luck."

Chapter Three

Outside it's so dark that Sarah can't see a thing. She holds Solomon's hand, and they walk together behind the smuggler. At the border of Ethiopia and Sudan, the immigration officers walk around the bridge with flashlights. Sarah, Solomon, and the smuggler are near the underside of the bridge. The smuggler sees the flashlights and tells his customers to walk slowly and silently. The light gets too close, and the smuggler tells them, "Don't move until I say to move."

"Okay," Sarah says.

Solomon hugs her. The light is getting remarkably close, and Sarah starts rapidly breathing.

Solomon whispers into her ear, "We will be fine, just pray." Then he kisses her on her forehead.

The smuggler's phone begins to vibrate. He tries to turn it off, but, in his haste, his hand pushes through a branch of the tree they're pressed up against, shaking it. The patrol officer walks toward the sound.

Sarah, Solomon, and the smuggler inch-crawl on their bellies beneath a cluster of low shrubs beside the tree, making their escape. The patrol officer comes to the tree and shines his light around the base of it. He casually glances around, looking here and there with his light. Then he saunters back to the bridge.

The smuggler says with a low voice, "We are lucky today!"

"God loves us," Sarah tells him.

They slide out from under the bushes and stealthily make their way toward the bridge. About one hundred and fifty feet from the bridge, they crouch low behind several large rocks. When the men with flashlights walk to the far side of the bridge, they scramble toward the dry riverbed under the bridge and creep underneath it to the other side. They wait again for the officers to continue their route to the far side of the bridge, then they creep up the bank and crawl to the nearest tree. From there, they slip away into the night.

After thirty minutes, they arrive at Gallabat village in Sudan. It's 3:30 a.m.

"Oh, this is nothing," Sarah says. "I thought it would take us all day."

The smuggler says, "This is nothing? If we walked legally, it would take us less than five minutes."

"But I was freaked out," Sarah confesses. "I thought they would catch us. Especially with your phone going off. Why don't you turn it off when you do this kind of thing?"

Ignoring her, the smuggler checks his phone. He sees a name on the screen and puts it back in his pocket.

***

Aster keeps calling her fiancé, Yoseph, but he doesn't answer. She walks to her friend's house and knocks on the door several times. Her friend says, "Who's this?"

Aster asks her, "Can you go with me to the bar? If I didn't get scared so easily, I would go by myself, but I never know if some drunk person will attack me. Better two people instead of one."

Her friend opens her door, looks outside, and turns back to Aster. "Are you out of your mind? It's too dark; we can go early in the morning. The bar will be closed anyway. What's happened? Are you looking for your Yoseph?"

"If you want to help me, let's go, I will tell you on the way."

Her friend gets dressed and looks at her to figure out what is going on. They leave the house, but the cloud cover makes it unnaturally dark and frightening. Aster's friend turns back home.

Aster relents. "It's okay if you don't want to go. I can't force you not to go."

Her friend stops and turns to Aster. "I turned back home because I need a flashlight and a knife."

They retrieve the items, and Sarah's aunt starts telling her friend the whole story. Her friend says, "Oh, I'm sorry. If she is here, we'll get her. Ask your fiancé; he knows everything."

"I called him several times. He doesn't answer his phone."

They keep walking. They see a man walking toward them. He staggers in a zigzag pattern, totally wasted, singing by himself.

Aster's friend says, "This's why I said we should wait till morning. Oh, my God."

With determination, Aster replies, "Can't you see? He can barely handle himself, let alone us. Just keep walking."

They keep walking and see an open bar. They enter one, but there is nobody inside except the bartender and bar back; they are cleaning after the long night. Aster asks the bartender if any other bars are open.

The bartender answers, "Just across the street; they should be open. Metemma Bar, right there." He points to a small, colorful building across the street.

They thank him and walk to the Metemma bar. There are some people inside, but Aster's fiancé is not there. Her friend says, "Let's go home."

"Let's try just one more time. Please."

Her friend agrees, and they walk to another cantina at the end of the street. Sarah's aunt sees her fiancé Yoseph sitting at the bar with his friends. They walk through the doors; Aster walks in first, and her friend follows her. Yoseph sees her, stands up, and steps to her.

"What happened, sweetie?"

"You know my niece, Sarah?"

He nods his head, yes.

"They told me she might be here." She explains what's going on.

He grabs his phone and calls the men he knows who work as smugglers. Some of them answer but have no information. The others don't answer at all. Finally, he hangs up in disgust.

"Sweetie, let's go home. We'll figure it out."

"No, my brother's hope is in my hands. Sorry, but we have to look at the other bars."

"Okay, let's go."

They leave the bar and then when Yoseph's phone rings. He grabs it and answers it.

The voice on the other side says, "Hey, you called me. Sorry, I was working."

"You had people today?"

"Yes, I just came from there."

"Where are you?"

"I'm on my way home."

"Okay, can you tell me what kind of people you helped?"

"I don't want to talk on the phone. I'll tell you tomorrow."

"I want to talk to you now. It is important. If you want, I can come over to your house."

"Don't worry; I can come to your house."

Aster whispers, "I hope it's not her."

They arrive home and sit on the couch. The smuggler arrives and enters; everyone looks at him. Without waiting for an introduction, Aster asks him straight out, "Tell me, who was there? Was it a girl?"

The smuggler responds, "I had a lot of people today. It was a busy night."

Aster grills him. "Do you remember their names?"

"I remember the last one I had was two young people, a female, and a male. The girl's name was Sarah."

"Yes! She is short, skinny, funny?"

"Yes, she is from Bahir Dar. Short and skinny, yes."

Aster gasps. "Oh, my God. It's her. My niece. Where is she now?"

The smuggler's eyes dart back and forth. "I'm sorry I didn't know that. They left Gallabat thirty minutes ago. I am deeply sorry."

Aster looks at the smuggler with begging eyes. "What should we do?"

The smuggler shakes his head. "It's too late; she's already in the city somewhere. We can't do anything."

Aster crumples into her chair. "Oh my God, what do I say to my brother's family?" She puts her hands on her head and begins pacing around the house, her face full of tears. "What can I tell them? I couldn't find her. No, they should know the truth. Oh, no. This is so hard. Her mom will die. Oh, God, give me the strength to handle it."

Yoseph walks up to her. "Sweetie, take it easy. What's done is done. You can't do anything about it now. You're only hurting yourself. If you're not strong, how can you tell them?"

Aster looks up at Yoseph. "That's why I'm worried about it. It's not for them; it's hard for me too, losing Sarah. She is such a sweet girl. I love her like my own baby. She is still so young, and she doesn't know anything. You know that road she wants to go on. How many people lose their lives? She might die. I don't want to think about it; I'm going crazy."

Yoseph hugs her tight with his one hand, and with the other, he wipes her tears. Then he hugs her with both arms and whispers to her, "Don't think like that. Please be positive. Pray to God. He will help her. Now we should just think about how we'll tell them. It's okay, my love, everything will be fine."

"I wish it were that easy."

"I didn't say that it's easy. I'm saying this is what we should do."

"How can we tell them?" Aster eyes look for an answer, searching all around the room; she looks at the smuggler, her friend, her fiancé. She is desperately looking for help.

31

Her friend, seeing Aster's frantic eyes, comes close to her and says, "Whatever happened is for a reason. God always has a purpose. It will happen if he desires it to happen."

"Are you finished talking philosophy?" Aster shoots back.

Her friend says, "I'm very serious. Take it easy. Find a solution."

While her friend is talking to her, Aster's phone rings. She grabs it from inside her jacket pocket. It's Belay. She looks at Yoseph. "I can't answer. I'm not ready." But the phone keeps ringing, and finally, she responds, "Hello?"

***

Tsehay stands next to Belay as the worried father speaks into his phone. He has it on speaker so everyone can hear. "Hey, sis, did you find something?"

"Yes, but..."

Tsehay watches her husband and says, "What happened? Ask her. She said, but."

Aster must have heard Tsehay's pain because Aster started screaming on the other end of the line. Then Yoseph's voice became loud on the phone.

Belay says, "Please, Yoseph, tell me what's going on. I heard my sister screaming."

"We have the information."

Yoseph tells him everything.

Tsehay sits down on the floor, crying. Looking up to the sink, she reaches her hands in front of her face. "God, please, watch her, everywhere she goes. I don't know what to do." Then she sits back to the floor, until the sunrise.

Early in the morning, Tsehay gets up from the floor and then dresses for a church.

Meron says, "Mom, can I come with you?"

"Yes, you can, but don't ask me anything. Just be quiet."

"Mom, how can you say that to me? You know I don't have anyone to talk to. No friends, no sister, no one cares for me. Sarah lied to me! How could she do that to me?"

"Please be quiet. Just for today. You have your younger sisters, brothers, me, your dad, and you have bunches of friends."

"You know that Sarah was my everything, Mom. But I'll be quiet if that makes you happy." Tears stream down her face.

Tsehay watches her daughter's reaction and says, "I didn't mean to hurt you. Come." She hugs her and kisses her on the forehead. Then she holds her daughter's hand, and they walk together to church.

When they arrive, they separate their hands, bend down on their knees, and whisper a prayer. Tsehay says, "God, please watch my daughter and save her from everything." She keeps praying for hours.

Meron prays a little bit and sits down, but she keeps looking at her mom.

Tsehay's tears continue without stopping, as one hour after the next pass.

"Mom, stop crying and sit down, or you'll hurt your knees. Please. I love you; I will be there for you. Anything you need."

"Thanks, sweetie, I'm thinking about Sarah. I can't help but think about if she has food or water to drink. Or, if she's starving or thirsty. I don't know how she'll survive."

"I know, Mom. Be strong. She'll be back soon. She'll miss us. She'll be back. I know she will."

Her mom looks at her, amused at how innocent her daughter is, and whispers to herself, "I wish I could think like her; she has no idea how terrible this world is."

"Mom, let's go home; I'll make a nice cup of coffee for you."

Tsehay looks at her and smiles, "You don't know how to make coffee."

"Ma, I know how to make it. I learned when you weren't home. Just for fun."

"Okay, we'll see." They get up and walk home.

33

Chapter Four

The passengers on the bus speak in a language that confuses Sarah. She looks at them, back and forth, right, and left. Then she looks out the window and admires the passing nature.

Solomon wakes up, glances at her, and follows her eyes to where she is looking, but she doesn't notice him. Solomon slowly touches her hair with his finger, and she lazily turns her head to him.

"Are you awake?" she asks.

"Yes, I woke up. I was watching you. You are such a beautiful girl."

"Oh, thanks. You're so sweet." She stares at him as she purses her lips and wiggles her nose.

His cheeks blush, and his lips quiver.

She can't stop looking at him.

He sees how she looks at him, and she turns back to the window. Slowly his head gets closer to hers. Sarah looks back at him, and they both slowly draw closer to each other. Sarah's breathing quickens, and her lips tremble. Her nervous energy crystalizes into fear, and she slowly starts to back up.

Solomon realizes she's backing away and backs up too. He sits partly back into his chair, pretending to look past her out of the widow but steals glances at her reflection. Neither one dares to talk about it the awkward moment.

After a long period of silence, she says to Solomon, "I wish I could understand what they're saying." Sarah starts laughing, and Solomon looks at her.

"Why are you laughing?"

"I'm thinking about it," she continues giggling; she can't stop.

Solomon starts laughing at her foolishness, and she looks at him and laughs even more. People around gawk at all the noise.

"Sarah, stop, stop. What's making you laugh this much? You're making us look foolish."

Sarah giggles. "The more you laugh, the longer you live."

"Okay, now tell me what's making you laugh this much." He looks at her, waiting for an answer.

"Think about it. If someone came over here and said, I want to kill you; we would just shake our head... big smile... maybe yes, maybe no. We have no idea."

Solomon starts laughing and says, "How, can you even be thinking about this? This is so crazy, but true." Then he looks away from her and sees people staring at them. He turns back to her and says, "Sarah look at them; they're watching us."

"I told you, we'll never know what they're saying."

"Sudanese people are very nice."

"How do you know that?"

"Didn't I tell you? My older sister lives in Port Sudan."

"Oh, you're lucky you have a sister here! You're staying with her until you go to Libya?"

"No, she lives far from Khartoum, so I'm not going to visit her. She might come to see me if she can, but I have a friend who lives there. We can stay with him until we meet the smuggler who will take us across the desert."

"Oh, are you serious? That's great! I was thinking about how we could get a hotel."

"There are hotels everywhere, but if a man and a woman aren't married, it's hard to get one room. Here in Sudan, it's not like Ethiopia."

"Why would we get one room? We need two rooms."

"So, you don't sleep alone? Wouldn't you be scared?"

Sarah turns back to the window and looks outside. Solomon continues talking for a while; then, he stops. He covertly stares at Sarah's reflection in the window. Tears streak her cheeks, and she quickly wipes them away with her hand.

Solomon asks, "Are you okay? What happened? What did I say? Did I hurt your feelings?"

"I was just thinking about how I would sleep without my family. It's my first time."

He smiles reassuringly. "There's a first time for everything. You'll feel better."

"Yeah, that's true, but even to sleep with you. I'm kind of afraid because I've never slept with a man. Most of the time, I sleep with my youngest sister."

His smile brightens. "It's okay; I'm not going to hurt you. Don't think that way. You can think of me as your brother."

"Thanks so much, you're genuinely nice."

The bus stops, and the driver starts describing the station in Arabic over a small, static speaker.

Sarah says, "I think he's saying we've arrived. Okay, where do we go now? Do you know where we're going?"

Now, it's Solomon's turn to start laughing, and she can't help but get caught up in it. She looks at him and says, "Why are we laughing?"

"I really like your translation. Gallabat to Gedarif is an all-day trip. He's saying it's breakfast time, and we're stopping for thirty minutes."

Sarah gets confused. "How do you know that? Do you speak their language?"

"I can understand a little bit. We can get something to eat."

"Where did you learn it?"

"You love asking questions. I'll tell you later."

"If you don't ask questions, you can't learn."

"Okay, I get it. I need something to eat; I'm so hungry. I bet you are too."

"Yeah, kind of," she said, "but I don't know what kind of food they have here."

"They have a lot, but let me give you some names; umfititi, foul mudammas, yogurt tahini, foul–fulminate, gourrassa, you name it."

"I don't know what you're talking about. Can you get me something good, and I'll just eat it.?"

"Okay, you can stay on the bus."

"What? Why?"

"Because you're supposed to cover your hair here."

"Oh, okay, wow. You have all the information."

"Yes, I'll be back. Stay here." He leaves the bus and walks to the small cafeteria.

Sarah becomes concerned about Solomon's knowledge and says, to herself, "How did he learn all of this? The culture, language, food, and place." She squeezes her face moving her lips together side to side. *There will be something.* She turns her attention to the outside. The walls of the buildings are wood, the roof grass, and all the people sit on the slatted floor as they eat and talk.

Solomon walks into the cafeteria and orders for himself and Sarah. He gets two different plates of food, two cups of tea and returns to the bus.

Sarah sees how people walk along with plastic bags of food and is amused.

Solomon enters the bus with a similar plastic bag.

"What is that?"

"Food. Our breakfast."

"In a plastic bag! It's cold, yeah?"

"No, it's super-hot. Can't you see the steam?"

"It's so crazy; I can't believe my eyes." She looks at the plastic bag, confused, and then reaches her hand to feel the plastic bag. It's regular plastic, not anything special.

37

Solomon opens the food and says, "Here in Sudan, it's normal that they sell a lot of liquid with a plastic bag, cheese, oil, milk, foul, hot or cold."

Sarah watches how Solomon eats. He picks up some foul with bread and feeds her.

Her eyes widen. "It's so nice; wow! Delicious!"

"I told you they have good food."

"Yeah, I don't know what I would do if you weren't here, I can't imagine. But one thing that confuses me; how did you learn the language? The culture? Even their food?"

"I will tell you when we get to Khartoum."

"Why can't you tell me now?"

"It's a surprise."

"Okay, whatever." Sarah starts looking at the others.

One Sudanese man looks at Sarah, and he says, "Linti hulwa."

Sarah looks at Solomon and asks him, "What did he say?"

"He says, 'You are so beautiful.'"

"Oh, that's nice of him." She turns back to look at the Sudanese guy, and Solomon looks at her.

"Do you like him too? You can go there and sit with him."

"No, did I say that?"

"Your actions say it. Actions speak more than a language. Your eyes are all over him."

"No, it's not the way you think. It's just the way he said it; it's so nice, you know. It's so surprising to me, compared to Ethiopian guys."

"What's wrong with us?"

"It's nothing. I mean, a lot of Ethiopian guys, even if they like you, they don't know how to say it; you know, nice words."

"First, Sudanese men like Habesha girls. A lot of people in the world like our women."

Solomon's eyes glance around with irritation.

"Are you angry?" she asks. "You look upset."

"I'm not. What, are you, my wife?"

"Oh, sorry, I didn't mean anything by it. I mean, are you upset because of a lot of other races like Ethiopian women? That's what it seemed like."

"No, I did not get mad or sad. Can we change the subject?" He looks away to avoid her seeing his face.

The Sudanese guy comes back and starts talking to Sarah. As she looks at the Sudanese man, Solomon responds to him in Arabic. Sarah tries to understand what they're talking about and tries to read their body language, watching them as they go back and forth.

In Arabic, the man asks Solomon, "Are you Ethiopian?"

"Yes."

"She is your wife?"

"No."

"She is beautiful. If you hook me up with her, I will give you whatever you want."

Solomon looks at him, rubs his forehead, then scowls and looks at Sarah. She studies his face. She understands something is going on and says, "Are you okay?"

"Yes."

"Your face has changed, just in the past few seconds."

"Oh..." he stops talking to the man and continues, "He just told me a sad story."

"Okay."

The Sudanese man speaks again to Solomon. "Tell me something. I gave you an offer, but you didn't answer. If I knew her language, I would tell her."

Solomon loudly says in Arabic, "What do you want?"

Sarah tries to quiet him. "Sol, you're talking so loud..."

"...This guy is driving me crazy."

"What's going?"

"He's just telling me about what's happening to the people traveling here from Libya."

"What happened?"

The Sudanese man is looking at them, but he doesn't know what they're saying. He just follows their eyes. Then he asks Solomon in Arabic, "Are you telling her? What did she say?"

"She says no."

"Why?"

"She says she has a boyfriend."

"Tell her I can buy her anything she wants. My father gave me his company. I have my own house, and I have two maids. She doesn't have to work in the home. The only thing I want is to have a beautiful baby with her."

The Sudanese man starts staring at her. His eyes are all over her, but she doesn't notice because she is studying the nearby houses.

Solomon says, "Don't' look at her like that. It will be hard for you to get her."

"Why is that?"

"When a Habesha woman knows you are all over her, it will be hard to get her."

"Okay, thanks for your advice."

"Women usually like to play hard to get."

"It's true. But I really like her. Imagine her kids; they will look like her."

Sarah turns back to them and realizes they're still talking.

"Oh, my God. You guys are still talking? I guess you forgot about me. It's like I don't exist."

"No, I didn't forget about you, my dear. I'm just interested in what he's saying."

"Oh, that's fine. Ask him if he can help us find our smuggler to Libya?"

"Yes, he's giving me some information about who to hire and where to find them."

"Good! That's smart because you know the language, it makes it easy for us. I'm so glad I met you." Her face shines. She smiles and looks super happy. "Ask him more!"

The Sudanese guy starts smiling with her and says to Solomon, "I think she likes me. Look how she's looking at me. Ya, Allah, she is so beautiful when she smiles. Tell me what she said? I want to know."

"I wish I could have him, he seems nice, but how about my boyfriend?"

"Where does he live, her boyfriend?"

"Back home."

"Forget about him. After a couple of months, he will have another girl. Besides, he's not her husband. But the best thing is knowing she likes me. We will talk when we get to El-Gadarif. You know, we will spend the night there. And don't worry, I will pay for our motel."

"Okay, thanks, and I will tell her more about you."

"Yes, please talk to her. I will get you whatever you want." Then the Sudanese man gets up to leave.

"Okay, I will."

Sarah says to Solomon, "Please tell him thanks for giving us the information. Or tell me how to say thanks in his language."

Solomon tells her, "Shukraan."

Sarah looks at the Sudanese man, "Shukraan!"

With a bright smile, he responds, "Afwan," and he turns back to his seat. Sarah looks at Solomon.

"He is a good person. Did he give you more information?"

"Yes, he did. He will make our travels quite easy. He also told me the best time to go to Libya and how to get into Italy."

"Wow, that's really great."

Solomon takes a deep breath and looks through the window, staring at Sarah's reflection. He starts chewing his lip, but then Sarah sees him, and he realizes it. He turns back and looks at the Sudanese guy, but he's lying back in his chair, with a towel covering his face. Solomon turns back to Sarah, looking deeply into her eyes. He starts moving closer to her slowly, but again she starts backing up. He stops. His eyes search hers.

"Who am I to you?"

"My friend. I see you like a brother."

"Do you like me?"

"What kind of question is that? I don't hate you. Yes, I do like you. That's why I say you're like my brother."

"No, I don't think you get my question. I mean, do you love me?"

"Okay, you're making me confused. I gave you the answer, but you keep asking me."

"Let me be clear. I want you to be my girlfriend."

"That's it? That was the question?" She starts laughing more and more. He gets angry.

"You can say no, but you can't play with my emotions."

She can't stop laughing. She says, "Why are you getting angry?"

"I swear to God I'm not playing. Or tell me, do you like that Sudanese man?"

She keeps laughing loudly. "What if I like him? He is human, yes?"

"I did not say he's not a human. Why are you laughing at me when I ask you a serious question?"

"Because you're asking me like I don't already know. I knew from the moment you met me."

"How did you know?"

"Your actions were talking louder than your words. When a guy looks at me, you get mad at me, but you don't even realize it. You think it's my fault when they look at me?" She starts laughing.

His anger melts into a smile. Finally, he chuckles at himself.

She says, "You see, you're laughing like I'm tickling you; because I tell the truth."

"I laughed because you surprised me. I was worried about how to tell you, but you already know it. It's so crazy. Even when I asked you, you acted like you didn't know anything."

She smiles. "I was messing with you."

The bus stops in front of a motel, and the driver says, "We will meet here tomorrow morning at five-thirty sharp. Have a good night."

Everyone gets off the bus. Sarah and Solomon get up and start walking to the motel, and the Sudanese guy walks in front of them. Then Solomon quickens his steps, reaches him, and they walk together. Sarah walks behind them. The Sudanese guy and Solomon start talking and laughing. Sarah watches them and smiles.

It's around 8:00 p.m. The night street is pretend-bright with street lighting. Sarah thinks to herself, "It's so hot, how do they live here? Maybe that's why their skin is so dark. But their outfits are perfect for this weather." Then she starts smiling at the dress-like garments worn by the men. "If they wore these outfits in Ethiopia, it would be considered disgusting, men and women wearing the same thing. I know they wear it because of their religion, but an Ethiopian Muslim man would only wear this when they go masjid. How strange."

Solomon looks back and observes Sarah. He sees that her face is shining, and she's smiling to herself. Then the Sudanese man turns and follows Solomon's glance toward Sarah.

"She is so happy, look at her. She is smiling all by herself, Mashallah."

"Yes," Solomon agrees. "She is always happy like this, and positive. I love her energy."

"Yes, I can see it. Look at her; she doesn't even notice us. She is in her own world. I need this kind of woman in my life. My other wives are always complaining and negative. They rarely smile."

"Oh, how many wives do you have?"

"I have four. My dream is to have seven wives, but if Sarah marries me, five is enough, because I want to spend more time with her."

Solomon smiles and says, "If she knows that you have other wives, she will say no."

"Why? I can give her whatever she wants."

"No, it's not about material things. In our culture, we marry just one woman."

"What? How can you live having just one wife?"

"One wife is more than enough to drive you crazy."

43

"Is that the law, or do you just want one wife?"

"We're Christian, so one husband and one wife, that's it. Even Ethiopian Muslims, they marry just one."

"No, a Muslim man can have seven wives, that is Sharia."

"Yes, I know, that, but it doesn't work like that in Ethiopia."

Sarah looks at them, and they meet her eyes.

"What are you guys talking about? You forgot about me."

Solomon smiles. "No, we didn't. You seemed to be enjoying your vibe." The Sudanese man walks into a large adobe building with a grass roof.

"Yes, I really like it. It is a different vibe here." She asks Solomon, "Can we get a room? I'm very tired."

"Okay, I'm just waiting until he comes back."

"Why are we waiting for him?"

"He just said, 'wait here,' that's why."

"Okay."

The Sudanese man calls out to Solomon from the motel. "Come here, guys."

Solomon looks at Sarah, "Let's go." Solomon opens the gate to the courtyard. The beds are set up outside the rooms, open to the elements, and the cool of the night. A lot of people sit or lie on their beds, reclining, and talking. Sarah looks at Solomon and follows what he does. The Sudanese man shows Solomon two beds, then walks to a third bed further down the line and puts his bag on a chair.

Solomon walks up to the bed and says to Sarah, "This is your bed."

"A bed? We are sleeping outside?"

"Yes, look at all the people."

"I saw them. I'm not blind. What I mean is, we're sleeping here all night? Or are we staying out here until they fix the room?"

"We sleep right here. In the summer, Sudanese people sleep outside because it's super-hot. If you sleep inside, you might die."

"Oh my God, how are we going to sleep here? Tell me this is a bad dream. This can't be true."

"Sarah, take it easy. It's not a big deal. I know in our country; we don't sleep outside. We must lock our doors to prevent burglars, but here, even in the big city, they sleep with the doors open. That's their culture -- nobody robs you; nobody stabs you or hurts you. And it's not like we're going to live here. It's just for tonight. I will sleep next to you. You'll be safe."

He points to the bed on the right. On the left, an old lady is lying down and talking to a neighbor.

Sarah quietly talks to herself, "Oh, my God. Please, Lord, help me. It's impossible." Then she puts her bag on the chair, sits down on her bed, and turns to Solomon, "Sol, where did we pay the bill?"

"We will pay tomorrow morning. Don't worry; I will take care of it."

"No, I have money, I can take care of my own bill."

The Sudanese man stands up from his bed and walks over to Solomon. "Let's go have dinner." It sounds very much like an order.

Solomon translates to Sarah, and they walk to the restaurant. Sarah looks at them, how they talk and act, but she doesn't understand what they're talking about. They wash their hands before they sit to order the food. The waiter comes almost immediately and explains the house special.

Solomon asks Sarah, "What do you want to eat?"

"I can eat whatever you eat because I don't know anything about Sudanese food."

The Sudanese man and Solomon decide together to get Molokai-soup, khuruf mathu (lamb stew), bamia biallahm (Okayra with meat), and shaiyah, (pan-fried meat), with some tamiya for an appetizer. Sarah looks at the other people at the restaurant to see how they eat.

"Solomon, they eat like us, with their hands. At least we have something in common."

Solomon responds, "We have a lot of similar customs. You'll see it when you get to Khartoum."

The Sudanese man asks Solomon, "Has she said anything about me?"

"No, but I'm talking to her. When she shares her feelings, I'll tell you."

"Please don't tell her about my life and my marriages. I will tell her after we are married."

"Okay, I won't tell her."

"Thanks, you are a wonderful gentleman."

"Anytime," with a fake smile, "brother."

"I will give you money when you get to Khartoum, and you can open your business."

"Wow, good! Thanks."

Then the waiter comes with a large plate of food. Sarah stares at the unfamiliar food and then watches the men.

The Sudanese man puts his hand on the plate and grabs some food. He eats and says, "It's very good."

Sarah looks at his face. She looks at Solomon, and he seems like he's enjoying it, too. Solomon grabs some food in his right hand and feeds it to Sarah. She squeezes her face like she wants to throw up.

Solomon looks confused. "You don't like it?"

"It's too mild."

"Oh, okay, that's the molokai. Try this one." He feeds her another one.

"Better, but can I get some spice or seasoning?"

After the waiter brings some sauces and spices, Sarah actually finds the meal quite tasty. As they finish, they wash their hands, and Solomon and the Sudanese man order hot tea. They ask if she wants to order tea.

"It's too hot; I can't drink hot tea."

"That's why you should drink hot tea," Solomon says.

"You are so crazy."

"Look, all the people are drinking hot tea. If they drink something hot, it somehow tricks their bodies, so they don't realize how hot it is outside."

She laughs and says, "I don't know how things work in Sudan, but I know that when it's hot, people drink cold stuff. Here, the

46

weather is terribly hot, and they drink hot drinks? For me, no thanks, I can't take any more."

"Okay, if you say so."

The waiter brings two teas, and the Sudanese guy takes notice. While looking at Sarah, he says to Solomon, "Why she didn't drink? Tell her the tea is specially seasoned. It can help her with the weather."

"I told her. She says no."

"Okay."

They keep talking. Solomon finds himself in the middle, sometimes talking to Sarah and sometimes to the Sudanese man. Then the waiter comes with the bill, and the Sudanese man takes care of it.

Sarah whispers to Solomon, "Why is he paying for it all? We ate together?"

"It's okay; he is our friend. Tomorrow we'll buy lunch."

"Okay. Please tell him thanks from me."

"Okay."

They walk out of the restaurant and go to their beds. Sarah heads into the hot baking bathroom to shower and changes into her pajamas. She enjoys the cold water, but the room remains stifling, so she quickly changes and crawls into her bed. For hours she lies there, sweating and unable to sleep, but finally, she drifts off.

Five o'clock arrives the next morning, and everybody begins waking up. Solomon goes to Sarah's bed to wake her up and touches her shoulder and kisses her on the cheek, waking her. She wakes up.

"Good morning," she mumbles. Then she gets up and gathers her things to get ready. She looks back at Solomon, "Where do we go to pay?"

"I already paid while you were sleeping."

"How much was it? Let me give you my share of the money."

"Shut up," he playfully scolds. "I'm not taking any money. Please don't ask me again."

"I don't want you to pay for anything else. I have the money. Please don't do it again."

"Okay, madam," he jokes.

The Sudanese guy comes over, "Good morning."

"Good morning," Solomon responds. "Thank you for everything you did for us. It means a lot."

"It's nothing."

"You paid for the room and dinner…"

"Forget about that. We will help each other in the future. I just want you to hook me up with her."

"Thanks, brother." Solomon swallows, even though his mouth is dry, and he looks away, unable to meet his eyes. "I will make sure she will be yours."

Sarah calls over from her bed. "Sol, let's go. I'm ready."

"Okay."

They walk together to the bus and sit. As soon as Sarah gets to her seat, she puts her head on the window and sleeps. Solomon sleeps on her shoulder and slowly hugs her with both arms.

The Sudanese man talks with the person sitting next to him. He gets up, sees Solomon and Sarah sleeping, and sits back down.

Solomon wakes up and looks around; everyone is sleeping. He hugs and kisses Sarah on her lips. She wakes up and sees him. He is shocked and says, "Sorry."

"It's okay." He hugs her tight; then, he tries to kiss her again.

"Stop, people are seeing."

"Don't worry; everyone is sleeping." He gets up, looking around, and sits. "I know it's dangerous kissing in public in Sudan. Forget kissing you; can't even hold hands, no one sees us."

"Kissing in public is so weird."

"Okay. I'm not gonna force you if you don't like me."

"I didn't say that. You know how we grew up; everything is behind closed doors and not open on a bus." Then she laughs.

"Why are you laughing? Sometimes you confuse me."

"I just imagine back home if people saw you when you kissed me. Oh my gosh, it would be weird."

"Yeah, that's true."

She gazes at him and smiles. Then they fall asleep again. After a long day of traveling, they arrive in Khartoum. It is around 8:00 p.m. and very hot. They deboarded the bus and took their bags. Solomon walks in front of Sarah and tries to hail a taxi. After a couple of taxis pass them up, he sees an empty one. He calls out, "Bajaj!" which is Arabic for a taxi. The driver stops, and he and Sarah climb inside.

The Sudanese man runs out and calls after Solomon, "My driver can give you a ride, don't take a taxi!"

Solomon says, "Thank you, anyway. It's okay; the taxi is already here."

The Sudanese man insists and gives the taxi driver money, offering an apology. Then they all walk together to the Sudanese man's car. The Sudanese driver helps with Sarah's bag. Solomon looks around, and before he enters the vehicle, he checks the plate.

The Sudanese man says, "Where are you going? Do you have family or...?"

Solomon responds, "...I have some family in Khartoum Thalathah."

"Oh, okay."

Sarah says, "Are you okay, Solomon?"

"I'm good. Why?"

"You look like you're anxious."

"Oh, yeah, kind of."

"Can you tell me what happened?"

"I will tell you when we get out of the car."

Sarah agrees with him, but she is slightly confused. She tries to figure it out, looking at each of them back and forth, but she sees they are talking and laughing. The car stops, and Solomon thanks them. Opening the door, he says to Sarah, "We are here."

Sarah gets out and says, "Please tell him, thanks."

Solomon thanks the Sudanese man and starts getting out of the car. Sarah follows him, but Solomon stops and makes Sarah pass him. Then he turns and says to the Sudanese man, "Oh, you forgot to give me your number."

"Thanks, I forgot. I know your house, but it's good to have a number."

"Yeah, that's right." He points the finger at the house beside him and says, "This is my sister's house."

The Sudanese man looks at the place and nods. "Good to know. If you have time, call me tomorrow. We can talk."

"Yes, I don't have anything to do. I will call you tomorrow. Thank you so much for everything you did for us."

"It's nothing. I did not do anything."

Then Solomon gets out of walks to the house's front door, Sarah follows him. He stops at the door and turns back to watch the Sudanese man's car. The car is still parked there, and Solomon knocks on the door several times. Finally, a man opens the door. The Man glances at the unfamiliar faces. Solomon puts his hand together close to his chest and apologizes. "Sorry, I think we are lost."

The Sudanese man, seeing the door open, orders his driver to leave. Solomon listens to the Sudanese man's car drive away and apologizes again. The man shakes his head and stares at them while he holds his gate. Solomon and Sarah walk back the road.

"Can you tell me what is going on?" Sarah insists. "I know something is not right, even though I don't speak the language."

"Yes, there is a problem. The Sudanese man gave us a ride because he wants to know where we live. That's why I lied to him. Now let's take a taxi to my friend's house."

"Oh, my God. He seemed like a nice guy."

"You can't trust people. He might be the police. We never know."

"That's true. You're smart."

They walk to the street and flag down a taxi. The taxi stops and asks where they're going. Solomon says, "Omdurman."

Sarah studies Solomon. "How do you know this place so well? It looks like you know the country and the language."

"I learned some Arabic in school, and I know a lot about Sudan. I had my sister and my best friend teach me."

"It doesn't look like someone taught you these things," she replied with doubt in her voice.

As they go, Sarah sees the river and the city. The Blue Nile and palms give beauty to the city. People walk along the river, most of them with kids. All the females covered their hair, and they wore a dress.

Solomon sits close to her and hugs her. Noticing how the river has caught her attention, he asks, "Do you know the name of this river?"

"Yes, I think it's the Blue Nile."

"Wow, good." He kisses her neck.

"Are you serious? Don't forget, that's my river. It was walking distance from my home."

"I know that. I'm just messing with you."

Talking and laughing, they move on, taking their bags and walking to the house gate. The gate is small compared to the neighbor's gate. Sarah stops at the door and looks at Solomon; he's not knocking on the door. So, she gazes at him. Solomon puts his bag on the ground and reaches his hand and opens the bag. Then, he grabs two house keys, holds them in his left hand, and closes his bag. Then he grabs his bag and holds it, and he puts the key in place to open the gate.

Sarah stands silently, watching.

He points his hand to get inside. She follows him, looking around the unfamiliar place. There are two big trees, two beds made of rope, four chairs made of rope, and a small brown chair made of wood. The ground is gravel and freshly wet. Solomon enters the key to the house door and opens it.

He says, "Welcome home." Solomon shows her the bedroom, the bathroom, and the kitchen.

Sarah is perplexed and asks him, "Do you have something to say?"

"Like what?" He studies her and says, "Oh," he laughs. "Is that because of the key? Surprise! My best friend mailed me them while I was Ethiopia because he travels a lot, for work."

"I feel like there is something you don't want to tell me."

"No. Why do you say that?"

Sarah stops and looks around like she's searching for an answer. Then she takes a long breath and says, "Never mind. Thanks for everything you did." With that, she goes to the shower.

Solomon goes to his bedroom, opens a drawer in the nightstand, grabs his cell phone, and calls his friend. "Teddy, I'm home."

"What time you get here?"

"We just got home."

"What? You said, we? With whom?"

"Oh, there is a girl with me; I really like her, and she doesn't know I live here. Please don't tell her. When you come, act like I'm new to this country. Please."

"That's strange. Why are you lying to her?"

"I didn't want to lie to her."

"You just told me you lied to her! Are you out of your mind?"

"It's not like that. She wants to go to Italy. And I told her 'me, too.' So, after that, I didn't know how to tell her that I live in Khartoum."

"You can tell her now."

"How?"

Sarah comes out of the shower and hears someone talking, so she walks in the direction of the voices, but she doesn't see anyone. She walks to the living room and turns on the TV but doesn't understand the language.

Teddy says, "Say that you didn't tell her so that you could surprise her."

"I don't think that will work. Besides, she's not staying here."

"What you gonna do?"

"I plan to make her fall in love with me and make her forget everything. Make her pregnant and get married."

"That will take time, try to keep her from leaving the house. If she goes outside, people will know about you, and she'll figure things out quickly."

"Yes, I will do that. I'll tell her we can't go outside because we don't have any documents. Don't forget; she is illegal."

"Use her weak side. By the way, I cooked dinner. Go check it out, and I will be there shortly."

"Okay, we can wait for you."

Sarah hears Solomon's voice and says, "Solomon, where are you?"

"Sorry, I was lying down until you got out of the shower. Are you hungry?"

"Kind of. Where's your sister?"

"Oh, she doesn't live here. This is my friend's house."

"I thought I heard you talking."

"Maybe it's the neighbors. They talk loud."

"Oh... okay.

They sit outside because it is very hot. Sarah starts sweating, she says, "I just took a shower, my God."

Teddy, an Ethiopian man, medium height, dark brown skin, short clean-cut-hair, and beautiful white teeth, arrives and walks toward them. He gives a hug to Solomon, shakes Sarah's hand, and says, "Welcome." He goes inside the house, drops his stuff, and takes a shower. Then he walks to the kitchen, warms the stew, sets the table, and says, "Come in, dinner is ready."

Solomon says, "Okay, thanks."

They walk inside. Sarah sees injera. She smiles happily and says, "It feels like I haven't had injera forever!"

Solomon agrees, "Exactly. That's how we grow up. It is hard for us to live without it."

Teddy laughs, "You guys, you can adapt to the culture."

"Maybe," Solomon responds.

Sarah gets Teddy's attention with a quick smile. "Where do you find injera?"

"There are a lot of Ethiopian restaurants here. I bought it there."

Sarah's eyes light up. "Oh, that's good. We can go tomorrow to see it!"

"We can't go out until we leave this country," Solomon cautions.

"Okay, but how do we find the smuggler who can get us into Libya?"

"Don't worry about that," Teddy interrupts. "I know a lot of people."

"Okay…" Sarah ponders the two men. Something is going on. The men seem to share secret glances and eye signals as they talk. Sarah gets up and walks to the bathroom; she notices that they lowered their tone and are speaking more slowly. After she turns the water on, she walks to the wall between the bathroom and the living room, and she starts listening.

"She looks suspicious. Are you sure she doesn't know anything?" Teddy asks.

Solomon shakes his head. "No. She is too young. I don't think she knows anything."

"Be careful around her and don't act like you know the city. She is beautiful, by the way. Get her pregnant as soon as possible. That's the only way you can know you'll have her."

"I will; trust me. I'm tired of living in this house by myself. I have money from work, but I don't have a wife."

Sarah turns back to the bathroom and sits down on the floor, shocked. She starts crying, then eventually adjusts herself into a kneeling position, and whispers a heartfelt prayer to God. Then she gets up, washes her face, and walks back out to them. When Solomon sees her, he changes the subject.

Sarah fakes a yawn. "I'm very tired; I want to sleep, okay?"

"Okay," Teddy responds. "Let's get the beds outside, and we can all sleep."

Solomon agrees, and they get up.

Sarah interrupts them, "I want to sleep inside."

The two men stop and look at her. "It is too hot," Teddy argues. "It's very dangerous to sleep inside. You could die." He looks at Solomon.

Sarah says, "It's okay, I can try, and I will open the window."

"Let her try," Solomon responds to Teddy. "She could come out in the middle of the night. She doesn't know how the weather is here."

Teddy warns him with his eyes.

Solomon immediately tries to cover. "The geography class taught us a lot. To know every country's weather." He smiles.

Teddy pretends to be impressed, "Wow, you know a lot of things. You are smart."

"Thanks to you, the geography class, and my sister. You all taught me a lot of things."

Sarah prepares to leave. "Have a good night; I'm very tired. The dinner was so great, thank you so much." She turns and walks to the bedroom.

Solomon walks behind her, enters the room after her, and says, "Aren't you scared to sleep by yourself? Do you want me to sleep with you?"

"I want to sleep by myself," Sarah says firmly. "I don't need anyone; I'm not a baby."

"Are you okay? You're acting differently since you came from the bathroom."

She gets quiet; her eyes look for an answer. Finally, she says, "Sorry, I'm having my period. I have really bad cramping. It hurts."

"Oh, sorry! Let me make hot tea for you. It will help you."

"Thanks," she says hesitantly.

Solomon walks to the kitchen, grabs the pot, pours in the water, and walks outside to tell Teddy, who is making up his bed.

Sarah gets to her room and waits for a couple of minutes, silently, staring at the wall and thinking. She smiles and rummages through her bag for a tampon. She walks to the bathroom and puts it in, carefully leaving the packaging on the top of the garbage in the trash can. Then she heads back to the room and lies down.

Solomon walks in with the tea. Teddy walks in behind him and says, "Sarah, you alright?"

"It's just a normal female thing."

"Do you need anything at the store?"

"Oh, no thanks, I have what I need." Then she smiles and looks down.

Teddy walks outside.

"It's normal," Solomon says to Sarah, misreading her smile. "Why are you getting shy?"

She looks down, again, not answering.

He gives her the tea and walks out of her room.

Teddy and Solomon sit outside, talking, and laughing as Sarah drinks her tea and drifts off to sleep.

"I don't think she is on her period," Teddy whispers.

"She is. She's innocent."

"You don't know that for sure. You lied to her. What if she knows the truth?"

"She doesn't know anything, trust me." Solomon gets up. "Let me go to the bathroom." He walks to the bathroom and notices the tampon cover on top of the garbage. He smiles and goes to tell Teddy.

* * *

A couple of days later, Sarah asks Teddy to go to church, then he talks to Solomon, and they agree. Solomon tells Teddy, "Can you take her? I don't want people to recognize me and say, welcome back."

Teddy agrees, and the two head to church. As their taxi rumbles toward the church, he points out several places and tells her the names of each one and their significance to the town. Sarah asks questions about each one. They arrive at the church, and after the service, they say the congregational prayers and head downstairs for a complimentary meal. Then they exit the building and sit outside. Sarah is intrigued by the congregation.

"I never thought there would be this many Ethiopians living here."

"Oh, this is nothing. You haven't seen anything yet."

"How many Habesha live here?"

"I don't know the exact number, but I think more than thirty-thousand."

"Really? And live here? Or are they like me, just passing through?"

"Oh, they live here. Probably even more than that."

"Can we please go to an Ethiopian restaurant?" she playfully pleads.

He resigns himself to it and nods his head.

They reach a restaurant called *Queen of Sheba*. The restaurant is outdoors inside a gate. There are several chairs and tables and some Habesha customers. In the back, there is a house. They walk in and sit.

After a while, a woman comes with a menu, she gives them some water, and says, "Hey" to Teddy.

"Hey, Azeb," Teddy replies.

Azeb and Sarah glance at each other. Azeb looks at Sarah and says to Teddy, "Is she new?" Some excitement filters into her voice. "Did you get married?"

"No, she is a guest."

Azeb smiles and rolls her eyes. She takes the order and walks to the kitchen.

Sarah gets up and heads to the bathroom to wash her hands.

Azeb sees her walking past, "Hey, Sarah."

"Hey, Azeb." They hug each other. Azeb and Sarah met a week ago at the store.

"You live with them?"

"Yes, do you know him?"

"Oh, everybody knows them. Where did you meet them?"

"Oh, I met his friend in Bahir Dar. Since then, we have traveled together. In the beginning, I trusted him, but after a while, I started having doubts. But one day, I heard them talking about their plans." Then she gets quiet. "Also, I heard Solomon on the phone while he was talking to someone about the store. I meet you. So, one day when Solomon and teddy leave home, I'll come to the store by myself. I'm glad I met you."

"Ah, you mean Solomon. Oh yes, He went to Ethiopia to visit his family. Also, he doesn't have any legal documents or passport. That's why you met him."

"Oh, my gosh. Yes, that's him. Do you know him well?"

Azeb smiles and says, "Everybody knows him; he is a smuggler. And Teddy too. They took a lot of people's money, especially for the people who are going to Libya. They send a lot of people. They don't care about their lives. Also, they rape a lot of innocent girls. They tell them, 'we will send you tomorrow, and tomorrow,' then when they get enough of them, they send them to Libya."

Tears roll down Sarah's face. She falls on her knees and begs to stay with Azeb. Azeb grabs her and pulls her up, hugs her, and wipes her face.

"You know I told you; I don't know anybody," Sarah says.

Azeb whispers in her ear what to do. Then Sarah turns back to her chair.

Teddy asks her, "Are you okay? You took forever."

"I don't know why, but I had bad stomach pains."

"Oh, you might be hungry."

"I think so."

Azeb comes with the food, and Teddy leaves to wash his hands. Sarah is happy to see her food and says, "It looks so yummy."

Azeb says, "The taste is great." Then she adds with a low voice, "After you eat, act like you are really sick."

"Okay."

Teddy comes back to the table and looks at Sarah. "Are you happy?"

"Oh, yes, thank you so much. It's a lot of food."

"I just want you to enjoy it. We can eat as much as we can."

While they're eating, Sarah goes to the bathroom several times.

After her third trip, Teddy asks her, "Is everything alright?"

"I don't know. I guess I have diarrhea. Excuse me." She walks to the bathroom again.

Then Teddy calls to Azeb and says, "I don't know what to do, she's sick."

"Wait here; I will be back soon." She grabs her scarf, puts it on her head, and walks out of the restaurant. Then, she grabs her cell phone and makes a call.

Sarah sits in the bathroom looking at the wall, then to the floor, and then leaves the bathroom.

Azeb comes back to see Sarah and calls her with a low voice. "Sarah, Sarah."

Sarah heard Azeb and walks to her.

"I called a friend of mine. He is a doctor," Azeb says.

"But I'm not sick."

"I know that. Don't worry. I told him. Just go and act like you are really sick. I will be there soon at your table."

"Okay." She walks in and sits down.

Teddy looks at her and says, "How do you feel? Don't worry; I told Azeb how you feel. She went to get you some medication."

"Oh, thanks so much, I feel so horrible and ashamed."

Azeb returns and talks to Teddy. They grab Sarah and walk to Azeb's bedroom, which is in the back of the restaurant. Sarah lies on the bed. After that, Azeb turns on the light and, they leave the room. Sarah laid on her belly. "Thank God." Then she sleeps.

The doctor arrives, Azeb sees him and takes him into the bedroom, but Sarah is asleep. They walk out of the room. Teddy sees the doctor and asks, "How is she?"

"I didn't check her while she was asleep," the doctor replies.

Teddy says, "I can wake her."

The doctor says, "No, let her sleep. She can wake up when she wakes up."

Teddy says, "Okay."

Azeb brings food to the doctor. Teddy's cell phone rings; it's Solomon, who has called eight times and texted a bunch more. Teddy gets up, walks out of the restaurant, and calls Solomon. They talk for a half-hour. Solomon gets mad after a while because Teddy took Sarah to the Ethiopian restaurant. Teddy tries to explain to Solomon, but he hangs up the phone. Teddy walks to Azeb's bedroom and sees that Sarah is up from her nap. He walks over to the doctor and informs him she is awake. The doctor gets up and walks to the bedroom. He checks her and gives her some medication.

Teddy tells Sarah, "Let's go home."

"Please let me stay here for the night. Can you please ask Azeb if that's okay? I'm still sick; I don't think I'll make it."

"No, we have to go home now. I'll call a taxi. Solomon will be by himself."

"It's okay. You can go. I will come tomorrow."

"No, I can't leave you by yourself. Solomon doesn't know anybody; here he's new."

Sarah looks at his eyes and smiles. "Yes, I know he's new. That's why I said you could go home, and I will come tomorrow."

Azeb walks in and says, "How do you feel?"

"I still feel so bad. Can I please stay here for tonight? I don't think I'll make it home."

"Yes, this house is not mine. It is God's house, and please feel free."

Teddy says, "Good night," and leaves.

Azeb turns off the light and goes to take care of her business outside. Sarah goes to sleep.

***

Teddy arrives at home. Solomon sits outside, glaring at Teddy. "Where's Sarah?"

"I tried to tell you what happened, but you hung up the phone."

"Just give me the answer."

"She's sick."

"What? What happened?"

Teddy explains to him what happened, and Solomon gets up and says, "Why did you leave her? You know what will happen tomorrow!"

"I was trying to explain to Sarah, but while I was talking to her, Azeb came in. I don't know what to say in front of her, so I just left."

"I hope she doesn't tell her about me."

"I told you to tell her. If you told her, I wouldn't get embarrassed in front of Azeb."

"Oh, are you just worried about that? I don't want to lose Sarah."

"She will come tomorrow, or the day after, when she feels better. All her stuff is here."

"That's true. I just need one chance. When she comes home, I'll get her pregnant. It's a good time because she has just finished her period. Then she won't have a choice except to live with me."

***

Azeb walks into the bedroom, where Sarah's still asleep. Azeb looks at her, and her eyes fill with tears. She mutters to herself, "I feel sorry for your mom." Then she leaves the room and closes the door behind her.

Sarah gets up and says, "Azeb?"

Azeb returns. "Yes. Sorry for waking you up."

"It's okay." Sarah walks out of the bedroom, looks around the house, and notices the restaurant is closed. She goes to Azeb and asks her if she needs help.

Azeb tells her, "It's okay. You can help me tomorrow."

Early the next morning, Sarah wakes up, walks outside of the house, does jumping jacks, squats, and sit-ups. Azeb stands outside, looking at her with admiration, but Sarah is in her zone. Azeb walks to the kitchen.

Sarah asks Azeb, "Do you know someone who works as a smuggler other than them?"

"Yes, I know a guy." She is quiet for a moment. "Actually, my friend's cousin wants to go to Libya, but I don't know exactly when."

"When did they come to Sudan?"

"Oh, they grew up here. They came when they were children."

"Why, do they want to leave?"

Azeb laughs and looks at her, "Why do you want to go?"

"To follow my dream."

Azeb explains how people go to Libya and then on to Italy. She also describes how many people lose their lives in the desert and the ocean.

Sarah looks very worried, as her tears start flowing.

Azeb continues talking about how dangerous the road is and how difficult it is to get into Italy. She says, "Do you want to go back to your family?"

"No, I can't. I'll take my chances. I'll never give up. I want to make my dream come true."

"Before your dream, think about your life! What if you die? This road is not easy. It's nothing like the way you imagined."

"I didn't say it's easy, but I'll make it with God! Besides, I already made it from Ethiopia to here." Then she smiles.

"Wow! Are you joking? I wish I were like you and thought like you. The road you came from is nothing like the road you're going to now."

"Oh my God, it was so hard. You didn't see it. It was dark, and the border patrol searched for us. I was scared and peed in my pants."

"You don't get what I'm saying. One day you will remember it."

"It's not that I don't believe you. I'm already here. It's too late." She looks at Azeb and says, "Thanks so much for your advice."

"I don't blame you. I wish people stopped for a minute and thought about it." Azeb goes on. "A lot of people lose their life by just following others. We tell all the people who are going to Libya how dangerous it is, but nobody listens. They just go, and after a couple of months, we hear they died in the desert or drowned in the ocean, and if they're lucky, maybe they make it. I'm not telling you to be scared, but it's the truth."

Sarah doesn't know what to say; she just stares at her. Then Azeb looks at her and hugs her. They hug for a while, and both cry.

***

Solomon wakes up with a headache and grabs medication, but there is no water at home. So, he gets up and walks to the supermarket;

it's kind of far, so he takes a taxi. When he gets to the supermarket, he gathers bread, soda, milk, water, and tomatoes. Then he walks to get onions, but he sees Azeb and Sarah together at the store. He turns to avoid them and goes in the opposite direction, but the store isn't that big, so he finally leaves without buying anything. He goes to another store and buys water. He calls Teddy to tell him what he saw. Then he tells Teddy to go to Azeb's place after work. Teddy agrees.

***

Azeb tells Sarah she can work with her at the restaurant until she goes to Libya. Sarah is happy to work with her, and she serves in the restaurant. The first day she was kind of confused because she had never worked at a restaurant before, but at least, there wasn't a language problem because all the costumers were Ethiopian and Eritrean. A lot of the costumers ask Azeb where she got Sarah from and also if she was single, but Azeb acts like Sarah's cousin. A lot of customers respect Azeb. She is well-known in the Ethiopian community in Khartoum. Azeb helps a lot of people when they come from Ethiopia, especially if they don't have a family. Most of the Habesha community who lived in Khartoum help each other.

After two days, Teddy comes to the restaurant and sees Sarah. She's wearing an apron, Teddy's kind of confused; he was about to turn back, but Sarah sees him, and he walks toward her.

"Hey, Teddy?" She says with a fake smile.

"Sorry, I was busy with work, and Solomon was sick, so I was taking caring of him."

Sarah acts like she is worried. "Oh no, what happened?"

"I don't know. I think it was the weather. You know, he's new, and until he adapts to the weather, it's not easy. How are you feeling?"

"I feel better, especially when I started eating injera." Then she laughs.

"That's true; we can't live without injera."

Azeb walks in and says, "Hey, Teddy, have a seat." And she says to Sarah, "Let him sit."

"Oh, sorry, Teddy; have a seat."

"What is the special of the house today?"

"What do you want? The kitfo is very good."

"You know what? I'll take it. If you have Kocho? I'll have that too."

"Yes, we do. I will get you the best one."

"After you get it, can you come back here? I want to talk to you."

"Yes."

Teddy looks around the restaurant, and a couple of people come to say hello to him and sit down. They start talking about Sarah. Teddy listens to them. Sarah comes back and sits with Teddy. Everyone turns and looks at them.

"Ay, Habesha has a problem. Now they think you are my girl."

"Who cares?" Sarah asks.

"Whatever. When did you start working here?"

"Yesterday."

"When are you coming home?"

"I can't come home. If you can, do me a favor and bring me my bag? If not, it's okay. There's nothing important in it."

"What? What are you talking about?"

"I want to work and stay here until I go."

"Solomon is waiting for you, and he's by himself at home. I thought you guys want to travel to Italy together. So, I'm looking for a smuggler for you guys."

"Don't worry about me." Then she gets emotional and walks to the kitchen, her eyes full of tears. She tries not to cry, but tears fall down her cheeks. She runs to the bathroom, washes her face, then returns with a fake smile. She walks to the kitchen and grabs the food plate, then walks into the restaurant and serves the food. She sees money on the table, but Teddy is not there. She puts the food on the table and walks to help the other customers. The people who had been sitting around Teddy see her when she puts food on the table, and they call her "Server."

She turns to them, and they say, "He left."

"Oh, thank you." She stops for a moment, then grabs the food and walks to the kitchen.

"What happened?" Azeb asks. "The food is not good?"

"No, it's not about that. It's Teddy." Then she starts looking at Azeb hopelessly.

"What happened to Teddy? Tell me."

"I don't know, when I went to the table with food he left," then she shows the money to her. "I got this on the table."

"Did you say something to him?"

"Yes. We talked. But I swear to God I didn't say any word to offend him or Solomon." Then she starts telling her everything.

Azeb takes the food and says, "Let's enjoy it. Don't worry. It's not your fault. He's just scared because you know about him and Solomon." Then she stops talking and looks at her, "Do you have something important in their house?"

"Kind of, I left all my clothes with them, but I have my money with me."

"Don't worry about your clothes. I will get you something. However, you can't take any clothes when you travel."

"What? I need something to change into, at least. I can't wear one outfit all week."

"Ha, you are not going on vacation. You can't have extra clothes, other than what you're wearing. Besides, it's not one week; it's much more than that, depending upon the driver. Some drivers know the road; some don't. That is if the border soldiers don't catch you."

"Oh, God." Sarah starts eating and tries to avoid the conversation. Azeb looks at her, realizing she doesn't want to hear these things.

***

Teddy walks home and sees Solomon sleeping outside on the bed. His head is wrapped in a scarf. Teddy looks at him and sits next to him.

"Whose scarf is that?" Teddy asks.

"Sarah's."

"Why are you wearing a wrap?"

65

"I don't feel well. Especially my head. And I miss her."

Teddy is quiet and looks at the floor.

Solomon turns his head toward Teddy. "Are you okay?" he asks, but there is no answer, Teddy is staring at the floor, and his eyes are darting back and forth. Solomon reaches his hand and touches Teddy.

Teddy, startled, turns to him. He looks like he woke up from a bad dream.

Solomon says, "Did you hear what I said?"

"I'm sorry. I didn't hear you."

"What? So, I've just been talking to myself? That's crazy! What is wrong with you?"

Teddy looks at him and says, "Are you ready to hear this?"

"Yes, tell me what happened? I'm a man, okay?"

"Sarah knows everything about us."

Solomon gets out of his bed and says, "What do you mean?"

"I said, she knows what we do and who we are!"

"That isn't true. How?" Then he puts his finger on his lips and says, "Oh yes! Azeb is behind all of this!" Then he gets up.

Teddy holds him and says, "Where are you going?"

"I'm going to talk to Azeb! She is always involved in my business. I let it go in the past, but not now! She came into my life."

"This time, it's not Azeb," Teddy says.

"Who the hell is it then? Tell me?"

Teddy looks at him and breathes.

Solomon says, "Why do you look at me like I'm crazy? Let me go, and I will find out for myself."

"Oh, look, it's Sarah."

"What? That doesn't make sense. Who told Sarah?"

"You..."

"...What the heck are you talking about?"

"She heard you the first day when you called me on the phone."

Solomon sits down on the bed with his hands on his head. Teddy continues talking, "She just acted like she didn't know anything."

Solomon breaks his silence and says, "She is a good actress. She acted well. I never thought someone could fool me." Then he laughs out loud and continues. "Not her. She acted like she doesn't know anything, but she fooled me. I will show her who I am! Not her!" He gets up and kicks the bed with his barefoot, then walks to the tree and starts beating it.

Teddy tries to stop him, but it isn't easy.

Solomon's hand starts bleeding, but he doesn't see it or feel it. He continues hitting it with his foot and sometimes with his hand.

Finally, Teddy sees his hand and is shocked. He runs to him and says, "Solomon, are you crazy? Do you see your hand? What are you doing?" Teddy grabs his hand and pushes him onto the bed. The blood is running all over his hand and also his feet. "Don't you feel the pain? Look at what you've done. We need to get you to the hospital."

"No, I'm not going anywhere. Not before I show her who I am! Now leave me alone." He tries to get up, then sees his foot is full of blood. He says, "Shit. She made me bleed all over my body. Especially my heart."

"Dude, take it easy. That is why I didn't want to tell you, but you forced me to speak."

"I never thought Sarah was smart! I thought she didn't know anything. But I was wrong!" He stands, then starts feeling the pain in his foot. He strolls inside the home, then goes to Sarah's bag. He searches for her money, but there is nothing except for her clothes and tampons. He says, "She played with our minds, she fooled us. I can't believe it. Please tell me I'm dreaming. This can't be true."

Teddy walks to the room and says, "What happened?"

"Come see with your own eyes. Then please tell me I'm dreaming!"

"I don't understand what you are talking about!"

Solomon grabs a receipt from her bag and shows Teddy, who gets confused. Then he takes the receipt from Solomon's hand and looks at it. The receipt is from Sarah, exchanging money from Ethiopian birr to American dollars. Then Solomon continues searching for her money, but there is none there. Also, she didn't use all of the tampons. The box is full; it's just missing one piece.

"That liar!"

Teddy tries to calm him down, but Solomon is mad, and his ego rises. He shows the receipt to Teddy.

Teddy says, "What is it?"

"This is a receipt from you when you took her to the money exchange."

"What are you talking about? That wasn't me."

"What? Who could it be other than you? I purposefully got her to exchange half the money at the border."

"Wow, I see that you don't trust me! That's fine. I don't blame you. This dirty job has blocked your mind, but I told you I don't have a clue."

"Okay, if you are not helping her, if I'm not the one, then who the hell is behind this? Tell me? I used to trust you with my life, but not anymore."

"What did you say?"

"You like Sarah, I've known that from the day we arrived. You have been trying to talk to her!" Then Solomon goes back into his mind and flashes back to how Teddy always looked her in the eyes and laughed at whatever joke she said. When she walked, Teddy would stare at the way she walked, the way she moved. He also gave her a lot of compliments about her unique voice.

Solomon wakes up from his memory and punches Teddy in the face. Teddy tries not to fight him, but he can't stop himself because Solomon is serious. They fight for a while. The neighbors hear them, and they jump in the middle to separate them, but Solomon wants to fight more. However, the neighbors pull Solomon apart from Teddy.

One of the neighbors takes Solomon to his house and says, "Hey, this is not Ethiopia! You're gonna end up in jail. What's wrong with you, guys? You two are brothers!"

"He is not my brother."

Solomon says, "I don't want to see him anymore. I will kill him, trust me!"

"What? Are you kidding me! You come here to kill people? That is your dream?"

"You don't know what he did to me. He ruined my life. I prefer to die or go to jail."

"No, you are bleeding too much, let's go to the hospital. Then we will talk about it."

"I'm not going anywhere."

"Okay, stay here for tonight, then we will talk to him tomorrow."

"No, hell no. I'll sleep at home." He gets up, but a neighbor sits him back down and gives him a glass of water. Solomon holds the water for a while, but then he throws the glass at the wall.

The neighbor holds his hand and says, "Please take a deep breath. You will feel bad tomorrow when you finally calm down."

"Why would I feel bad? Because he slept with my future wife? The girl I love. The girl I want to marry and build a family together, but he stole her from me and hid her. Just tell me why?"

"What? Oh, you had a girlfriend?"

"Yes." He starts telling him about Sarah.

"I never saw her."

Solomon explains his past experience. A while ago, he got married in Ethiopia and brought her to Sudan, but one of his close friends took his wife from him and took her to Libya, then to Italy with him. Since then, Solomon has never had feelings for any girl. He just used them for sex. But now he likes Sarah and wants to build a family with her.

The neighbor says, "I understand, but you can't live in the past. How do you know Teddy slept with Sarah?"

"I know it! I have a lot of evidence. I'm not just talking. I know it for a fact. But why my girl? Why can't he find a girl for himself? Why? Why?" He starts punching the couch.

"Please be patient. I'll talk to him to find out."

Teddy and the other two neighbors are talking. Teddy explains to the man what happened, and the man feels sorry. He says, "He will calm down. Don't worry."

"I don't get it!" Teddy cries. "He is my brother! How could he suspect me? What is in his head? I'm not an animal. How could I sleep with his girl?" Then he stops talking and laughs. "She doesn't even like him. She is the one who escaped from him. He can go to Azeb's restaurant and talk to her, but I'm done with him. I can't live with him. I can't even trust him with my life."

"Teddy, relax. He might be mad, but we can't judge him."

Then Teddy gets up and grabs his bag. The two neighbors walk toward him to try to stop him, but Teddy insists. The neighbors ask him, "Where are you going?"

"To be honest, I don't even know where I'm going."

"Okay, but please call me." Then he hugged Teddy. They walk out together until they get to the gate. The Second neighbor walks toward his home while Teddy stands to wait for a taxi. The other neighbor hold's Teddy's hand and begs him to stay, but Teddy doesn't want to stay.

The neighbor says, "Remember one thing. We are your family, and we're here for each other. We need to support each other as brothers. No one other than us will help us. Please stay here. I will talk to him. No matter what, don't forget, we are in the same country."

"Thanks, I know that. I promise I will call you."

A taxi arrives, and Teddy drives off in a taxi.

***

Sarah worked with Azeb for two months. Now she has experience working in a restaurant as a server. She also met a lot of Habesha. They tell her about their life in Sudan. Sometimes she feels bad for them because a lot of people work as maids. A foreigner can't go to school here in Sudan.

Sarah does her usual morning exercises. Azeb comes from the supermarket, looks at Sarah, and says, "Sari, you have a surprise."

She smiles, "What is it?"

"There are people leaving tonight."

"Where are they going?"

"Libya."

"Wow! Great."

"Also, there are people I know who will go with you. There are girls your age, and they are cousins."

"Oh, that's great. Oh God! What would've happened to me if I didn't meet you that day at the store?" She hugs Azeb and keeps talking. "Do you remember the day I met you? That day I felt so happy."

Azeb says, "I was so surprised how you came outside by yourself? You didn't even speak the language."

"I just wrote down the road name and the cross street." Her mind went to flashback to Solomon's phone conversation. Solomon sits outside, talking on the phone while Sarah was inside the living room, reading an Amharic fiction book. She overheard Solomon giving a direction to the person he's talking to. He said it over and over. Sarah grabs a pen and begins writing the address behind the book.

The next day Teddy and Solomon told Sarah they were going to the store for clothes for Solomon, and they left her by herself. Also, the key was on the table. She got up, changed her dress, and left after them. She took a taxi and gave him the address; she exchanged her money and also met Azeb. Then she took the same taxi home before the men arrived back home.

"Wow, you're so smart, but did you tell them?"

"No, hell no. Because I know what their plan is. I just act like I don't know anything."

Azeb says, surprisingly, "What?"

"No, because they think I'm dumb. I heard them when they talked to each other, they said, she doesn't know anything." Then she laughs.

Azeb looks at her, amused, and says, "I'm still surprised how brave you are, but what did Solomon say about that specific store?"

"That is a lot of Habesha where they meet and shop. I think the person he's talking to is new because he repeated over and over the address. Did you shop there?"

"Yes, that place is well known by the Habesha community. The owner is Ethiopian. No, I haven't been in that store for years. I went that day because I had a meeting."

"Oh, my God! That's' why my mom said everything happens for a reason!"

"That is true." Azeb looks at her for a moment, and says, "Did they know we met before?"

"No, they don't have a clue. How would they know? They think I never went outside. I just asked them to take me to the church. Then I begged Teddy to take me to a restaurant, so he took me here. I was worried until I saw you because I didn't want to end up at another restaurant."

"Oh, I know you will feel that way, but we only have one church. So, people come after church because it's close to the church. That's why I told you to do so."

"Worked perfectly." They walk together to the kitchen.

Sarah was serving, as usual, and Solomon stands outside. He sees Sarah, but she doesn't see him. He walks back and forth, then steps inside and turns back to leave. He says, "It's okay; I will come tomorrow."

***

Azeb walks into the living room with grocery bags in her hands. Then she starts putting the food, bottles of water, several cans of pineapple, snacks, packed injera with Shiro (chickpea) stew, dry injera, and Shiro powder in a big bag. In the other plastic bag, she puts a blanket. Another bag has one pair of pants, one shirt, a couple of pairs of underwear, tampons, and a ski mask. Sarah walks into the room and sees Azeb packing everything.

"What is it?"

"That's for you."

"It's a lot. What am I going to do with all this?"

"You're gonna need it. You will need to eat it." She looks at all the stuff and says, "Trust me. If you don't finish it, you will give it to someone."

"Thanks so much." She hugs her and says, "I'm gonna miss you." Then she cries.

Azeb says, "No, don't cry, just be strong."

"Okay, I will." Then she looks at the blanket, points her finger, and says, "Is that for me?

"Yes, it's..."

"For what? I'm traveling in the desert. It will be super-hot."

"Maybe, or maybe not. The desert can get quite cold at night. Just take it with you; it'll help you."

"Okay, thanks."

Azeb checks her watch and then says, "Oh, they will be here shortly. Come, let's eat first." Azeb prepares Sarah's favorite food and puts it on the table.

Sarah walks to wash her hands and turns back to the table. They eat together.

A knock on the door startles them. Azeb says, "Who is that?"

"It's me," the smuggler says, standing outside.

"Oh, come in."

"No, I can't. Please hurry up. I have a lot of people outside."

"Okay, just five minutes."

"Are you joking.?" He walks inside and looks at Sarah. She just sits and eats. "Who's going?"

Azeb points at Sarah. Then he looks at her and orders her to get up. Sarah gets up and looks at Azeb as tears fill her eyes. Azeb gives her a tight hug.

He walks out and says, "Ya Allah hurry up. Otherwise, I'm leaving her."

Sarah takes the plastic bags and walks after him, then Azeb grabs the rest of the stuff and walks behind her. The smuggler opens the door to the car, and Sarah gets inside.

Azeb gives her the rest of the bags, then says, to the smuggler, "Please give me a minute." She runs back inside, but the driver leaves.

Azeb comes back with a plastic bag and sees that the vehicle has already left. She says to herself, "My God, what is she wearing? I wish I would have dressed her. What do I do now?" She grabs her phone and tries to call the smuggler, but he doesn't answer. She sits on the porch and says, "Oh, God, I didn't even introduce her to my cousin."

Chapter Five

Sarah sits next to the window in the vehicle, looking at people who are walking, at the buildings, and then the trees. She sees a family walking together and stares at them, but the vehicle was moving so fast she couldn't see them anymore. Without realizing it, her tears streamed down Sarah's cheek. She turns around but can't see anything because the car is so dark and very quiet. Sarah turns back to the window to look outside.

After a while, the vehicle stops, and the smuggler whispers, "No one is allowed to talk. Be quiet." He presses his finger onto his lips. Everyone nods with fear in their eyes.

The smuggler gets out, and everybody gets quiet. They don't even move. They look like they are ready to run. After a couple of minutes, he comes back with more people. The car is full now; it's more than twelve people. He urges them to sit. The car moves before the new passengers can sit, and one of the girls falls on top of several of the others.

One new girl screams, "Please stop for a moment. I'm feeling pain. I'm pregnant."

"Be quiet," the smuggler says. "Otherwise, I'll throw you out of this car."

"Please, don't. Do you have a sister or mother? Can you please stop the car for just a minute?" She tries to hold back from vomiting, but it's too hard to stop. She puts her hand over her mouth, but it's impossible. She throws-up on several of the other passengers. Everyone starts screaming.

"Can you please stop for her," Sarah pleads. "She's sick."

Several people speak up for her, and the car suddenly stops. Without a word, the smuggler grabs her and puts her on the sidewalk. The car starts and leaves her. She tries to move, but she can't.

Everyone in the car starts screaming. One of them says, "We're not going anywhere if you won't stop this car."

The driver continues driving for a few minutes. The people scream more and more.

The smuggler shouts, "Be quiet!" Then he gives an order to the driver to turn back.

The pregnant woman sits on the sidewalk, crying and saying to herself, "Oh God. Why is this happening to me? What did I do wrong? Please don't leave me like this. Where am I going? I don't even know where I am."

Her clothes are covered with vomit. She tries to clean it off with her hand, but it's impossible. She says to herself, "I don't even have another set of clothes. Oh, God, please." Then she bends down on her knees, her eyes closed, her hands up to the sky, her eyes full of tears.

The smuggler's voice surprises her. She looks at him, and she bends down and kisses the road. "Thank you, God!"

The smuggler opens the door for her, and she sits. People ask her how she is feeling. She says, "I feel better now."

One of the men, who called is Kaleb, puts his hand into his pocket, grabs some snacks, a napkin, and gives it to her. She appreciates it and starts cleaning her hands.

The smuggler says, "Please be quiet!" His voice is intense and robust.

Sarah looks at the pregnant lady. "She's pregnant. Why is she going? It will be tough for her, but if she can make it, I can too."

After they ride for a couple of hours, Sarah says to herself. "I thought we are taking some big cars. Wow, this taxi is going into the desert, it is unbelievable."

Outside is very dark, and they can't see anything -- no moon, no stars, and nothing moves on the road. Everything is quiet. Sarah continues thinking, *How many days will it take to get to Libya? Maybe five days, maybe six days, or less or more. Oh no, not more than six days.* She's concerned, and out loud, says, "But where are we going to take a shower?"

The smuggler hears her and says, "I said everyone must be quiet."

Sarah stops talking. After a while, they arrive at a house in the middle of the desert. The car stops, and the smuggler says, "One by one, stroll after me."

Everyone stands; the females go first, and then the men walk after them with their stuff. Outside it is very dark. They can't see anything; they hold hands entering the house. There is a small light in the corner. The house is empty and full of sand. Everyone stands, and the smuggler gives them an order to sit. People sit on the floor.

Sarah looks around to see how many people there are, and she starts counting. There are twelve people, and she says to herself, "How did that little taxi hold this many people?"

After thirty minutes, more people come. They are from Sudan, Eritrea, Somalia, and Ethiopia. All smugglers come together to collect the money from the people. They ask the people to pay, and everyone goes into their pockets to reach for the cash. After all the people pay the smugglers, they start talking one by one.

"We have a couple of hours to stay here," one of the smugglers says. "If you guys need to take a nap, you can. We'll wake you up, but don't open your bags because we don't know what time the cars will arrive." Then he leaves.

Sarah looks at what the other people are doing. Four girls sit next to her, and they start braiding their hair, but it isn't good.

Sarah moves closer to them and says, "Hey, I can help you; I know how to braid hair."

One girl whispers into Sarah's ears, "We're not braiding the hair to look nice."

"Oh, okay." Sarah moves back. "Why are you doing it then?"

"To hide our money inside our hair."

"How?"

The girl motions Sarah to watch more closely. The girl divides the hair with her finger, rolls the money together, puts it inside the hair, and braids it. Sarah is shocked and surprised. All four girls do the same thing.

"Would you like for me to braid your money into your hair?"

Sarah says, "Yes, please."

The girl does Sarah's hair.

"Thanks so much, it means a lot to me."

"It's okay; we are a family. Sorry, what is your name?"

"Sarah."

"Oh, it's my sister's name. My name is Winta. Are you Ethiopian or Eritrea?"

"Ethiopian. What about you?"

"Eritrea, Asmara."

"Wow, I heard Asmara and Bahir Dar look the same."

"Oh, are you from Bahir Dar?"

"Yes."

"That's where I was born. I left when I was fourteen."

"Why?"

"The Ethiopian government deported us."

"I'm sorry about that."

"We lost everything. We didn't even have the time to sell my family's house, we just left."

"I'm very sorry. I had a lot of friends who were deported and separated from their family too. Things like that shouldn't happen, but they do. It's not right."

A couple of years ago, there was a war between Ethiopia and Eritrea, and many Ethiopians were deported from Eritrea, and many Eritreans were deported from Ethiopia. However, they often only deported a few members of the family. For example, if the husband was an Ethiopian living in Eritrea with his wife and children who were Eritrean, he would be deported to Ethiopia by himself. Or, if the wife is Eritrean living in Ethiopia, it was the same thing. In both cases, the children could choose to stay with their mom or go with their father. That's how a lot of families got separated from each other.

Winta has the same story. Her father is Ethiopian, and her mother is Eritrean. That is how Winta got deported with her mother. Winta wanted to stay in Ethiopia, but her father died when she was two.

While Sarah and Winta talk, the smugglers return and wake everyone up.

Smuggler Four says in Arabic, "Come out." He points to the Sudanese, and the Sudanese follow him. There are three Toyota Land Cruisers outside. It's 5:00 a.m. and still dark. The car has no passenger seats so they can fit as many people as they can inside.

Then one of the smugglers jumps on top of the car, and everyone gives him their bags, and he ties the bags down very tightly.

People enter the car and sit, and the smuggler says, "Get as close as you can. This car has to take forty people. Half inside and the rest of you can sit on the top."

Smuggler Three brings a Somalian to another car.

Sarah tries to look outside, but it's impossible. She walks to Winta and whispers, "This is getting so scary."

"Don't worry; we'll be fine."

Smuggler Two gets the rest of the people to the car. After they put their stuff down, he says, "Women inside, men outside."

The pregnant woman sits in the front next to the driver. The rest of the women sit behind. Sarah looks confused because there is no chair, but she sees everyone sitting on the floor. She sits next to Winta. Inside the car, more than eighteen women crammed, and the rest of the people sit on the roof.

The drivers start following the lead car. After they drove for thirty minutes, one of the guys falls from the top of the car.

The smuggler says to the driver, "Please stop for a minute."

The guy hops from the car waving his hands, but running on the sand isn't easy, so he keeps falling. He gets up, tries to run but falls again. After a couple of minutes, the car stops. He stands up and gets to the car. The smuggler grabs the guy's hand and pulls him up.

Then the smuggler says, "Don't sleep! Stay awake. Do you understand me? If you fall again, trust me, I will leave you there." Then he says to the driver loudly, "Let's go."

"Wow, now we can see the light outside," Sarah says to Winta.

"Yes, finally, the sun is rising."

"Can you imagine if people lived here?"

"You are so crazy! How could you think of that?"

"I'm just saying, what if?"

"They will die. This desert is super-hot. There is nothing."

"How do you know that?" Sarah asks.

"Sweetie, I studied geography in college for four years."

"Oh, great. Good for you, the school gave you a Bachelor's Degree after four years of studying. Now, you'll earn a Master's Degree after seeing for yourself what the Sahara Desert looks and feels like."

"Sarah, stop, you joke a lot." Then she laughs loudly, and everyone turns back to look at her.

Winta says, "Oh, sorry," but she can't control her laughter as others laugh with her.

"Stop, Winta, you are the craziest one. I just told the truth."

Winta looks at Sarah and keeps laughing.

Sarah continues talking, "Let me tell you something. I chose this road because I wasn't good at geography."

Winta keeps laughing and then says, "Sarah, please stop."

Then one of the girls tells Winta, "Your friend, she is so funny. Did you guys grow up together?"

Winta looks at her to respond, but the girl keeps continuing to talk, "Or are you sisters?"

"We met just yesterday, but I feel like I know her. She is so sweet, very open, and so funny. Sorry, what's your name?"

"Aida." Aida is an Ethiopian with light brown skin, around five feet tall. Her medium length hair frames her chubby cheek and big eyes. "What is yours?"

"Winta." She points her finger at Sarah. "Her name is Sarah."

"Welcome to our group," Sarah says.

Aida smiles and says, "Thanks."

Then Sarah says to Winta, "Oh, I forgot to tell you."

"What?"

"About my geography class," Sarah says.

Winta and Aida look at her, then Winta says, "What about your geography class?"

"I wasn't good at geography, and one day my teacher said you should learn about geography practically because you are not good at theory, then he gave me a prescription for this road to learn geography."

Aida and Winta laughing loud, but Sarah is serious and looks at them.

Aida says to Winta, "My gosh! You know she is so comic."

"If we can't make jokes and laugh about it, I think this road will be too hard," Sarah says. "And I don't want to think about it."

"That's true, Sarah," Winta says.

"Exactly," Aida agrees. "Let me introduce you to my cousins." She turns back and calls two young girls.

One of the girls says, "My name is Liya." She looks like she's sixteen and is very quiet.

The other girl is around fifteen and is shorter than Sarah, with dark skin, average weight, and short hair. She looks humorous and says, "My name is Mazaa."

"Nice to meet you all," Sarah says. "I came by myself, and now I have a lot of friends."

"We are all family; we are not just friends, okay?" Mazaa says. And she gives hugs Sarah, then Aida, Winta, and Liya. Sarah cries, and they wipe her face.

Sarah says with her sweet voice, "Thanks so much, everyone, for thinking of me as family. I'm blessed to have you." Tears form.

"Please stop crying. You look good when you laugh." Winta says.

"Look at me; I'm so sweet when I cry too." Then Sarah laughs.

Everyone talks, makes jokes, and laughs to pass the time. It looks like everyone has known each other for a long time, but a lot of people just met in the car.

There are three different cars: one car full of Sudanese people, the other vehicle filled with Somalian, and the last one is Eritrean and Ethiopian, or Habesha. The cars go one after another. There is no road; they just drive on the sand. The men on top of the car are covered in dust. They wear masks covering their faces, but there is a lot of sand, and they can't even see how it looks in the desert. Some men cover their eyes with their hands. They can barely see. When they open their eyes, sometimes their eyelid fills with sand. Some men's eyes are full of tears, but even though they don't see each other, they still talk and laugh.

After driving for six hours, the cars stop for lunch. The smugglers get up first, and one says, "Everyone, get out; we have one hour for lunch."

When the women get out of the car and see the men, they barely recognize them because their bodies and faces are covered with sand. Liya's cousin stands close to her, but she doesn't know who he is until he calls her name. She turns back, but she doesn't know who called her.

He says, "It is me, Kaleb."

"What the heck, what happened?"

"The sand." She tries to clean him up, but he says, "Don't worry."

Then Aida, Mazaa, and Sarah walk over. Mazaa says to Kaleb, "This is Sarah, our new sister."

Kaleb is an Ethiopian and about six feet two inches with a medium weight, brown skin, and a generous man.

After they introduce them, they grab their food and walk a little bit and sit on the sand.

Sarah and Aida find wood for a fire while Kaleb, Mazaa, Liya look for stones to cook with. They start lighting the wood and put the pan in the fire; then, they cook whatever they have. After they finish cooking, they put their food on top of plastic bags, and they start to eat.

Sarah grabs the bottle of water and says, "Let's wash our hands."

Kaleb looks at her. "You must be joking. How could you think of washing your hands?" He grabs the water and puts it down. "We have to be lucky to not run out of water. A lot of people lose their lives on this road from thirst."

Sarah looks around her at everyone eating, but no one is washing their hands. Then Kaleb says, "Eat before the food is finished." She tries to clean her hands by wiping them together.

Kaleb says, "Sorry, Sarah, you are a sister to me now, and I don't want to see you suffering later."

"I know that, but I never eat food without washing my hands. It's just hard for me."

"All Habesha wash their hands before they eat. That's how we were raised, but you see everyone is eating -- even the Somalians and Sudanese. Everyone is eating. Just eat, God will protect us."

"Thank God that I have met you guys. Azeb told me she had a cousin going this week, but the smuggler didn't give her time to introduce me."

"Who is Azeb?" Kaleb asks.

"Azeb has the restaurant, Queen of Sheba."

"Oh my God, is that you, Sarah? She is my cousin, she told me about you?"

"Wow, you guys are her cousins?"

"Yes, we are," Aida answered.

"It's so amazing! I can't believe this, thank God!"

The smugglers walk around and tells everyone it's time to get up. Everyone wraps up their food and put the food in the car. The men get on top, and the women get inside. Sarah's leg sinks in the sand as she walks, and she turns back to tell them, "I'm glad we are so small because if we were any bigger, we would get stuck here."

"That's true," Mazaa winks at Sarah to watch Kaleb, who is struggling to walk, and Sarah laughs.

Sarah says to Winta, "Where have you been? I didn't see you?"

"Oh, my food is with my friends, that's why." Then Winta turns back to show Sarah her friends.

People keep making jokes. Sarah looks at the desert, but there are no trees; nothing to look at but sand forever and forever. It's nothing but dust, sand, and crushed rocks.

Aida asks Sarah, "What are you looking at?"

"I'm looking at the desert. I get amused by nature. Look at this desert; there is nothing. Now imagine our country, full of everything: mountains, rivers, lakes, and trees. Sometimes it's good to see everything because you can appreciate it when you don't have it anymore."

Everyone listens to her, and Winta says, "That's true. People don't appreciate what they have until they lose it."

Everyone gets quiet for a while, and Sarah says, "Let's sing."

"I have a horrible voice," Winta says.

"We are not singing for *American Idol*. It's just to pass the time."

"Yes, let's sing." Aida agrees.

"Whose song do you want to sing?" Sarah asks.

"Aster Aweke, or Teddy Afro."

"No, let's sing Tibebe Workye."

"Which one?"

"*Meda lay kere Ibie Meda lay. Dagmegana aynishin lalay midiri lay!* When translated, it means, my heart left in the field. I can't see your eyes again on earth."

"Okay, but it's kind of sad," Aida says.

84

"Looks like he sings it for people like us," Winta says.

"I know the song is for the people who lost their beloved ones."

Then Sarah starts smiling and says, "We have to sing for ourselves. We might make it to Italy, or we might die before we get there."

"Sarah, don't say that," Mazaa says.

"That's the truth," Winta says. "This is my second time traveling on this road..."

"...What?" Sarah says.

"The first time I got deported from Libya. I tried to stay in Sudan, but there is nothing, just working for the madam my entire life. Instead of working as a housekeeper, I'd prefer to die on this road. That isn't my dream, but the first time I went on this road, we lost seven people in the desert."

"What, seven people died?" Aida asks.

"Yes, please let's talk about something else," Winta says. Her eyes fill with tears.

"Let's sing," Sarah suggests again.

"Sari, please sing a Tibebe Workye song," Winta says.

Sarah jokingly says, "Yes, I will! I have the best voice on the planet." Then she laughs.

Aida starts singing, and Sarah says, "You're great."

Then she follows her singing, and when they finish one song, they sing another.

After a long day of driving, they stop, and the smugglers get out and say, "We are staying here for tonight."

Everyone gets out and take their stuff with them. Outside, the sunset looks like the sun is tired. Everyone finds wood for a fire, but there is not enough. Then they cook their food first. Then everyone makes a circle around the fire and talks. There are three circles of Sudanese, Somalian, and Habesha, but when they need something, they help each other because everyone is family. It doesn't matter where they come from.

Kaleb says, "Before it gets too dark, we have to make our resting place, then we can come back to pass the time with talk and laughter."

"Okay." Aida says, "Me and Sarah, we can make it; we just put our blankets down to save our place."

Sarah and Aida go to set up the place. Aida grabs a couple of blankets, and Sarah helps her to set up. Then Sarah opens her plastic bag, there is no blanket, then she opens the other one, and there is nothing. She opens the last one; it's a trash bag; she looks at it and starts laughing.

Aida looks at her and says, "Are you okay?"

She can't stop laughing and shows her the trash when Aida grabs the trash bag from Sarah and runs to Kaleb to show them. Sarah runs after her, but they fall several times before they get to Kaleb.

Kaleb saw them and walks toward them and says, "Are you guys, okay?"

Aida, while she falls on the sand, shows the bag to Kaleb, "Look at Sarah's blanket."

He smiles and says, "She may bring it by accident."

"I didn't even see it." Sarah laughs.

"Don't worry; you can share it with us."

Then Kaleb grabs their hands from the ground, and they walk together.

One man, from Asmara, Eritrea, but he speaks fluent Amharic, talks as everyone listens to him. He tells them he went on this road twice because the Libyan police put him in prison for eight months and then deported him to Eritrea. Then he escaped from Eritrea by Tesseney, which borders Eritrea and Sudan and finally made it into Sudan. The next time the Libyan government deported him, but this time two guys hijacked the plane and forced them to stop in Sudan. He says, "However, I can't stop trying, no matter what, until I get into Italy."

Everyone asks him questions about the road, and he answers them.

Then everyone goes to sleep; the weather gets colder. Everyone is sleeping on the sand, but the sand is freezing. Sarah can't sleep, and she stands, then she starts looking at how other people are sleeping. She says to herself, "Why am I cold? How are other people sleeping? Why can't I sleep like them? Or, do they not feel the cold and are faking it?"

Kaleb sees Sarah and says, "Are you okay?"

"Oh, I'm fine. I'm just looking at how other people sleep."

She sees several Sudanese men and the way they made their place to sleep by digging a hole in the sand large enough for their body to fit. Sarah says to herself, "I think they have experience."

"What did you say?" Kaleb asks.

"Oh, sorry. I was talking to myself, but I was amused at how that Sudanese guy made his place to sleep."

"Why don't you sleep? Are you scared, or do you feel cold?"

"I feel very cold! I don't know how I will sleep."

"Just try. The sand will get hot."

"Okay."

She goes to sleep, but the blanket isn't enough for everybody because she slept in the end, and she just had enough to cover half of her body. She starts shaking as her tears come. The entire night she tosses and turns because she can't sleep.

When the light shows up in the sky, the smugglers get up and say, "Wake everyone, we have to start driving before the sunrises."

Everyone wakes and starts eating something fast. Then they put their stuff in a bag, but Sarah can't move her body; it was so cold, and she is still shaking.

"Sarah, are you okay?" Kaleb asks.

She can't even talk. Her body is shaking. He holds her in his arms and puts her in the car. He puts two blankets on her.

Winta sees Sarah and feels terrible for her. Everyone talks about her, and say, "She will be fine; maybe the cold will make her blood freeze. We have just to give her some heat." Then some people keep talking.

But Winta, Aida, Mazaa, and Liya are quiet, Then Mazaa says, "Now I realize who makes us laugh."

Everyone agrees.

It's been a few hours when Aida checks on Sarah. Sarah is sweating all over her body and finally asleep.

Aida is scared and shows her to Winta; then, they try to wake Sarah.

The old lady says, "Leave her alone. She is sleeping and also breathing normally; I think she just needs rest."

Then they look at her with hope.

"Trust me; she'll be fine."

Everyone keeps chatting.

After a couple of hours, Sarah wakes up and looks around, but she doesn't remember anything. And she says, "Oh my gosh, it's super-hot."

Aida says, "Oh, I'm glad you woke."

"I'm sorry I wasn't able to sleep all night. I was dying from the cold, and I have never felt cold like that in my entire life. Look at me now; I'm sweating. Oh, God!"

"It was so cold last night," Winta says. "And it's boiling now. That's why they called it the desert; the days are super-hot, and nighttime is freaking cold."

"I hope it doesn't get too cold tonight."

"Don't worry; I'll sleep at the end, and also, I can give you my blanket," Winta says.

"Thanks." They keep talking away.

* * *

After eight days in the desert, there are still long stretches ahead of them, seemingly as endless and imposing as the day they began. The tightly packed women bounce and sway in the seat-less vehicle to the muffled sounds of the men talking loudly on the roof, mixing with the sound of the engine taxing heavily through the sand.

Sarah wipes the sweat from her brow. "Oh God, when will we arrive in Libya?"

Winta looks out the window. "Maybe three or four more days."

"Oh God, another four days?"

"If we're lucky."

Aida looks at her two friends pleadingly. "Our water and food won't last us for four days!"

"We can help each other," Winta responds, and she is quiet for a moment.

Something interrupts the loud talking on the roof of the car. Then there is yelling and the sounds of fists pounding on the roof and the top of the driver's door. The car stops.

One of the men on the roof has become unconscious. The smugglers try to revive him with water and pineapple juice but to no avail. He is lowered to the ground and hauled inside the car with the women. His head rests on Sarah's thigh. As the car takes off, Sarah and the women cover him with a blanket and prop his head up to receive small amounts of carefully poured juice.

Minutes later, Sarah touches his forehead. "We have to put more blankets on him; he's very cold."

The older woman adjusts the blanket to look at the man's face and jerks back with a scream. The dead man's eyes have rolled back into his head, leaving only the whites showing. The old woman's screams trigger more screams and cries from the rest of the women, and they beat their fists on the car to stop.

All three cars grind to a halt, one after another, and the Habesha women flee from the car, running to the other vehicles.

Men from all three Land Cruisers come and take the body out of the vehicle, laying him on the sand while they deliberate what to do.

After a brief minute, a smuggler says, "We don't have time, we have to take him there." He points to a small nondescript knoll of sand, a short distance from the car -- all the men, Sudanese, Somalian and Habesha murmur that they want to bury the body. The women stay close to vehicles, crying.

A large collection of men from the different trucks carry the body to the knoll. Arriving, Kaleb sees other newly dead bodies around the base of the large dune, half-covered by blowing sand. He tries to get closer to see who they are. They are all women. He grimaces, shakes his head, and in disbelief, walks back to the body where the men are using their hands to dig a shallow grave.

A Sudanese man stops digging with a loud curse, and immediately the men all get and scramble away. At the bottom of the new hole, a small patch of torn fabric and dark skin has been uncovered. The area is a graveyard, and no one knows where the boundaries are.

The men argue briefly with each other, then carry the body to a spot a few dozen feet away. Not wanting to uncover another body, they scoop out an unusually shallow depression and slide the body in.

As they work, Kaleb notices that the men's faces reflect the death and lifelessness of this awful place. No one talks. They scoop just enough sand over the fallen traveler to form a small mound, and then one by one, and in small groups, they rise to their feet and walk back to their car. A few looks back at the other half-covered bodies around the base of the massive dune.

The women still stand near the cars, crying.

The smugglers herd them back into the vehicles. "Let's go; this is nothing. Get in! Everyone stop crying."

***

After three days, everyone has depleted their food and water. The driver keeps driving, but the peoples' faces become darker, dirtier, and their lips are dry, smush, and broken. No one sings, makes jokes, or even talks. Everyone's eyes squeeze and small.

Sarah leans over to Aida and quietly whispers, "In case of an emergency, If I die, my family's phone number is..."

"Please, Sarah, stop saying that. You are the strongest one -- please don't say that! We'll make it!"

"No, I don't think I can." A small pair of tears follow each other down her cheek.

Winta grasps Sarah's arm. "Pray to your God."

The old lady says, "Let's pray together."

The women all start praying, each in their own religion - Muslim, Protestant, Orthodox, and Catholic. The different prayers mingle into a single, urgent liturgy. At the same time, they are praying the car rolls to a stop.

More sad news arrives; two Somalian men the following vehicle have died. Sadness fills the small Landcruiser, but no one has the energy to scream or cry out loud.

The men assemble, again, to carry the bodies away, but no one has the energy for digging. Instead, they convey the body a short distance from the car, they stroll quietly, and they like dead men themselves, return and file into the waiting vehicles.

Kaleb and one of the Sudanese men, while they are turning back to the car, see a moving hand on sand several feet away. They walk toward the moving hand.

A pregnant woman is lying down on the sand, and half of her body covered in it. A week ago, she traveled with other smugglers, and she became unconscious, so they thought she died. So, they buried her and left.

Kaleb and Sudanese man, when they see her, tears fall, and they dig into the sand and take her to the car.

The smugglers say, "She looks like she is gonna die soon, we don't have time for that. Leave her, let's go."

Everyone from the three cars says, "If you can't help her, we're not leaving."

Finally, the smuggler agrees. "Okay, but she has to pay."

People share and pay for her. She just looks at them, but no words come; only tears.

Thirst has become an obsession. At one point, the cars stop, and the men take turns peeing into a water bottle and drinking the dark amber liquid. A few women exit the vehicles to stretch their legs. They see what the men are doing and are disgusted by their behavior.

Winta quietly stands on the other side of the vehicle away from the men for nearly a minute. Then, nervously holding her own small bottle, she squats down and tries to pee into it. She makes a mess of her hand but manages to get a small amount. She holds her nose and drinks it.

Sarah watches her friend from several feet away and gags. "I'd rather die," she says to herself. "I can't do it." Her gut heaves and wretches, trying to vomit, but her stomach is empty.

"Let's go," a smuggler barks and everyone gets back into the cars. Soon they're back to powering across the endless expanse.

After a couple of hours driving, the loose sand begins creeping higher and deeper, and the excessive weight of the passengers causes the vehicles to trough deep into the sand and get stuck. The driver turns the lead car off, and the smuggler gets down from the roof, telling everyone to get out. Once the passengers have disembarked, they are given orders, and the driver speeds off towards a location he says is more stable, half-mile or so ahead.

Walking through the deep sand is challenging to begin with, but with the added fatigue of starvation, thirst, and oppressive heat, several members of the group are overwhelmed and collapse. Dusty, benevolent hands scoop them up, and the stronger members help the weaker ones. Winta holds Sarah. To everyone's great relief, the Land-cruisers sit waiting at the appointed place.

More hours pass. Without warning, the cars roll to a stop, and the people are once again ordered out. This time a smuggler orders the immigrants to bring their bottles and walk behind him, and for the first time in several days, a fire of hope sparks in their hearts. Clutching their bottles, they arrive at a small oasis, and people begin breaking from the group and running toward the waterhole, stopping around the rim of the lagoon. The banks are precipitously steep, and the water stagnates deep below, shrouded in darkness. A putrid smell wafts upward like a warning.

The smugglers go down first, cautioning, "Watch your step. There are sharp stones, so be careful."

Sarah can barely contain her happiness and tries climbing down, but the walls of the lagoon are crumbly and treacherous. "The women stay here. The men come down," orders a smuggler.

"Stay here," Kaleb says to Sarah, Aida, Mazaa, and Liya. "I will get you water." Stepping sideways, he digs his feet into the banks and scales his way down with the bottles. The water is barely fit for camels -- green, dirty, and bobbing with dead rodents. It stinks so severely he must hold his nose with one hand while he fills the bottles with the other.

Another man balances gingerly on the sharp stones at the water's edge, filling his bottles beside Kaleb. "Oh, my God," Kaleb mutters to him, "How are we gonna drink this?"

The other man keeps filling his bottle. "Better than pee."

Kaleb nestles one full bottle in the rocks and begins filling it. "At least I know where my pee comes from."

"Well, to get pee, you'll have to drink something."

Kaleb momentarily releases his nose to screw a cap onto a bottle. "If I knew this road was like this, I swear to God I wouldn't have moved one foot from my home. My poor cousins."

"Trust me; you would have come anyway."

Kaleb's indignance flares. "How do you know? If I get to Italy safe, I will tell everyone how dangerous it is."

"No one will believe you. They'll say, 'Oh, he arrived at a nice place, and doesn't want to share with others.' You can't talk to people when they want something."

"How could you know that?"

The man looks at Kaleb. "Did you believe how bad it was when people told you?"

"I was told it was bad, but nobody warned me it would be like *this*."

"Well, I was. My brother went by this road, and he told me not to follow him. He told me how dangerous it is. He told me how many people lost their lives, but I didn't believe him." As the man talks, Kaleb notices the emotion taking over his voice.

"Oh, please don't cry, you're a man. A man doesn't cry. A man has to be a man."

The two men fall into silence, finish filling the empty bottles, and make their way back up the sides of the lagoon.

Sarah hurries to Kaleb as he climbs over the rim and reaches for her bottle, but stops short at the sight of the opaque and gritty, green liquid. "What is this?"

"Water."

"But why is it green?" Aida objects.

"I don't know! But we don't have a choice; we should drink this." Kaleb says.

Mazaa breaks from the huddle of women and strides toward Kaleb. "I don't care; I will drink it." She takes the bottle, then hesitates, wincing.

Winta walks up beside her and gently takes the bottle from her hand. She wraps the corner of her shirt tightly over the top of the bottle, holds her nose, and drinks through the cloth. When she finishes, she looks at the circle of wet, green dirt and small insects on her shirt.

"Hell no! I can't!" Exclaims Mazaa from beside Kaleb. "What about Sarah? Is she going to drink it?"

Winta offers the bottle to Sarah, but she shakes her head no.

Aida walks to them, grabs a bottle from Kaleb, and says, "I prefer drinking to dying." Then she covers the mouth of the bottle like Winta did and drinks a long drink. Immediately she doubles over and vomits it out—all around them, people are choosing to drink or not to drink.

The smugglers approach the scattered groups of people. "Let's go back." They walk back to the cars, and the people walk behind them. Sarah turns back and notices the second pregnant woman unsteadily slowing to a stop. "Are you alright?"

The woman doesn't answer and suddenly falls. "Help! Help!"

People run to the woman. She is lifted, taken to the car, and laid down inside. Some women go to pour the green water into her mouth, but this sparks an argument. They finally agree to splash water onto her chest.

Sarah asks one woman, "Did she drink the water?"

The woman says, "I don't think so... she was so scared to drink it, because of her baby. I think she is dehydrated."

94

Sarah looks back at the pregnant woman, wondering if she'll be the journey's next victim. Suddenly a smuggler opens the door of the Landcruiser, wordlessly hands them a can of pineapple juice and a fresh bottle of water, then walks back to his vehicle. The women give their friend a small drink of the juice. She swallows slowly, and in a few moments, opens her eyes.

Chapter Six

The small caravan arrives at the Libyan border and pulls to a dusty halt in the shadow of a small mountain. Ahead of them, several Libyan men begin getting out of cars hidden in a small recessed area at the mountain's base, surrounded by large rocks and a smattering of palm trees.

Sarah hears her driver mutter something in relief, and immediately he gets out of the vehicle. The other Sudanese smugglers also step out of their cars. The Libyan smugglers walk toward the Sudanese. In Arabic, one of the Libyans asks Sarah's driver, "You guys, okay? We thought you guys died or got lost on the road. You guys took more than two weeks."

"We lost three people. Ran out of water."

"That's normal," one of the other Libyan driver's chimes in, casually.

"Also, we lost the road, that's why it took us forever. Alhamdulillah, we made it."

"I'm sorry," the Libyan responds. "The most important thing is you got here safe."

"Yeah, we are here." The Sudanese driver exhales.

The Sudanese smugglers make all the passengers get out of the car. The people climb out one by one and find places to sit on the rocks.

Sarah takes in a palm tree and is immediately transported home. "Oh my God," she sighs wistfully looking around, she sees a house a great distance away.

As she strains to make out details, Aida walks up beside her. "I think we are in Libya," breathes Sarah.

"I think so too."

The two women turn to watch the Sudanese and Libyan smugglers confer.

"Yes, we've made it."

Winta drops to her knees in the sand and raises her hands to the sky. "Thanks, God. For taking care of us." Then she rises, pats the sand from her pants, and approaches her friends with her hands in the air. "This is Libya!"

Sarah smiles. "Yes, I figured it out. I'm so glad. We made it!"

As the Sudanese Land Cruisers drive away, throughout the parking area, the exhausted travelers congratulate each other and hug. As the celebration begins, the Libyan smugglers walk into the scattered crowd.

Standing in the middle, the spokesman barks, "From now on, we're the ones who can guide you to Tripoli! Each one of you will pay three-hundred USA dollars."

For a brief moment, the people stare at the Libyan in shocked silence. Then a cascade of protests erupts.

"We already paid the Sudanese smugglers!"

"We've already paid for this trip!"

The Libyan smuggler raises his hand. "That is for them to get you here. Our payment is separate. If you don't want to pay, that's up to you." Then he starts back to his vehicle, and the other Libyan smugglers follow.

Exasperated cursing and quiet arguing can be heard throughout the small crowd.

"We don't have any option, let's pay and get out of here."

"Why are we paying them? They are taking advantage of us!"

The Libyan smuggler calls back to the group, "If you want to pay, pay. Otherwise, we are leaving before the police come."

People start searching for money in their pockets, their bags, or wherever they've hidden it. The Libyans idle lazily around their vehicles, waiting for the travelers to collect their cash.

"They will pay," the spokesman says confidently, as he lights a cigarette. "What else will they do?"

Men take money from their pockets, underwear, shoes, and socks. Women reach into their bras, underwear, shoes, and several women unbraid their hair. Some people simply don't have enough money. Sarah is one of them. After a couple of minutes, the smugglers walk back to the group. "Who's coming?"

The people all press forward, calling out with hands raised, offering cash.

The smugglers start collecting money. One of them calls out, "The people who paid stay on the right."

The small crowd continues to pay the smugglers and assemble in the agreed-upon spot. Soon only ten people are left, looking alone and scared, Sarah and two other young women, and seven men. The lead smuggler regards them dismissively. "If you don't have the money, you can stay here."

Mustering her courage, Sarah calmly shows him her one-hundred-fifty USA dollars. She is about to speak, but he cuts her off. "Are you deaf? We said three hundred USA dollars." He turns and walks away.

Sarah's eyes tear up, but she strides after him. "Please, in the name of ALLAH..." She grabs his shirt desperately, but he turns and pushes her violently. Sarah crashes to the ground, smacking her head on one of the many red rocks littering the landscape. Immediately blood begins to flow. As she tries to sit up, the blood drips into her eye, stinging her. The smuggler walks away.

Kaleb runs up to Sarah and grabs her hand. He uses the corner of his jacket to wipe the blood from her eye and forehead.

"I'm Okay," Sarah says quietly. "I prefer he kills me, over leaving me here."

Kaleb smiles, "You think we're gonna leave you here? We're hoping they would just accept whatever money you had so that we could save as much as possible. We can pay the difference."

"Oh, thank you!" Sarah throws her arms around Kaleb, trying not to cry.

The large group of travelers sorts through their leftover money to see how they can pay for those who will be left behind. The money is collected, and an older Somalian man brings the money to the Libyans. The money is counted and isn't enough. Two men are singled out and forced away from the group at gunpoint. As they stand far off, watching the road helplessly, a smuggler turns to the rest of the group. "Ya, Allah, get in, get in the car fast, fast, the police are coming."

Everyone races into the cars. As soon as the doors close, the drivers peel out and speed away. Sarah watches through the window as the two abandoned men get left further and further behind. With silent horror, she thinks of how close she came to suffer their fate. They have nothing. No food, no money. No chance.

After only thirty minutes, the car stops. Ahead of them, up a small embankment, another road crosses their path. Beneath this road, cut into the embankment beside their parked vehicle, is a round, iron door.

The Libyan smuggler steps out of the car and quietly patrols the area. He comes back and issues a short order, "Follow me slowly."

The people quickly exit and walk behind him.

The smuggler opens the weighty metal door and steps inside. A wave of heat from within hits the travelers as they snake their way behind him, through the door into the low, narrow chamber under the road. The space is about five feet high, and most people can't stand up straight. At the other end of the corridor-shaped room is a similar iron door.

The smuggler addresses the group. "Stay here until we come back. We have to make sure the road is clear."

He exits the door they came in through and clangs the door shut, plunging the room into darkness. The travelers hear a loud locking sound, the muffled noise of the engine start, and the tires spitting up gravel and small rocks as the car pulls away.

A couple of people feel their way to the doors, but they're locked at both ends. The travelers sit in the excruciating heat of the small room, making small talk. As minutes pass, anxiety grows over whether the smugglers plan to return. Every time the sound of a car is heard, people sit up and look at the door. Is it the smugglers or just people driving past overhead, oblivious? Is it the police?

For hours, the men and women sit in the dark, hot prison. The heat is sweltering. It's uncomfortable to sit or to stand.

Sarah asks Winta, "How long will we stay here?"

"I don't know."

"I thought you came here before?"

"They always change the route. Also, these are different people. There are so many smugglers, both bad and good. God knows what kind these are."

Sarah takes this in, as Winta keeps talking.

"But Libyan people are the bad people of the earth. They call us, donkeys, crazy, black, animals..."

"...Why do they call us Black? They're African too!"

"They don't believe they're African."

"What?"

"They think they are Arabs." Winta shakes her head and laughs dismissively.

Sarah joins her. "Wow. It's so crazy." Sarah looks at the water bottle in her hand, full of the green, particulate-filled liquid from the lagoon. "I think I have to drink this water. I don't have a choice."

Winta says, "You should drink. Do you want a light?

Sarah says, "Yes, please."

Winta reaches for her small flashlight in her jacket. There are a couple of flashlights, but it's not that bright for Sarah to see the water.

Sarah opens the bottle and pulls the tail of her T-shirt over the opening. She holds her nose tightly and drinks. She gulps down half the contents before stopping. "I hope I don't get sick." Then she looks at the bottle. "Oh, my God, I drank that much?" Then she inspects her T-shirt. There are tiny dead insects and small rocks caught in the green-stained patch of fabric. "Oh, my God. Did I drink this? Wow, if someone told me they drank this kind of water, I would think they're crazy."

Winta shakes her head. "If we didn't experience this ourselves, we would never understand."

Sarah agrees. "That's true. If someone told me this story, I never could have believed it. Sometimes it's good to experience awful things, to understand other people's pain."

The two sit in quiet agreement for a few moments. Sarah finally breaks the silence. "When are they coming?"

"Soon, I hope; otherwise, this heat is gonna kill us."

For no discernable reason, Sarah suddenly became aware of the odor wafting off her own body. "I just realized how bad we stink. We literally smell like dead animals."

Winta smiles. "The heat makes it worse too. Don't forget we didn't get to shower for over two weeks."

"Oh my Gosh, it's crazy. I never thought it could be this way. Please, God, let's just get where we're going. Let's get safe. I'm really scared."

***

As the sun nestles colorfully into the horizon, the two abandoned men plod sluggishly through the sand. Hours earlier, as the four cars had driven away from the mountain-meeting point, the two men started walking after one of the cars. In a few short minutes, they could no longer see the car, just its trail of dust. Not long after, even that had disappeared. The men, with little discussion and no other options, had simply kept walking in the direction the car had gone.

Four hours they stumbled, as the sun-scorched them.

Finally, the shorter, darker-skinned man lets out a groan. "Oh, God, I'm so exhausted. I don't think I'm gonna make it."

The taller man snaps back, "Aren't you a man? Keep walking."

The shorter man looks down. "I'm a man, but I'm a city man. I'm soft."

The taller man looks over. "I'm a city man too, but I was a soldier. I trained in Massawa."

The shorter man looks over. "Oh, are you Eritrean?"

"Yes."

"But you speak Amharic fluently."

"Thanks. You from Addis?"

"Yes, around Chirkos. Do you know Addis?"

"Yes, I do. Before the war, I used to go to visit my uncle and aunt. I remember it well."

"Did you fight in the war?"

"I did."

The two men trudge in awkward silence. How easily someone becomes an enemy. Minutes pass, and the Eritrean offers an explanation.

"In Eritrea, you have no choice. After high school graduation, every man and women have to train at a military academy before you can work; before you can go to school, anything. So, I went."

The Ethiopian wonders how to respond, and finally says, "In Ethiopia, we have a choice. None of my family ever entered the army."

The Eritrean keeps walking silently, looking straight ahead. Then he admits, "I wished we had a choice. I didn't want to fight." He paused. "In fact, I'm on this trip because I'm running away from the army."

The Ethiopian regards the Eritrean with surprise. "I have family in Ethiopia, as I said. Why would I want to kill Ethiopians? I have no quarrel with you."

"We're Habasha," offers the Ethiopian. "We're brothers. It's foolish."

The Ethiopian suddenly notices the Eritrean has stopped walking. He glances over, worried that his words have caused a reaction, but the Eritrean is staring straight ahead. The Ethiopian looks in the direction of the Eritrean's gaze.

Far ahead, on the horizon, are the shapes of tiny houses.

"Oh, my God! We made it!" The Ethiopian grabs the Eritrean in an embrace, and they both laugh. They pick up their pace and begin walking briskly toward the distant structures.

***

The dark room under the road no longer swelters like a furnace but is still uncomfortably warm. People are lying and sitting mostly in silence. A few men are whispering to each other. Suddenly, the metal portal scrapes and clanks open. The people in the tunnel jump and all look to the doorway in fearful silence. A silhouetted man steps through the door. People instinctively grab hold of each other's hands and arms of those beside them.

"Get up," the new man quietly demands. "Follow me."

As they rise to follow him, the people ask each other, "Who is this?"

"Is he ours, or is this someone new?"

"Is this the police?" Nobody knows the answer.

As they step through the doorway, the cold, dessert nighttime air cuts into the sweaty, exhausted travelers, but there is comfort in the sound of the familiar Libyan's voice.

They follow him mostly in a single file, and the smuggler yells at them to get in the car. "Ya Allah! Fast! Fast!! Get in! Are you crazy?!"

He starts pushing them, kicking them, slapping them wherever his hand can reach their bodies. Everyone tries to move faster, but there is a hesitation in the line as the men try to let the women enter first. The smuggler is so beside himself that he almost doesn't seem human.

After everyone gets into the car, the driver takes off at a crazy speed. The vehicle bounces hard over the bumps in the road, sending people against the roof and causing several to cry out.

"Shut the F**k up! Shut your mouths, Stupid idiots! You guys don't have a country! No land! We are the only ones that can help you get what you want."

The two pregnant women become sick, but the driver and his smuggler sidekick don't care. People bang their hands on the side of the car in protest, but they keep driving. Very soon, the vehicle pulls over.

They arrived at a house in the middle of nowhere. There's nothing nearby except for palm trees and an old, corrugated metal fence that snakes around the house in tired disrepair. The smuggler exits the car to open the gate, and the vans rumble inside, then stops, and the people are ordered out. The smuggler, at the entrance, points them to the house, and the weary travelers trudge toward the front door.

The house is one big empty room. There is nothing. No rooms, no furniture. The lead smuggler walks inside and curtly announces, "We're gonna come back tomorrow. For now, I'll bring you something to eat." Then he exits the house.

Another car enters the compound. It's another smuggler, but a new one no one has seen before. He gets out and calls to the others in Arabic for assistance. The smugglers, sitting lazily in the house and on the rocks outside, indicate to the travelers to go and help. Several men rise and shuffle out. Together they haul in fifty-kilograms of pasta, fifteen-liters of oil, fifteen-kilograms of red onion, fifteen-kilograms of tomatoes, salt, one big pan, and five big plates. The travelers look at the growing pile of food with wide eyes, and the weary looks on many faces finally start to brighten. As the smugglers begin to file out, one of the Eritrean travelers walks behind them and asks in Arabic, "How are we gonna cook this? And what are we gonna drink? We need water."

The smuggler points to a pile of sticks outside the house and retorts, "Do you want me to cook for you? Stupid. Water is there, tap water in the bathroom. You can drink that. Say thank you for bringing you food, ungrateful fool. You've never seen this much food in your life. Your poor country doesn't have anything like this to offer you!"

The Eritrean responds, but this time in his own language of Tigrigna. "My country offers me everything. We have a better life.

We only come here because we didn't appreciate what we had there. I wish I could go back."

The smuggler doesn't understand. "What did you say?"

The Eritrean responds in Arabic. "Nothing." He saunters back into the house.

As the smugglers drive out of the compound, the travelers watch from windows and the doorway.

One of the smugglers rolls down his car window and sticks his head out, yelling back at the house. "No one is allowed to go out of this house. Also, stay silent! I don't want any trouble from the neighbors. Good luck, donkeys! Orphans! Ha-ha!" His laughter trails off as he pulls his head back inside the car and rolls up the window. The vans gradually disappear in a shrinking cloud of dust.

Sarah listens intently, studying their body language. "They are so rude," she states loudly.

"Lower your voice!" Kaleb glares at her.

The men build a small fire outside and find rocks to arrange under the pots. Two men fill the cooking vessels half-way at the bathroom sink, then take it back out where the fire is beginning to crackle and smoke. When the water reaches a boil, they add the pasta, and when the pasta starts to cook, they add oil, salt, tomato, and onion. Soon the aroma fills the air, and the pot is brought inside the house. They scoop large helpings onto each of the five plates, and groups arrange around each one. Everyone prays according to their religion.

With no utensils, people eat with their hands, and for the first time in several days, people are laughing. The plates are refilled again and again. The meal is simple but delicious, and a memory none will forget. After they eat, most of the travelers say another round of prayers before splitting off to find a spot to sleep. Here and there, people lie on their blankets on the ground or pull them around their shoulders as they settle in for the night.

Sarah sweeps aside the dust with her hand on the broken concrete floor, to prepare a place for her and her friends. As she does, she can't help but notice the early protests of an upset stomach, after putting so much food in a stomach four days empty. She wonders if others are feeling the same, but looking around, people seem content, so she lies down and tries to get some rest.

* * *

The Eritrean and the Ethiopian walking through the desert are nearing the border city of Al Kufrah. Their hearts lift at the sight of the houses with their lights, and give each other another hug. "We made it."

"But where are we gonna sleep?" Asks the Eritrean.

"I have one-hundred USA dollars. We can sleep in a hotel, and tomorrow I'll call my brother in the USA. He will send me money, and we can go to Tripoli."

"Good! I have fifty USA dollars for a phone. And I'll call my sisters and brothers; they live in Italy."

"Wow, all your family lives in Europe? How did they get here?"

"Oh, they went when they were young. Our parents came here a long time ago. I stayed with our grandmother, but she passed away."

While they talk, the city rises closer and closer before them. Their energy levels pick up with excitement, but from out of nowhere, a white police car with red doors and Arabic lettering stops in front of them. At the sight of this, the two men stop abruptly, and the Ethiopian suddenly realizes he is peeing himself. "Oh, God!"

The officers get out of the car. The men stand silently, with wary eyes. Soon, six police officers walk toward them.

The first officer yells, "Look at these crazy donkeys. Black animals."

They draw their handguns and use them to club the men to the ground. They fall, as the officers continue beating them while they writhe in the dust, desperately protecting their heads with their clenched hands. Under the shower of fists and boots, their faces and clothes become streaked with blood, and they begin losing the strength to protect themselves. As the officers step back to rest, the two men can't even get up. They cry in pain, but the officers laugh and throw insults at them. Then they are dragged to the cars.

A few short minutes later, the car arrives at one of the city's many prisons. The officers open the vehicle and pull the men out, dragging them inside the concrete building. There is a large room filled to overflowing with Ethiopians, Eritreans, Sudanese, and Somalians. The two travelers are shoved onto the floor, and the police close the iron doors behind them.

One of the inmates approaches the two fallen Habesha to see if they're okay. He helps them to a sitting position and shows them where they can sleep. Other inmates come over, help them remove their clothes, give them blankets and cups of water.

The prison officer opens the door. Behind him is a long table with many scantily filled plates. "It's dinner time. Go get it. I don't have time. Do it fast."

As the men filter through the doorway and back, one of the guys grabs two plates. The officer pulls the second plate from his hands and asks him why he has two?

"I was trying to help the new guys. They can't move."

The officer looks past him to the two fallen travelers. "If they can't come, let them die. I don't care about animals."

The inmate's jaw muscles begin to flex and clench, but there is nothing he can do. He stands there silently.

The officer raises his voice. "Are you deaf? Get out of my face. All of you are worthless!"

As the inmate turns to leave, the officer viciously strikes him between the shoulder blades with his gun. The inmate collapses to the floor, and his plate of food explodes as it hits the ground. The officer leans over and shouts at the inmate, "No food for you either, so get to your room."

The inmate gets up and slowly limps back into the holding room.

The meal is by no means glamorous. Everyone re-enters the holding area with a plate of white rice, bread, and a glass of water.

There is no seasoning of any kind, and the water is tap water, but it's better than nothing, so the prisoners eat their food together.

***

The following morning the travelers in the deserted house wake-up, and while they wait for the Libyans to arrive, the idea spreads of cooking the leftovers for breakfast, and people set about the task. Once the meal is prepared and eaten, the pots are used to collect water for washing, as the single shower in the house doesn't work. People take turns outside, pouring the water over themselves, as friends hold a blanket for privacy. After everyone's taken a shower, the women fix each other's hair. They talk and make jokes as people pack for the next stage of the journey.

***

A week later, the smugglers still haven't returned. The travelers have been eating the same food every day, and it's nearly gone. Had they known they needed to ration it, they could have stretched it further, but the entire group fell prey to the illusion that this was just a quick stopover. People are scared and don't know what to do. Different ideas have been thrown out all week, but nothing has been agreed upon by the group. As evening falls, one of the men finally says, "Guys, let's see what is outside the fence."

Another man quickly scolds him. "They said we are not allowed to go outside the compound or even to look."

Kaleb lifts his voice over the argument, "We can see without opening the gate. Until then, do we just sit here? We have to do something."

Everyone agrees with Kaleb, and a scattered crowd begins moving closer to the fence. Two men lift Kaleb on to their shoulders, and he scans the surrounding terrain. Beyond the compound, there is nothing, not a house, car, or anything for endless miles.

As the men lower him back to the ground, he concedes, "Everyone, we were fooled. There is nothing."

Someone exclaims, "Are you sure?"

"Yes!" Kaleb jumps to the ground, and he and the two men who hoisted him up open the gate and walk the perimeter. There is nothing except for the distant glow of an unknown city at least a dozen miles away. They re-enter the compound, lock the gate, and relate to the others what they saw and didn't see. As a group, they begin to discuss in earnest what to do.

One of the men says, "We should divide into groups of five or six and leave one group at a time to prevent suspicion. Hopefully, we can catch taxis to Benghazi. Then we can find a bus to take us the rest of the way."

Some people disagree. "What if the police catch us?"

Others beg. "Let's wait here; they might come back because they need the house!"

Kaleb says, "The taxis are a good idea because they only care about the money, but the bus is not good. Too many people on the bus, and we'll stand out. What if the police catch us? The taxis are enough."

"And where do we find a taxi? We don't know where we are!"

"We'll have to walk until we find a road. There has to be a road between us and that." He points in the direction of the city.

Everyone agrees with Kaleb's idea, and they make preparations to go. The first group of six exits the compound. People gather around, hugging them, and wishing them well. "God be with you!"

The people leaving ask for prayer and turn to begin their long journey. After a couple of hours, the second group sets out. It's now deep into the night, and the rest of the people bed down.

The next day the rest of the large group sets out the same way. Sarah, Aida, Kaleb, Mazaa, and Liya are the last ones to leave.

Chapter Seven

K aleb walks at the front of the group, and Sarah brings up the rear. It's extremely dark, causing them to walk slowly and carefully. The five members all hold each other's hands. After about forty minutes, miraculously, they come across a road. The group is torn. They're scared to walk too close to the road for fear of the police but have to stay close enough to be able to flag down a taxi.

"Stay here," Kaleb instructs. "I'm going onto the street to get a taxi, but if I don't come back, keep continuing down this route."

Aida grabs Kaleb's sleeve. "No, if you go, we're going together, not by yourself."

Kaleb gently pulls her hand from his shirt. "If the police catch me, I don't want you guys to end up in prison."

"We can hide, and when the taxi comes, we can run over," Liya offers.

Sarah has a suggestion, "I can go to stop the taxi because I'm a girl; he'll stop for me."

"That's a good idea," Kaleb concedes, "but no."

"Don't worry; I'll take care of myself." Not waiting for an answer, Sarah begins walking toward the road.

Mazaa calls after her, "Be careful, Sari."

"Don't worry!" She calls back.

The rest walk as a group and hide behind a cluster of palm trees. Sarah stands by herself very close to the road, but no taxis come.

Sometime later, the group decides to walk a little bit more, and while they're walking, they continually scan the road forward and backward for cars. Finally, they see a black and white car from far off with a small yellow taxi light.

Sarah runs to the road. The driver stops and asks her in Arabic, where she wants to go, but she doesn't understand. She tries to reason with him in English, "Wait, my brother speaks Arabic..."

He doesn't understand her.

She turns back and calls Kaleb, but the driver speeds off.

She goes back to tell Kaleb. "He spoke Arabic. I tried to speak to him in English, and he left me."

Kaleb, laughing at her, and says, "What did he say?"

Sarah laughs. "God knows."

"We have to leave just in case he comes back with the police," Kaleb says.

They continue walking, and about twenty minutes later, Sarah asks the group, "Where did they leave us? We've been walking for hours."

Kaleb agrees. "That's true, they scammed us, they made fools of us. They just gave us some food and dumped us."

Aida responds, "The past is passed. They're Libyan; we can't expect anything else from them."

"But they were smart," Sarah concedes. "They gave us some food, left us in an empty house and told us we couldn't go out. I swear they fooled us good." Then she laughs, and the others laugh with her, despite themselves.

Mazaa joins in with Sarah. "Exactly, they treated us like babies. Do you remember our mother's when they went to the supermarket? How they used to fool us, they'd give us a toy or something to eat."

The women laugh loudly.

Kaleb is frustrated by their conversation, "You guys shut up, don't make me mad. They don't know who we are. We're Ethiopian. The only country in Africa never colonized. But they met us here, in a place where we have nothing and can't do anything. I wish I could meet them again in Ethiopia. I'd show them."

Sarah tries to calm him down. "It is okay. One day we'll make fun of them, but no matter what, for me, they are smart, in a horrible way. Also, I can't help but wonder who started this idea of getting someone's money and then just leaving them? Are they human?"

"I think they learned from their moms," Mazaa responds.

Kaleb sees another taxi and runs to the road, waving. The taxi stops for him. Kaleb addresses the driver In Arabic, "We want to go to the capital city."

The driver looks at him, confused. "You mean, Tripoli?"

"Yes."

"Oh, no, I can't go there. But if you want, I can drop you at the nearest city."

"How long will that take?"

"About an hour."

"Another hour? Driving?"

"Yes."

"Okay…" Kaleb turns back to call his cousins, and when the driver sees more people coming, he tries to drive off. Kaleb quickly explains, "They're my sisters."

The driver stops again and studies Kaleb. "You will pay one hundred US dollars?"

"Okay. Can you take us to a motel?"

The driver pulls the car off the road, and Kaleb jogs over to his window. "Why are you pulling off the road?"

"I know you guys are traveling illegally."

"Oh, okay. Thanks."

"It's not for you. I don't want to go to jail because of you people."

Sarah steps beside Kaleb. "Ask him if he knows someone to take us to Libya."

"We're in Libya. I understand what you're trying to say."

Kaleb turns back to the driver. "Do you know someone who can help us get to Tripoli?"

"I have a friend; he has a big van. I will call him." Then the driver grabs his cell phone and calls his friend. He talks to him briefly, hangs up the phone, and says, "My friend said okay. He'll come to meet you tomorrow morning."

"How does he know where we'll be?"

"That's our work," the driver responds with a deep sharp sound. "This is not the first time."

"Oh, sorry."

The five friends load into the car. Sarah settles herself in the backseat and looks out the window as the vehicle leaves the road behind and plows through the dust and dunes. "I feel like we are still in the desert." She points her finger out the window. "Look at the sand."

"We don't have a choice, it's for our safety," Aida says.

"I know, but... I've been wishing..."

"What?"

"If I knew this would happen, I would never have even thought about stepping out of my mom's house for a minute. But I realized too late. I got all that information from your cousin, she told me everything, but I was already in Sudan. It seemed too late to go back. But now I wish I'd listened to her."

Mazaa considers her sympathetically. "If you knew, you wouldn't have come?"

"I would've stayed home."

"I'm glad you didn't know then," Mazaa says, with a spreading smile.

Sarah looks at Mazaa, surprised. "What? I thought you loved me."

"Yes, I do. That's why I said it. If you didn't come, who will make me laugh? Especially in that awful Sahara Desert. Without you, that two weeks would have been two years!"

Aida agrees. "That's true. Without Sarah, it would have been harder." They hug her.

The car arrives at a building. A gate opens, and the taxi stops inside the fence.

The driver turns to the five friends and says, "Don't go out. Stay here; I will book a room for you. If people see you, they'll call the police."

Sarah follows him with her eyes and turns back to her friends. "What if he leaves us here?"

"Sarah, stop joking like that," Liya cautions.

Mazaa agrees with Sarah. "You never know, he might."

Aida, looking at them both, says, "You guys are crazy. How could he leave us with his taxi?"

Sarah responds, "The smugglers left us in their house." Then she looks at them. "But actually, this is better; we can drive to Tripoli. We have a car." She laughs. Liya looks at Sarah and shakes her head.

The driver comes back with a room key. He shows them the room and gives them the key. They walk fast to their room, jubilant at the prospect of their first bed in three weeks. The room is small with one bed. The walls are faded orange, the floor is cracked concrete and dusty, and the bed is covered with an old blanket. There is a small bathroom, but there is no shower.

Mazaa looks at the bed, "But it's just one bed."

Aida is exhausted but clear, "It will be enough."

Suddenly there is a knock on the door. "Be quiet," Kaleb warns. The knocking continues, and a voice says, "I'm the room service."

Kaleb opens the door. The man is light-skinned and handsome but doesn't even remotely resemble a motel staff member. Dressed in black slacks and a dark, plaid shirt, his sunglasses perched on the top of his head like a tiara. "I'm your driver for tomorrow morning. Do you need anything? It will take two days because we are driving off-road, but we can get food on the way. I will get you something to eat. You will pay five hundred US dollars."

"Five hundred dollars is a lot. Can we give you four hundred?"

"If you don't want to pay, that's up to you." Then he walks out, and Kaleb calls after him.

"Okay."

"You will pay half right now, then the other half when we get to Tripoli."

"Okay, I will give it to you tomorrow morning."

"I want the deposit right now. Otherwise, you can find somebody else."

"Okay, let me give you now, one-hundred. I'll give you the rest in the morning."

The man accepts the money and walks out. "I will come early. Five a.m."

Kaleb locks the door and walks to the bed. But again, there is a knocking at the door. Assuming the driver has returned with some piece of forgotten information, Kaleb opens the door without ceremony. Standing there is an ancient woman, tiny and deeply wrinkled. She is neither angry nor sweet. Her eyes stare with the dullness of routine.

"Will you need something to eat? We have a full menu. I know you can't go out; I can bring you food here," she says, in Arabic.

Kaleb eyes her warily, "Let me ask them." Everyone except Sarah hears this conversation, and when he turns back, they answer his question before he can ask it.

"We're not hungry." Sarah hears the chorus of dissent and agrees but asks for water.

Half an hour before the driver is supposed to arrive, there is sharp rapping on the door. Kaleb gets up. Walks to the door and cracks it open. "It's me," the driver assures him. Kaleb rouses the girls with his hands and speaks to them, "Wake-up."

When they open the door again to head to the van, the driver demands the remaining deposit, and Kaleb gives him the one hundred and fifty dollars. There are two men with the driver, and

Aida, Sarah, Mazaa, Liya, and Kaleb glance over at them as they move to the car. The new men watch the women walk and don't avert their eyes when they notice. The party enters the van, and compared to what they've been in up until now, it is the height of luxury. The windows are darkened, and it has all its original padded seating.

Kaleb and the women sit in the rear two rows, and the driver and his two friends sit together in front. They wind through the streets of Al Kufrah toward a desert road leading out of town, and once outside the city limits, turn off the path onto the sand. The girls watch through the windows. "Here, we go again."

"What if they drive us back to Sudan?" Sarah muses.

Annoyed, Liya shoots back, "Sarah, sometimes you don't know what you are talking about. Can you wish for something else?"

"It's a joke."

Mazaa smiles, "Liya doesn't like those jokes."

Aida agrees with her. "She's allergic."

"Whatever," Liya defends herself. "Sometimes, Sarah's jokes become real."

Sarah likes the idea of this new power. "Okay, let me wish something..."

Kaleb shakes his head. "Sarah, you're a CD that won't turn off."

"If you don't want me to talk, I can be quiet, but I don't want to be quiet." She laughs.

"Why?"

"I love entertaining people; I love seeing people's happiness. I love it when people laugh and smile. I just love seeing people's happiness."

"You have a pure heart," Kaleb concedes. "That's a good thing."

"Yes, my mom says that every time. I don't like it when people cry. I'd rather be the one crying than see others hurt," she pauses. "I'm very sensitive. I feel people's pain." She looks at her four friends, with whom she's gone through so much. Only three weeks have passed since they met, but they have shared what seemed like a lifetime's worth of hardship. "One thing I'm not joking about is that

I won't ever forget you as long as I live, you guys. If you weren't here for me, I would be dead by now."

"It's nothing," Kaleb responds. "We must help each other. One day you will help us."

The van stops, and one of the men turns and asks them if they want to use the bathroom.

Sarah smiles, and her eyebrows dart up. "Yes!"

All the girls want to use the restroom, but when the driver slides the side door open, there is nothing but more sand.

"Oh God," Sarah sighs. "We're still in the desert."

The four women walk a little bit away from the car. They take turns covering each other, forming a human wall to block the sightlines from the van as they pee one a time.

When they finish, they jog back to the car. The driver's two friends stand outside the van. They look at Sarah without blinking. They continue watching her as the girls get into the vehicle.

The driver calls out to the men outside. "Let's go."

They get in, and as the doors to the van close, the vehicle lurches and roars forward.

Spirits are high, and Sarah's jokes get people laughing till the tears come. The passengers are having a good time. The next few hours are spent in laughter. After a long day of traveling, the van arrives at a large building that looks like a construction site. It's maybe one quarter finished. The first floor of the building is all concrete and has several rooms, but everything above is still a work-in-progress. The Libyan men go to the first floor and check around, then return.

"It's fine." They open the van side door and usher the five friends out and into the building. The building is on the outskirts of some unknown city, with one side facing the open desert. There are no other houses around. The building doesn't have lights or electricity and is extremely dark.

Kaleb walks behind Sarah, following the three men. One of the men says to Kaleb, "You're staying here for tonight."

Kaleb responds, "That's fine, as long as it's safe."

"There is no choice; we can't enter the city."

Kaleb and the girls sit on the concrete floor. There is nothing to cover themselves with or put on the floor because they left their blankets back at the abandoned house.

After the Libyans leave, Sarah takes her friends' clothes. "Oh my God, we've stayed in the same clothes this whole time. It's so sad."

Mazaa looks at herself. "I never thought I could stay in the same clothes for two days, but I've worn this for over three weeks. Why did you have to remind me?"

"It just crossed my mind."

They try to sleep, but sleep doesn't come easy; the concrete is very cold and uncomfortable.

The driver and his friends contemplate sleeping in the van.

"How can we sleep here? Let's go to sleep at the hotel." The driver smiles. "No, let's sleep here. I have a surprise for you guys."

The driver steps out of the van and walks back into the building to Kaleb and the girls. "You guys want to use the bathroom?"

"Yes!"

The Libyan man produces a flashlight and aims it at another entrance to the room. "The bathroom is downstairs, through there. Be quiet and walk slowly. I'll guide you there, one at a time."

"Okay." Kaleb turns to the girls. "Who wants to go first?"

"Please, I want to go." Mazaa is up instantly and follows the driver.

When they return, Aida leaves with the driver, and then Liya. When Liya returns, Sarah says to Kaleb, "Go first; I'll go after you."

"I will go after you," Kaleb yields.

"You've been asking about the bathroom for hours."

"Please, Sarah, go." Sarah picks herself up and follows the Libyan down the stairs and through several hallways to the bathroom, illuminated by the dancing light of the flashlight. When they arrive, he points out the toilet through a doorway with no door. She settles herself onto the small bathroom facing the wall, not realizing that the Libyan is standing in the doorway, leering at her exposed rear.

He takes out his phone to call his friends and steps away from the door, but as he fumbles with the buttons, Sarah emerges from the bathroom. He lowers the phone, but makes no move to leave, and stands unashamedly staring at her. Sarah takes in his menacing gaze with a growing alarm and quickly moves past him into the hallway. The man doesn't stop her, but walks behind her, not offering to lead. The passageway is exceptionally dark, and with a growing feeling of sickness in her stomach, Sarah realizes the beam of the flashlight is fixed on her back and rear. When they get to the room, she sits down beside her friends, too scared and confused to talk. Kaleb gets up and leaves with the Libyan toward the bathroom.

Arriving at the bathroom, the driver issues a plain decree. "I need one of the girls to stay with me for tonight."

"What? It's impossible; they're my sisters."

"I'm not asking; I'm telling you."

Kaleb looks at the driver. He turns to walk back to his sisters without using the bathroom, but the driver grabs his hand and jerks him back. "I'm not asking your permission to f**K your sisters, I'm telling you. Otherwise, I will kill you here, and no one will ask any questions. You're an animal here."

The driver pushes Kaleb toward the bathroom. Kaleb pushes him back and starts pushing the driver's arms away, but the driver pulls a small handgun out of the waist of his pants, beneath his untucked shirt. He points it at Kaleb, who freezes in fear. Then the driver's phone rings. He grabs it from his pocket and puts it up to his ear. He listens for a few short seconds then puts it away.

"We have one of the girls. Sit here and cry like your mom, you pussy."

"No, no, no! Please, I'll pay you more, please!"

"I don't need your money! But if you try to do something, I will kill you, trust me."

"Please, I'm begging you!" Kaleb falls to his knees.

The driver kicks him down with his foot. "The choice is yours if you want to die. Also, if I want, I can f**k them right in front of your face."

119

"Please, kill me before you do that!"

Kaleb tries to rise, but the driver pistol whips Kaleb hard across the side of his head, knocking him flat to the cold concrete. The Libyan man takes off his belt to tie Kaleb's hands, but Kaleb again tries to get up and kicks at the Libyan man with his foot. The Libyan man clubs him over and over on the head with his pistol. Blood runs down his face, but Kaleb continues to struggle, shielding his head with his arms. The Libyan's arm gets tired, and he resorts to kicking Kaleb in the ribs and head, finally knocking him unconscious. He drags Kaleb through the bathroom entrance. The Libyan man pulls Kaleb's hands behind his back and ties them to one of the plumbing pipes. Then he takes off his scarf and ties Kaleb's feet together. He rises to his feet, spits on Kaleb's face, and kicks him hard one more time in the belly with his foot. Kaleb hangs loosely. His blood runs over his face, his jacket, pants, and the floor. The Libyan turns and runs out of the bathroom and down the long, dark passageway.

Back on the main floor, the three girls' mouths are taped, and they sit back-to-back in a triangle. Their hands are tied behind their backs and to one another. Their faces are streaked with tears, and they kick their legs to try to loosen the bonds on their feet. The room is dark and silent, and the air is filled with a terrifying expectation of what's to come. They struggle to untie their hands, but the more they try, the tighter and more durable the ropes seem. The ropes bite into their wrists, and the friction of the rope pulling and scraping against their torn skin becomes searing.

***

Sarah's hands are tied behind her to the exposed metal wall studs. Her mouth is covered with tape. The tape is dotted with droplets of the tears dripping from her eyes. The driver's two friends stand to one side of her, watching her and waiting. When the driver arrives, she looks to see who it is, then quickly looks away. Without any verbal signal, the three men close in on her. They untie her hands, and the driver presses her tightly against the wall. The other two men fumble with the button and zipper of her pants, sending Sarah

120

into a panic of kicking and squirming. Between her violent movement and the tight fit of her jeans, the men can't get them off, and one of them slaps her face viciously while the driver pushes her down to the floor.

They finally yank the jeans down her legs and off. The layers of tape muffle Sarah's crying and begging. Unable to speak, she casts her eyes wildly around the room, but there is no one to save her. *I hope they kill me.* She thinks. *God, forgive me for whatever I did. This is my punishment for what I did to my family. For hurting them; I disappointed them.*

The Libyans take their guns from their pockets and put them on the floor, a short distance away. Sarah stares at the guns. At the same time, the driver presses Sarah's shoulders hard into the floor, and the two accomplices get down on their knees on either side of her. The man on the right grabs her right arm and her right leg with the other. The man on the left does the same. They use this leverage to pull her legs apart. Sarah resists, but they are too strong.

The driver lets go of Sarah's shoulders and removes his pants. Moving to her spread legs, he rips down her underwear and begins to f**k her until he feels satisfied. "She is so sweet, like honey," he exclaims.

Sarah can't handle the pain; no one will ever understand the pain. Her vagina steadily drips blood. The second man, exchanging places with the driver, simply removes his underwear and uses them as a rag to wipe off her pelvis, and he penetrates her.

Sarah's face, a mask of tears and snot, twists and mutates with pain and terror. She begs for water, but nobody understands her through the tape. Or they do and don't care. Halfway through the second rape, Sarah faints, which only makes the rapists' job more manageable. When the second Libyan finishes, the third switches places with him and begins. When the third man finishes, the driver wants to go for a second round, but Sarah's body doesn't move. Her eyes are wide open, her head cocked at a strange angle, and she is unresponsive. Her body is cold to the driver's touch, and he recoils. He shuffles backward on his knees. "I'm not fucking a dead body."

The three men's pants, hands, and thighs are covered with Sarah's blood. They wipe themselves mostly clean with their underwear, dress, and leave.

***

After a couple of hours, Kaleb awakens. He tries to lift his head and open his eyes, but they're cemented shut with dried blood. He scrunches his face and eyes repeatedly, trying to break the crispy blood out of his eyelids and finally cracks them open and raises his head, but there is nothing to look at in the darkness. He feels dizzy. His head drops again, but after a few seconds, he wills himself to keep trying. He moves his hands slowly back and forth behind him to loosen the ropes. As he works, horrible thoughts of what might have happened to his sisters besiege his mind. Failing to free his hand, he lets out a furious, desperate scream. He knocks his head back against the pipe.

"I'm worthless! I'm not man enough to protect my sisters!"

He keeps trying hard to untie his hands and yells the accusations of failure filling his mind. *Why didn't he kill me? Why did he leave me? He called me a pussy. That's true! I am! If I were a man, I would have saved my sisters.* He keeps knocking his bloody head back against the pipe.

The girls hear the echoes of Kaleb's screaming, far away. Aida touches Liya and Mazaa's shoulders with her shoulder, and they press close together. They try to talk through their taped mouths, but their voices are hopelessly muffled. When they hear Kaleb screaming, fear and heartbreak overwhelm them, and their crying intensifies.

Liya prays, *Please, God, help us; you are the only hope we have. What are they doing, these Libyans, to my brother and my sisters? Please, God, help us! Please!* The ropes burn her wrists with every movement.

Mazaa desperately prays in her mind, *Oh God, I hope they are not killing him! No, no, no. And where is Sarah? Oh, God, why? WHY!?*

122

Aida also prays desperately. *God, please take me first before him! I don't want to see his dead body. I don't want to think! I love you, Kaleb! I do!*

***

After several hours pass, Sarah starts to move her fingers. Her eyes are closed, her mouth still taped, her tongue slowly moves inside her dry mouth. "Please, water, I need some water…" There is nobody else in the room. She tries to open her eyes, but she can't see. The room is utterly dark and quiet. The pain in her lower body throbs and aches as she tries to move but can't raise herself up. After a couple of minutes, her finger stops moving, and her hand drops to the floor.

***

Kaleb drifts in and out of consciousness, immediately struggling to free his hands with each waking. Finally, several hours after the beating, he pulls a hand free. He gathers his legs toward him and pulls at the scarf around his ankle. It is incredibly tight, so he bends far forward and uses his teeth for extra leverage on the knot. After several minutes, he finally pulls an end loose, then another, and unwraps his legs. He tries to get up but becomes woozy and disoriented and falls, striking his head on the ground.

A wound over his right temple opens, and fresh blood adds a layer of slickness to the dried blood caked and scabbing on his head and cheek. He takes off his jacket and ties it around his head. Then, leaning into the wall and steadying himself against it with his hands, he slowly gets up. He trudges heavily down the passageway to the stairs and begins up the steps. He stumbles and falls backward, collapsing in a heap at the bottom of the staircase. He pulls himself up and starts over. Finally, he makes it to the top and staggers down the hallway into the room where he last saw his sisters.

Bursting into the room, he sees three girls sitting back-to-back, with their hands tied and their mouths taped. "Oh, my sisters!" he exclaims and runs to them. He removes the tape one at a time, letting loose an explosion of exciting questions and thanksgivings.

Unable to focus on their words, he groggily begins trying to solve the puzzle of the knots on their wrists.

"You're alive!"

"Where were you??"

"Where is Sarah?"

"Is she with you??"

"Where are the Libyans?"

"Oh, praise God!"

Kaleb begins biting and pulling at the ropes to try to get the knots undone. He manages to loosen one, then another, then another, untying the young women one at a time. When the last girl is free and rubbing her sore wrists, he breaks into tears and hugs them.

The girls pepper him with questions.

Aida tries to check Kaleb's head, but he takes her hand, "I'm fine, let's go find Sarah!" He gets up, but again staggers and slumps to his knees before falling back onto his bum.

Aida runs over to him. "Kaleb, are you okay?"

Liya kneels on the other side of him. "Sarah isn't with you? We thought you were together!" They put their hands on him and hold him to keep him sitting up.

Kaleb looks up at them. "I thought she was here."

"Oh my God," Liya gasps.

Aida touches the jacket on Kaleb's head. "You should rest for a minute."

"Oh, my God, no, no, no, no," Mazaa erupts. "We heard the car start and drive away hours ago. We thought they had you. They must have taken Sarah!"

"Maybe," Kaleb mumbles. He rubs at a clot of dried blood, irritating the corner of his eye. "But she could be here somewhere. Left behind, like me." He begins to rise. "Let's go look."

Liya takes Kaleb's arm. "Are you sure you can walk?"

Kaleb nods.

Aida looks at the two of them with shock. "You guys, we have to leave! We have to get out of here! What if they come back?"

"We can't leave without Sarah!" Mazaa says in horror.

"We don't even know if she's here!"

"Aida! How can you be so selfish?"

Kaleb fixes his eyes on Aida. "Are you glad I came back? Are you glad I didn't just run out when I got free? How can you say this, Aida? We're going to look for her."

Kaleb, Liya, and Mazaa walk past Aida to the doorway leading deeper into the building. Exasperated, she follows.

They work their way downstairs and search through all the dark rooms, calling Sarah's name, finding nothing.

"I told you," Aida insists. "She's not here. If she were here, she would have come to us, as you did."

Mazaa looks at her. "We wish for the best, Aida. What do you wish for?"

Aida's eyes fill with anger. "This is reality," she says. "Let's go find a taxi before these monsters come back. And Kaleb needs medical help; look at his face." She reaches her hand toward his head.

Kaleb erupts angrily. "I said I'm fine; I'm not leaving this building until we find her!"

Aida stares at him suspiciously. "Maybe there's something you're not telling us?" Aida questions. "Why do you care so much for some girl we met on the road? You're caring too much, more than for your own life! Think about yourself first."

"We're worried about him too," Liya pleads, "but think about Sarah. Is she alive or dead? Is she here, or did they take her with them? She is our sister too. When we find her, we can go to the pharmacy or clinic for him."

Not waiting for an answer, Liya walks up the stairs to begin checking rooms on the main floor. Mazaa follows her. Kaleb looks at Aida disapprovingly; then, he goes too.

They comb their way through the first floor, as the first pale incandescence of dawn fades onto the walls through the building's open window frames. Again, they find nothing.

The group hurries to the stairwell.

"I told you guys, she's not here. She's not here.!"

While Aida protests at the base of the stairs, Kaleb, Liya, and Mazaa continue to the second floor, reaching the top of the first set of steps, they around a corner in the stairwell and come upon a pair of men's underwear, soaked through with large blotches of blood.

All three look at the garment with a welling emotion. *What does this mean?*

Aida trails them up the steps and stops short at the sight of the underwear. "Oh, my God!" She gasps.

"Can you please be quiet for a moment?" Mazaa looks at her and at the underwear on the steps. Tears stream down her face.

Kaleb, Liya, and Mazaa climb quickly to the second floor. The crying increases in volume.

"We've lost her," Liya sobs.

Kaleb keeps walking.

"I don't think so. We're gonna find her."

In the hallway on the second floor, Liya points to another pair of bloody underwear. Kaleb's posture droops.

Mazaa walks up beside him. "Don't lose hope, please let's check the floor."

"She's dead," Kaleb says simply. He stands like a man seconds away from falling asleep.

"He told the truth." Aida agrees. "We won't find her." She points again at the gory lump of cotton. "Are you guys blind? Don't you see this?"

With strange calmness, Mazaa speaks to Kaleb. "If she is dead, we'll find her body, and at least we will know for sure. But if she's alive, we can still help her."

Aida walks down the stairs and turns to see if they'll follow. Mazaa creeps down the hall toward more rooms. Liya follows Mazaa. Kaleb does as well. Aida folds her arms as if to stand her ground on the stairs and screams, "They're going to kill us!"

Kaleb calls back over his shoulder. "I don't care; we're already dead. There's light in the building now, and it will go faster." Then he looks back at her. "What if you were the one missing?" He points ahead at Liya and Mazaa. "What if it were them?"

Mazaa agrees and says to Liya, "If we die, we're gonna die together. If God has a plan one way or the other, what can we do? Let her stand there if she wants to stand there."

As the trio moves further down the hallway, Aida looks fearfully down the stairs and then runs after them.

They search after room after room. As they search, Liya is continually praying.

***

Sarah slowly begins to gain consciousness. She slowly opens her eyes and tries to look around, but there is no one. She sees the sunrise, now pouring in through the open sections in the wall.

She gingerly moves her hand toward her mouth. The tape has dried tight to her face, but with several tries, she tears the clingy trespasser away inch by inch, until it detaches fully and breathes deeply from her mouth. She struggles to get up, but her body is unresponsive. "Am I paralyzed?" Focusing her foggy mind, she manages to turn her foot sideways, but why won't her legs work? She feebly calls for help, but no sound comes out. Her voice is gone.

As she continues to wake-up, she feels cold. Pain and stiffness begin, flooding into her consciousness, reminding her of the night before and the danger she faced. Sarah keeps forming the names of her friends with her mouth and trying to push the sound out, but a hoarse whisper is all she can muster. She observes her lower body, speckled and blotched with dried blood and completely nude. She looks up to the sky through the patchwork wall.

"Why, God? Why did they do this to me? I wish they had killed me. Why have they left me with a dead body?" She looks again at her lower body, then back to the sky, and her thoughts now pour out of her mouth in sharp rasps. "Dead body, dead mind! Why didn't they kill me? Why?" Her eyes moisten. "Where are you, God? Why have you left me? I thought you loved me. Protected me. Cared for me. But I was wrong!"

***

Liya stands motionless for a moment. "I hear her. I'm hearing her voice!"

Everyone comes to a dead stop and listens for several seconds. "I think it's in your mind," Kaleb says.

"I don't hear anything." Aida moans.

Liya takes long strides and briskly toward the last few rooms on the floor, calling Sarah's name loudly. "Sarah! Sari! Answer if you can hear me. Sarah!"

***

Sarah hears her name being shouted, but can't get up, and can't manage any sound other than a scratchy whisper. The sound of people calling her name drifts closer and louder.

She recognizes Liya's urgent voice, "Kaleb! There's blood here! Over by this room!" Liya's face appears in the doorway, scanning the room.

***

Sweeping the room with her eyes, Liya sees what looks like a pile of discarded clothes with legs in the corner. She screams at the sight of Sarah, quickly covering her own mouth.

Kaleb arrives at the door, followed by Mazaa. They look in horror at what appears to be the tortured, half-naked corpse of their friend, but then Sarah groans and moves.

Liya bolts to Sarah. Kaleb runs after her, pulling the jacket off his head. He drops to his knees beside Sarah and uses the jacket to cover her lower body, not believing what he's seeing. He can't control himself and breaks down. He grabs her and hugs her tight. "I'm so sorry! I'm so sorry!" Sarah's eyes are open, and she looks at him, but she doesn't answer.

Aida reaches the doorway and stands watching. Liya and Mazaa hug Sarah. "Sari, please don't cry. We're here now. We are here!"

Aida calls into the room from the doorway. "Why are you holding her; she's covered with blood!" She lowers her voice as if trying to somehow prevent Sarah from hearing. "She might have a disease." Everyone ignores her.

Now that they've found Sarah, they have to get out of the building as quickly as possible.

Kaleb is on his knees, with Sarah's shoulders and head propped up against his lap and chest. Together with Mazaa, he tries to lift her to her feet, but when she stands, Sarah's legs don't work. Her pain wells up, and her face grimaces. While Kaleb and Mazaa bear Sarah's weight, Liya ties the arms of Kaleb's jacket around her waist, so that the body of the jacket covers her front. Then she rapidly removes her own jacket and ties it around Sarah's waist to cover the back. As soon as she's covered, Kaleb picks her up with one arm under her back and one arm under the crook of her knees. Liya walks beside him, also holding the weight of her legs. They hurry to the staircase and make their way out of the building.

They walk along the road, stopping every five minutes or so to take a break. While they walk, Sarah feels a painful tingling in her legs and feet, like a hundred pins pricking her at once. The way she lay on the concrete floor all night caused her legs to fall asleep, but her traumatized mind didn't register this.

Liya sees a taxi. She runs and stops it, and in a stroke of incredible luck, the driver is Sudanese. She instantly feels safe and quickly strikes up a conversation, making up a story about their "sick friend."

The driver gets out of his car and walks to Kaleb to help him. When he sees Kaleb's and Sarah's injuries, he tears up, intuitively knowing the truth. "Libyans are animals. They are the Devil." He looks at the helpless girl. "Ya Allah."

They carry Sarah into the car and lay her down. The Sudanese open the trunk of the car to grab blankets and passes them to Kaleb. Kaleb covers Sarah.

The driver speeds to Benghazi in a short couple of hours and drives through the gate of an apartment filled mostly with Sudanese people.

Stepping out of the car, he says, "I will be back." True to his word, he returns within five minutes. "I have a doctor friend. I talked to him; he is going to help her, at least to give her a pain killer. He can help you too."

The two men help Sarah out of the car and walk her into the house clinic. The doctor meets them at the door and guides them to a clinic bed in his apartment where he checks her, gives her some pain killers, and starts an IV. A nurse is assigned to Sarah, and the doctor leads Kaleb to another room to begin cleaning and stitching his wounds. When his stitches are finished, the Sudanese driver takes the cousins to another apartment in the building, which houses a small home-restaurant. They eat delicious Sudanese food -- their first proper meal in weeks.

The nurse attending to Sarah gently removes the jacket and the rest of Sarah's clothes. She begins to clean Sarah carefully with wet napkins and sanitary wipes and treats the external wounds with medical alcohol. When she finishes, the doctor comes in to begin a more thorough examination of Sarah's internal wounds. The nurse excuses herself and hurries to her living quarters on an upper floor of the same building to grab a dress and shoes for Sarah to wear.

The nurse returns and assists as the doctor finishes, and then he leaves, and she dresses Sarah. Sarah nods her head to say thank you, and the nurse gives her a comforting smile.

Sarah is thirsty, but she doesn't know how to ask. She moves her hand close to her mouth and swallows her saliva. She moves her hand back and forth in a beckoning motion, and the nurse, understanding, shows Sarah a water bottle. Sarah's eyes lighten, and she slowly nods her head, yes. The nurse leaves the room to consult with the doctor and gets his permission. She returns and lifts Sarah's head as though holding a baby, giving her the water with a plastic cup. The simple act of kindness causes Sarah to cry uncontrollably.

Mazaa goes back to the clinic to check on her friend. The doctor ushers her into the room, and Mazaa asks. "How do you feel, Sari?"

Sarah doesn't answer, but tears continue to run out of her listless eyes.

"I'm sorry, Sari, I'm so sorry. I feel for you." Mazaa's emotions start to overwhelm her, and she has to leave the room.

Liya approaches the clinic and sees Mazaa crying in the hallway and approaches trepidatiously. "What's happened to Sarah?" Mazaa can't talk, so Liya runs inside.

With the nurse's assurances, Liya realizes that it's Sarah's spiritual state, not her physical one, that is so devastating to Mazaa, and she's similarly struck. She grabs Sarah's hand. "Please, Sarah, be strong; we can't be strong without you." She goes to hug her hurting friend, but the way they embrace shifts Sarah's body causing a sharp pain to open beneath Sarah's abdomen. She yelps in pain, and Liya retreats quickly.

The doctor comes into the room and asks, "Can you call your brother?"

Liya runs to Kaleb in the hallway and says, "The doctor is looking for you."

Kaleb walks with Liya to the clinic.

The doctor approaches Kaleb. "I want to talk to you by yourself." Kaleb agrees and tells Liya to leave the room. Liya is not happy to go but does.

"Doctor, what is it?"

"Let's go to the office. I can't talk right here." He indicates toward Sarah with his head.

"She doesn't speak Arabic," Kaleb assures him.

"I understand, but the body language, it doesn't need words."

They walk through the adjacent room to his office, and when the doctor sits down, he continues, "She needs special attention from you and her friends, she can't be left alone. She is damaged physically and mentally. The physical part will get better soon, but the mental aspect will take years."

"What happened to her?" Kaleb asks. "I know she was raped."

"Yes, by several men."

"Several?" Kaleb can feel his face get hot, and his eyes moisten.

The doctor tries to keep the conversation calm. "I'm telling you because you are stronger than them. You must be strong; otherwise, she can't be cured. If you care for her wisely, she will get better soon, even though it's hard to forget an experience like that."

Kaleb fights hard to keep his voice level against the rising emotion. "If you had met her before, she is so sweet. The only thing she knows is making people laugh; she has a pure heart."

"She can stay for a few days. There's not much more we can do here, but the rest will be good for her. She must rest and heal. She will get better."

"Okay, how much do I have to pay?"

"Nothing. You're my people. However, we need to find a place for you and your sisters to stay. You can stay at my house if there's nothing else."

"Oh, my God!" Kaleb exclaims. "Thank you! God bless you." Kaleb shakes the doctor's hand vigorously.

He leaves the doctor's office and returns to Sarah's side. He touches her hand. "You will be fine."

She looks at him without moving her head, her eyes still tearing.

He pulls a napkin from the box on the counter and wipes her face with it, but the tears he wipes away are just as quickly replaced by new ones.

Then to Kaleb's surprise, she speaks in a quiet, husky voice. "Can you please tell the doctor I don't want to live."

"Please, Sari, don't say that. We need you. Your family needs you."

"I don't want to live. I'm already dead. I'm dead!" With that, she starts crying convulsively.

"Please don't say that," Kaleb begs.

***

At the house clinic, Kaleb stands outside Sarah's closed door, leaning heavily against the wall. His head tilts up, but his eyes are closed.

The Sudanese taxi driver approaches. "How is she?"

"The doctor says she will get better; she will stay here for a few days to rest."

"What about you?" Asks the driver.

"I'm fine. The doctor said we could stay at his place, but I feel bad because he's already done so much."

"Come to my house. We have a room. You can all stay with us."

Liya passes the two men and delicately opens the door to Sarah's room. Sarah sees her. The other cousins follow Aida in, and when Sarah sees Aida, she turns her face to the wall.

Kaleb looks at Sarah. "She needs us. I'm not leaving her. I'll stay here; you guys go sleep."

Liya and Mazaa disagree immediately. "We are not going anywhere."

"Please, guys, go sleep. I'm here for her."

"You're sick too, Kaleb!" Liya insists. "You should be resting. Go to sleep."

Aida walks to the driver's side. "I'm going to sleep. I didn't sleep last night."

"Go then," says Liya.

Aida looks at the Sudanese man, and he looks at Kaleb.

"It's okay, go," Kaleb says. "We'll be fine." The Sudanese man and Aida leave.

Liya, Kaleb, and Mazaa sit on chairs around Sarah's bed, making jokes and chuckling, but Sarah doesn't respond or laugh. The nurse arrives and gives Sarah sleeping medicine, and soon she is asleep. The three cousins stay by her bed the whole night. Kaleb falls asleep, sitting on a small couch.

In the middle of the night, the doctor walks into the room. He looks at Kaleb. "You need rest too. You lost a lot of blood."

"I will. Thanks for everything you did for us."

The doctor looks at Sarah. "I did it as much for me as for you. For my daughter and for me."

"Yes, any human being would relate to Sarah's pain."

"Yes." The doctor pauses. "I lost my daughter to the same situation." The small man's eyes begin to tear up. He goes to speak again, but the words catch in his throat. He waits a moment, then forces a sad smile, but can't speak.

"I'm sorry for your loss."

The doctor nods his head. He waits another moment, then clears his throat. "She was my only child. She killed herself a month after she was raped." Words become difficult, but he continues. "I wasn't… there for her. That's why I remain here to help others. There are a lot of women and men whose dreams die on this road."

"I'm really sorry. Yes, I saw that with my own eyes." Kaleb looks back at Sarah. "She was a butterfly, one of the happiest girls I've ever met in my life. She was so fun to be around, but…" His emotions begin to rise, and he struggles to control them. "But they killed her happiness."

"Is that your sister?"

"No."

"She is our sister," Mazaa responds. "She doesn't have to have the same family to be our sister."

"Exactly," the doctor says. He leads them away from the bedside, and as Sarah sleeps, the doctor quietly instructs them. "Don't ask her what happened in that building." The doctor tells them. "Do not ask her. Try to act like it is nothing. It sounds harsh, but for now, there is no sense in making her remember it. For now, we need to get her mind on other things. Help her to forget. Even though it will be an emotional struggle for her entire life."

"Okay." They agree.

"It's true," Liya acknowledges.

The doctor walks out, and Kaleb, Mazaa, and Liya return to their seats. They chat quietly and doze while the sun rises. At 7:00 a.m., the nurse walks into the room and sees them.

"Good Morning."

They all greet her with, "Good mornings," and the nurse politely asks them to leave the room she while she cleans Sarah. They file out and sit outside.

The nurse wakes Sarah. Sarah looks at her and closes her eyes again. The nurse says, in English, "How do you feel today?"

Sarah is surprised to hear English words but simply says, "I don't want to feel better. I want to die. Could you help me to die, please?"

The nurse is taken aback and isn't sure how to respond.

"I'm already dead, but I'm just breathing." Sarah gets emotional. "Can you please help me?"

"Please don't cry! Please try to think about your family. What will happen to them if they lose you? I'm not saying it is easy to recover, but..."

"...They will cry for a month." She looks at her hopelessly. "Then, they will forget. Whether I'm breathing or not breathing, there is no difference. I'm dead."

"A month? Your mother will cry her entire life! Or she will die." Sarah screams at the nurse. "DON'T SAY THAT!!"

The cousins out in the hallway jump and stare at the door, then look at each other.

Sarah keeps screaming, "I'M WORTHLESS! A dead body with a dead mind! DON'T TRY TO SCARE ME! She will be FINE! And I will be relieved!" She looks at the nurse contemptuously. "You know what, you don't get it."

"I'm telling you the truth. Your doctor lost his daughter in the same circumstance. Her mom cried nonstop for six months; then, she died six months after her daughter. That's why the doctor moved here to stop thinking about his family. Helping others helps him feel better. It helps him heal."

Sarah listens to her quietly. The nurse helps Sarah rise from the bed and take a shower. In the bathroom, she gives Sarah new underwear and changes her tampon in case the bleeding hasn't stopped yet. The nurse also offers Sarah new clothes. While Sarah changes, she quietly says, "Thank you."

The nurse takes her back to the clinic bed. "The doctor will be here shortly. Let me call your family."

The nurse sticks her head out into the hallway and invites the cousins in.

Mazaa sees Sarah in her new dress. "Wow, Sari, you look so beautiful."

"She is always beautiful," Kaleb agrees.

"Sari, let me tell you a joke." Liya tries to make Sarah laugh.

Mazaa looks at Liya and smiles.

Sarah looks at them with unmoving eyes. Liya looks at Sarah's eyes, and she forgets what she wants to say. Something in Sarah's eyes is unfamiliar. It scares her, and she becomes emotional. Embarrassed, she turns to slip out of the room. Mazaa calls after her in Arabic.

"What are you doing? Don't you remember what the doctor said? Try to be strong."

"I need to pee, badly," Liya responds in Amharic. She abruptly turns and walks out the door.

Mazaa tries to pass it off as humorous. "Ay, Liya, that was her joke... to tell us about her pee." Then, she laughs, and Kaleb does as well.

"Hey, everyone." Aida walks into the room, rubbing her eyes. She hugs Kaleb, then begins inspecting the thick bandages on his head. "How do you feel?"

"I'm fine."

"And how about you?" Aida asks Sarah. Sarah doesn't answer, so Aida keeps talking, "You look great, looks like you are ready to go."

Still, Sarah says nothing.

"Sorry, Sari... are you mad at me?" She sits on Sarah's bed next to her. "I went to sleep because I was so tired, I didn't sleep at all the other day."

Kaleb and Mazaa try to signal to Aida not to speak subtly, but she doesn't see them.

"I want to talk to you outside," Mazaa says, grabbing her hand, leading her outside. "Are you out of your mind? Are you trying to remind her of what happened? We're trying to help her forget."

"No, I wasn't," Aida explains. "I saw she didn't want to talk to me, that's why I was explaining to her."

"She doesn't want to talk to any of us. She's been crying the whole time."

"She'll forget soon."

"Sometimes, I wonder if you're human. Think about if you were in her place, would you forget so easily? No, I don't think so."

"Why do you wish this for me? Oh, my God!" Aida looks at Mazaa in shocked disgust.

"You see! In her position, it hurts to even think about it. When we see people's pain, we don't feel it until we experience it. Then it hurts. But sometimes we have to think, 'What if it was me?' Then life will get new value."

Aida doesn't answer; she just stares at Mazaa.

Kaleb moves to Sarah. "Sari, please don't cry!" He wipes her face. When he touches her face, she flinches and jerks her head away, turning from him. He stops, surprised by her reaction. He withdraws his hand. "Your eyes will shrink," he says, quoting a favorite Ethiopian saying. "Be strong. You are the strongest person I ever met in my life."

"How will I be strong?" She speaks to the wall. "How? Sarah is dead." Then she points to her body. "This is a dead body. Don't think I'm alive because I'm breathing." Then she screams, and the cousins jump.

"It's okay, please, Sari. We're here for you," Kaleb tries to help her calm down.

Mazaa hears the screaming and quickly walks back inside the room. "Sarah, we're your family, we're here for you!" She hugs her friend and weeps.

The family remains in the Benghazi apartment for a week, until Sarah's body heals.

Chapter Eight

It's been a month since Sarah left Sudan. Sarah, Kaleb, Liya, Mazaa, and Aida arrive at Tripoli, the capital city of Libya. The Sudanese taxi driver takes them to a fenced-in neighborhood, heavily populated with Ethiopians, Eritreans, Sudanese, Senegalese, Nigerian, and Chadians. Libyans do not come to this sector and would be in danger for their lives if they did. The majority of businesses here are Sudanese, Chadian, and Senegalese that included coffee shops, clothing stores, restaurants, hair salons, and others. The neighborhood is called Crimea.

"You'll find so many Habesha here." The driver points at the gate in the fence.

"Is this the Sudanese place, Crimea?" Kaleb asks.

"Yes, it is."

Everyone thanks the driver and exits the car. They walk through the gate, and up and down the street, looking through the many shops. On their tour, they meet a couple of Habesha, and one of them takes them to a small restaurant. The restaurant is Ethiopian.

When they see Ethiopian food, everyone's hearts warm with happiness. The place mostly serves take-out food and is cramped inside, so they sit at a small table outside. The owner comes out to take their orders. He has no menu, but rattles off the items from memory, diligently reciting his vegetarian options. Many Ethiopians belong to the Orthodox church, which endorses fasting from meat and dairy on Wednesdays and Fridays. Accordingly, this being Wednesday, the group orders the veggie combo.

"While we wait for the food, let me walk around to find out from the locals where we can stay," Kaleb says.

"It's a veggie combo; it doesn't take long," Mazaa suggests.

"Okay, I was trying to save time."

"I never thought there would be this much Habesha here," Aida says, surprised.

"This is a place where a lot of people work to make money for their journey," Kaleb says.

"Will we work here?" Liya asks.

"Yes, there is no other choice," Kaleb responds.

"Sarah, will you work here?" Mazaa asks.

"I have to," Sarah answers quietly. She has become very quiet since the tragedy. She doesn't make jokes or laugh when others do.

"Sarah needs to rest for a while, first," Kaleb offers, though the suggestion sounds more like a verdict.

"Don't worry. I'm fine; I can work!"

Then the food arrives, and the group walks over to a small counter with a plastic basin and pitcher to wash their hands. They return to the table and take in the wonderful appearance and smell of the food. A large plate is covered with injera, topped with a variety of warm vegetable and legume-based stews. A second plate sits beside it with several folded injera for dipping and scooping.

"Wow, the food is delicious," Kaleb proclaims after eating his first mouthful. Then, true to custom, he begins to feed Sarah her first two mouthfuls. Aida watches him.

"I never thought I would see Injera here," Mazaa says, surprised.

"If there is Habesha, there is injera. No matter where," Liya says.

"Someone is making a joke," Mazaa says.

"I'm not making a joke. That's the truth."

Kaleb turns to offer Aida her first mouthful, but she ignores him, dipping and eating her piece of injera. He then offers the first bite to Mazaa and Liya. They accept and then begin their meals.

"How's the food?" The owner asks.

Except for Sarah, they all compliment the owner enthusiastically.

After they finish eating, they walk to one of the coffee shops, and Kaleb orders tea for everyone. He says, "I will be back soon; stay here."

"Don't worry; we'll wait here," Liya says.

"I want to come with you," Aida says.

"If you want, you can come."

She pushes back her chair and follows him but stays a few steps behind to avoid conversation.

As they walk down the street, Kaleb meets several Habesha working in the shops they pass. Aida is still not talking to Kaleb and enjoys the steady procession of tightly packed stores.

Liya and Mazaa talk and laugh. Sarah is in her own zone, not even hearing them. They notice tears coming down her cheeks.

"Are you okay, Sari?" Liya questions.

"Yes, I'm fine."

"Sari, you're crying," Mazaa says, "and you say you're fine?"

Sarah puts her hand to her face. "I'm really sorry; I don't know why I cry."

"Let's talk about our family." Mazaa tries to change the conversation. "I'll start. I was born in Gondar in the countryside; my mom died when I was a kid. My aunt brought me to Sudan after that. That's where I met Liya and Kaleb, my cousins."

"What about Aida?"

"She's lived in Sudan for less than three years. She's not my blood family. She's my aunt's family, but..." She looks at Liya. "She is my first cousin. Unfortunately, her mom died when she had her younger sister."

140

"I'm really sorry about that," Sarah says. "For both of you."

"I don't remember my mom," Liya says. Then she looks down. "Don't worry; it was a long time ago."

Now it's Sarah's turn to change the subject. "Let's talk about something else."

***

Walking around the market, Kaleb suddenly stops. He examines a man across the street in disbelief, then calls out his name. "Samuel!"

Samuel looks over. His face erupts in surprised happiness, and he runs over. The two were childhood best friends in Sudan, and they welcome each other with a sincere hug. Samuel greets Aida as well and offers to sit for coffee. Kaleb enthusiastically agrees, and the three walk to the coffee shop, seat themselves, and order their coffee.

"When did you guys come here?" Samuel asks.

"We got here today."

Samuel invites them to stay at his place for a couple of days until they get their own place and money. They share stories of their travels over wonderfully aromatic, traditionally blended coffee, and Samuel gives them hard-earned advice about life in Libya. When their cups are empty, Kaleb leaves to bring his sisters.

The family returns to the coffee shop, and Samuel takes them to his place in a taxi. Samuel lives with ten people inside one room. The room is about two hundred square feet, but there is no bed, just a couple of flat sponge mattresses on the floor. The occupants aren't too worried about comfort because none of them plan on staying for long.

"Hey, everyone," Samuel announces, "I've brought guests. They just got into the city today."

The reception is warm. "Welcome!"

"Feel free; this is your home too."

Kaleb acknowledges the greetings, humbly. "Thanks."

They offer two of the thin mattresses for the new guests to share. Sarah looks around to absorb the situation. There are a couple of girls, but the majority of the residents are men.

141

Sarah whispers to Liya, "Can I sleep in the middle?" Liya agrees.

The next morning, the girls were already up as Samuel gets up to shower and get ready for work. The house has more than thirty people from Ethiopian and Eritrea, but there is just one shower. The men cook breakfast for everyone. After breakfast, the women's taxi driver arrives, and they go to work. One of the girls is sick and stays home, spending her day with Liya, Sarah, and Mazaa. Kaleb leaves the house with Samuel, and Aida goes with them.

The girl explains to the cousins about Libyan work life. In Libya, there is almost no work for foreign men. Coffee shops, for instance, only employ females because that's how businesses make money. A lot of guys go there to get females, literally. The men buy the coffee, then proposition the waitress of their choice for sex. The waitress can say yes or no. If they say yes, the man will pick them up after work. Everyone is happy -- the man gets the woman, the woman receives the extra money, and the shop owner sells copious amounts of coffee to the Johns.

"Arab, Sudanese, Chadian, they love Ethiopian and Eritrean women." The girl explains.

"They don't love us; they just want to use our bodies," Sarah responds with emotion.

"But not all the men are the same," the girl begins to explain.

"Trust me; all men are the same." Sarah gets angry. "They all have the very same mother. It doesn't matter where they come from; they are the same. They just have a different name and a different nationality."

"No, that is not true," the girl disagrees.

Sarah's eyes fill with tears, and she walks back over to her foam mat. She covers her face with a borrowed blanket and silently cries, thinking about the girl's seeming-indifference. "Why don't people feel other people's pain?"

"Did I say something bad?" The girl asks.

"Oh, don't worry. You didn't," Mazaa assures her.

After a long day, Kaleb returns home and says, "Hey," to his cousins. "Where's Sarah?"

142

"Asleep," Mazaa responds.

"Is she okay?"

"She slept all day," Liya responds. "She didn't even eat. Ask her; maybe she'll say yes to you."

Kaleb walks to Sarah and touches her to wake her up, but she doesn't stir. He walks back to Liya. "She is fast asleep."

Liya tells him about their conversation with the local woman.

Kaleb walks back to Sarah and crouches down beside her again. "Please, Sari, wake up, I know you are not asleep. At least eat dinner. Dinner is injera."

Sarah pulls the blanket off her face. "I'm not hungry. And I don't feel like getting up. Can you please understand me?" Her voice is emotional.

"It's okay." Kaleb rises and respectfully walks back to Liya.

In the days to come, the cousins get jobs at different coffee shops, promising each other not to accept the advances of patrons. The cousins settle into a routine of the women going to work, while Kaleb stays behind to cook and clean.

After a week, the girls return home from work, and Kaleb tells them he's found a place to live. He takes them to the new place, and at first, the girls are alarmed that they're leaving Crimea. They arrive at their new address around 8:00 p.m. The neighborhood is clean, and the cream-colored two-story building faces the gravel road. They march up the stairs to their room, and to their delight, Kaleb and Samuel have spent the day setting it up. There are two real, actual mattresses, each fitted with sheets, blankets, and two pillows. There is also a single burner propane stove, a pan, knife, cutting board, salt, and onions. Down the hall is a shared bathroom, with a section of ceiling oddly missing and exposed to sunlight.

The next morning, Sarah doesn't feel good and stays home, but her friends leave for work. Their new taxi driver is also Sudanese, and while he waits for them, a small group of young boys outside starts throwing rocks at his car. When the girls come out of the building, the little gang of boys throws rocks at them too. Liya, Mazaa, and Aida run as fast as they can to get into the car.

The driver explains to them that this is how they treat foreigners outside of Crimea. The young ones learn from the older ones. "Especially in this area. That's why the rent is so cheap."

Sarah waits until Kaleb leaves for the store, then she gets up and walks outside with the kitchen knife and cuts the clothesline, coiling the rope and taking it back inside. Leaving the knife in their room, she takes the rope to the shared bathroom, but there is a short line of people waiting to go in, so she heads back to the room. She looks around the room and climbs up on the windowsill to tie one end of the rope to an overhead pipe. She starts tying the loose end of the rope into a loop but stops short at a thought. She hops down from the ledge and finds a pen and paper in Kaleb's belongings. "Sorry about everything I did." she writes. "This is my family's phone number...."

***

As Kaleb walks to the store, he sees four men watching him from across the street. They hold large rocks. Suddenly they run across the street toward him. The adrenaline from pure fear shoots through his veins like ice water, and Kaleb turns and sprints home with the men in close pursuit. He runs back to the apartment, slamming and locking the gate behind him. He breathes deep gulps of air and drops onto the stairs, exhausted.

***

Sarah steps back up onto the window ledge and reaches for the rope, but her foot slips. She cracks her shin on the sill and falls slowly to the floor. Outside, Kaleb hears the tumult of Sarah falling and runs up to the room. He sees Sarah on the floor, and the rope hanging from the ceiling. For a shocking moment, he stares in disbelief, then races to her side and grabs her.

"Why? Why?" He hugs her, but she flinches and squirms violently at his touch. Kaleb pulls back physically but remains insistent. "I'm sorry! Please, Sarah, don't hurt yourself." He grabs the paper and reads it.

The place they're living in becomes worse and worse. Every day they must run to their taxi under a hail of rocks. They can't go shopping without danger.

"How long must we keep doing this? Find a new place for us," Aida demands.

"I'm looking; it's not that easy," Kaleb responds.

"The other day, I got hit by rocks while I was taking a shower!" Mazaa exclaims. "They threw them right through the hole in the roof. I don't know how they even knew I was in there!"

"They always make him run when he goes shopping," Liya says.

Sarah comes back from the bathroom with blood dripping down her forehead. Everyone gets up looking at her.

"What happened?" Kaleb asks.

Mazaa and Liya echo his question.

Kaleb regards her warily. "Did you... hurt yourself?"

"...Rocks," Sarah simply says and walks to the bed to lie down as the cousins look at each other.

**

After a week, they find a place on the street called Sharia Ahada A'ashar. It's a large U-shaped, single-story building like a motel. Each of the seven rooms has its door facing the courtyard within the U. The entrance gate is at the open end of the U, with the single bathroom at one end of the building near the gate. The shared kitchen is at the opposite end of the courtyard from the gate, in the portion of the building connecting the two wings. All the rooms are rented to Ethiopians and Eritreans, and many of the rooms have at least eight people.

While setting up the room for his cousins, Kaleb was told of a man living in one of the rooms who sells exceptionally good homemade injera. Now, they buy dinner from him and settle into their new room to rest.

In the morning, Liya rises from bed and notices Sarah is gone. Assuming Sarah is in the bathroom, she gets dressed and prepares for the day. After a while, Sarah still hasn't returned, and Liya becomes concerned. She goes to the bathroom to look.

Sarah isn't there. She becomes worried. Returning to the room, she wakes up Kaleb and says, "Sarah is not in the building. I looked for her everywhere, but she is not here."

"Are you sure?"

"Yes!"

He walks to the shared kitchen and bathroom and asks the people if they've seen her, giving them a description. Then he returns to the room. "Do you have any idea where she went?"

"No, I don't," Liya says. "I heard her when she walked out; she didn't change out of her pajamas."

Kaleb looks at Liya, completely confused, "I don't know where to go."

***

Sarah wakes early in the morning to go to the bathroom. She heads to the bathroom and stands in line. A little boy comes out from the room next to hers and crawls toward the bathroom. A smile curls Sarah's lips, and she intercepts the little traveler to play with him. He is delightful, happy, cute, and sweet. "I wish I was like you," Sarah says quietly to the giggling baby. "I would have a clean mind, I could laugh, I would be happy, and my mom would protect me."

After a couple of minutes, his mother comes out of the bathroom.

Sarah looks at her, and she can't believe her eyes. The girl sees Sarah and screams!

"Oh, my God, I'm sure I'm not dreaming!" They hug each other.

Sarah exclaims, "Eden?" with a cheerful voice.

"Sari, when did you came here?"

"To the city? A couple of weeks ago."

Eden takes her in. "It's unbelievable. I never thought you would come on this road. Does your family know you're here?"

"No, they don't."

"We have to let them know where you are! We will call them later. Oh, my God. Who did you come with? Did you come with a guy?"

"No. I came by myself. I'm with others now, but you don't know them, I met them on the road. But they are very nice and caring people."

They talk for hours. Eden is Sarah's neighbor from back home in Bihar Dar. She left Ethiopia when she was very young and grew up in Sudan. She lived in Sudan for many years, working as a maid, until she got tired of the monotony of her life and desired a change and a family life. She met a man while traveling to Libya and became pregnant. They tried to go to Italy to have their baby there, but the first smuggler stole their money, and the second one got them caught by a police boat. She ended up in prison for two months. Luckily, when they discovered she was pregnant, they let her and her partner go, and the baby was born in Libya. Her baby is now ten months old. Financially, it will be a long time before they can afford the next leg of the trip to Italy.

Sarah is laughing for the first time since her awful night in the deserted building. Eden makes breakfast, and they eat together. They keep talking about their childhood memories, their families, and the school they went too. Eden is older than Sarah, and they were in different classes, but they went to the same school and remembered many of the same people and stories.

"Do you remember when you were a kid," Eden says, "We used to make fun of you!"

"I don't. About what?"

"We used to say your family found you on the street. You believed us, and you cried."

Sarah laughs loudly, "Oh, yes, I do remember. You guys were bad."

Then there is a knock-on Eden's door. "Come in."

Kaleb enters. Sarah looks at him and suddenly becomes conscious of the time. She stands. "How did you know I was here?"

He doesn't give her an answer but just stands there looking at her, surprised, because her face is shining.

Sarah looks at him. "Are you okay?"

"Yes," Kaleb is confused. "I heard your voice from next door when you laughed."

"Oh, my God, sorry, I forgot to introduce you," Sarah indicates toward Eden. "This is Eden, my childhood friend."

Kaleb shakes Eden's hand and responds, "Kaleb."

Sarah turns to Eden. "He's like my brother."

"She told me about you guys; she is so happy to have you in her life."

"She's a sweet girl."

Eden gets up and gives him the remaining breakfast from the stove.

"Let me wash my face; I just got up. Then we can eat together."

"We just ate."

Kaleb walks to his room to tell Liya. Then he comes back and eats. "It's so delicious."

"Yeah," Sarah makes a joke. "Women from Bahir Dar, we know how to cook."

"You'll have to prove that," Kaleb jokes.

After a couple of hours, Eden and Sarah make ready to go to the phone center. In Libya, illegal immigrants cannot purchase cell phones or sim cards without a government ID, so immigrants travel to these stores to make calls.

Eden gives Sarah a hijab and scarf to cover her head and face. They hail a taxi. At the center, Eden speaks to the man at the counter, then, Sarah steps through one of the small doors into a phone booth. She nervously dials her family home number.

***

Tsehay, Sarah's mom, sits in her living room, enjoying coffee with her neighbors. Sarah's sister, Meron, is in her bedroom practicing her singing. The phone rings. The maid picks it up. "Hello?"

"Hey."

The maid recognizes Sarah's voice; her eyes go wide, and she spins to face Tsehay.

"It's Sarah!" Tsehay's coffee cup shatters on the floor in a wet explosion. She is instantly out of her chair and running to the phone. "Are you sure?" She grabs the phone.

"My sweet baby!"

"Hello, hello, hello, Mom..." Sarah's voice sounds older but is unmistakable.

"It's true! It's my baby!" Tears run down her cheeks.

Sarah listens to the emotion overwhelming her mother. "Mom, please talk to me, don't cry."

"Are you alive? Is this true, or am I dreaming?" Tsehay is nearing panic, and her guests sit on the edge of their chairs, trying to decide how to respond. "Sari, my sweet baby! I thought I lost you!"

Hearing her mother's emotion unlocks deep feelings, and Sarah breaks down. "Mom, I'm so sorry, you didn't deserve this. I'm a bad and selfish child." Her tears pour down.

"Don't worry, my baby. I just want to know you still exist; you're alive! Praise God."

"Mom, I'm really, really sorry for everything I did. I couldn't find a phone to call you."

"It's okay, I understand. I'm so glad to hear your voice. This is a miracle! It is! It feels like a dream." She turns back to her neighbors. "My baby is alive!" She speaks with intense focus into the phone. "Are you okay?"

Powerful sobs are lined up in Sarah's chest, waiting to break free, but she holds them back with all her strength to try to speak coherently with her mom. "I'm great. I'm fine."

"I don't know if I believe you! A month ago, I had a terrible dream, and I thought I had lost you. Thank God for allowing me to hear your voice."

Sarah feels caught, not wanting to lie but not able to reveal the depth of horror she's experienced to this caring woman. Feelings overwhelm her, and she suddenly hangs up the phone.

Eden hugs her and holds her tightly. "You have to be strong; I know you missed your mom, but you have to call her back. You can't hang up on her." Eden asks Sarah for the number and types it in for her. The phone is picked up before the first ring finished.

"My darling, are you okay?"

"This is Eden, Almaz's daughter. Do you remember me?"

"Oh... um, yes. Yes. But what happened? Is Sarah still there? Is everything okay?"

"Yes, yes, just a little phone problem. She's fine. She just needs a moment. We just discovered each other this morning. How are you, auntie?"

"I'm fine. We're good here. I thought you were living in Sudan."

"Yes, but I came here two years ago."

"Oh, good. I'm glad you guys met. How is she?"

"She is good. Here I'll put her back on the phone..."

***

The call is over, and Sarah sits on the floor of the phone booth crying. She whispers, "Mom knows what happened to me. I wish she were next to me to hug me; I would be fine."

"Baby... my dear..." Eden sits beside her and puts her arm around her.

"I'm fine; I just can't handle my mom's pain. Her voice was so...caring... and hurt..."

"It's normal, be strong. Of course, your mom is worried," she says. "You did well. You told her the truth that you're okay. That will give her peace."

Sarah is quiet, and the tears keep trickling. "Which truth do you know?" she imagines herself, asking Eden. "My fake laugh or my real ruin, which one? My mom knows the truth, God told her, but I lied to her because I'm a liar. But if I tell her the truth, she'll die. She could never handle this. I'm telling no one. No one! I will keep this to myself until I die."

"What did you say?" Eden asks.

Sarah realizes her thoughts are escaping her mouth as murmurs. "When? I didn't say anything."

Eden lets it go and starts cleaning Sarah's face for her. They pay the attendant for the call and walk out of the phone center. Eden takes Sarah to a nearby store to buy a hijab and some new clothes.

The next day Sarah, Liya, Mazaa, and Aida leave for work, work all day, and meet their transportation to go home after closing time. They have a new contract with a Sudanese taxi driver, a very nice man, who comes in the morning to pick them up and returns them at night. Sarah struggles intensely with interaction at the coffee shop... the language was already a barrier, but now the very sound of Arabic fills her with dread, anxiety, and almost a homicidal anger.

The motivations of the men coming for coffee fill her with disgust, but virtually *all* customers are men, leaving her feeling trapped all day. Jobs are scarce, and she doesn't want to ask for money from her family, so she's determined to keep showing up for work, but once she's there, she is continuously retreating from the customers and hiding from any interaction. In three weeks, she is fired from eight coffee shops.

"What is your problem?" Eden asks Sarah.

"Nothing, I just... hate them. I just hate them. I don't understand..." She is going to finish the sentence with the word "Why," a lie, but Eden cuts her off.

"But you don't need to understand the language. It's not a problem. If you know the words for coffee, tea, water, and soda, that's enough."

"I know all of that. Liya, Mazaa, and Kaleb taught me."

"Then, just remind yourself that you're not living here forever. It's temporary or ask your family to send you money for transportation."

"I'll work," Sarah says simply, not willing to explain that merely hearing the customers' language makes her want to kill them.

"That's what I want to hear from you," Eden says with a twinkle. "I have a Sudanese friend who owns a shop; I'll talk to him."

"Thanks!"

"You look so sad, Sarah," Eden says, assuming it's because of the firing. "Let's go find something to entertain ourselves."

Sarah walks to her room to change her clothes and puts on her hijab and scarf.

"Where're you going?" Kaleb asks.

"Eden wants to take me to the city," Sarah answers quietly.

"Good, you should relax your mind."

"Have a great day, Kaleb," Sarah walks out.

Sarah, Eden, and Eden's little boy arrive at the park. There is playground equipment, a Ferris wheel, and lots of places for adults to rest and visit while the children play. Sarah sits on a wooden bench, watching everyone.

Eden plays nearby with her son. Eden walks over to Sarah and asks her to play, but Sarah just wants to sit and absorb the happy energy of the people here and the kids playing. She is enjoying it. There are no men in the park, at all, just mothers and children, and this suits Sarah simply fine. All the women's faces are covered, but Sarah can tell by the children that she and Eden are the only black people there. After spending a long day in the park, they go back home.

When Sarah arrives home, Kaleb is cooking dinner, and everyone is just returning from work. Sarah begins swapping stories with her friends, and soon they're settling down to eat. As they eat their first mouthfuls, there is a knock at the door. "Come in," Kaleb calls.

Eden opens the door. "I'm making coffee, don't go to sleep yet, guys."

"Eden, come and have dinner with us," Kaleb beckons her in.

"Oh, I just ate."

Kaleb insists. "Let me feed you."

Eden comes in and sits down, and Kaleb feeds her two separate mouthfuls, reflecting a courtesy of Ethiopian culture. Then Sarah takes a small portion of food and also feeds Eden. As Eden chews, her eyes suddenly begin to tear, and she stands up from the table. Sarah starts laughing, and Kaleb immediately knows what's happened.

"Are you crazy? She's dying."

Eden can't swallow the scalding-hot mouthful. "Don't forget I will pay you back," she says through a full mouth and chokes out a giggle.

"You fed me an all-spice bite the other day; this is payback."

"You fed her the mitmita, didn't you?" Kaleb asks Sarah.

"Yes, I did." She laughs again.

Mazaa shakes her head. "Sarah is crazy."

Eden has to excuse herself to spit out the food while the cousins laugh, and then leaves to begin preparing the coffee ceremony in the courtyard in front of their rooms. As per custom, she invites everyone in the building. There are more than forty people, most of whom are men who can't find work. Violence against immigrants in Libya is common, and these men face a high probability of physical attack whenever they leave the compound. Just going to the store is difficult, and finding work is nearly impossible. They mostly rely on the generosity of family members sending money. It's a frustrating life, and private, protected moments of community like this are welcome.

People begin emerging in small groups from different doorways and gather around the coffee ceremony. When the coffee is ready, Eden pours it into small cups, which Sarah helps to pass around. A sudden, wrenching cramp stabs Sarah's stomach, and she has to put her cups down. A rush of nausea pushes toward her mouth, and she hurries to the bathroom where she vomits violently into the toilet. The private discomfort in Sarah's stomach has been building for several days but going to a doctor is out of the question in Libya. A deep feeling of tiredness follows her nausea.

Eden enjoys watching the people drinking and chatting, and here and there asks a person, "How is it?"

"It's so good!"

Ethiopian coffee ceremonies involve three consecutive rounds of roasting, brewing the beans and take from two to three hours. During the second round, Sarah returns and sits down beside Eden.

"Are you okay?" Eden asks.

"I don't know why I'm feeling weird," and explains her stomach pains.

"Are you pregnant?"

Sarah is shocked but doesn't say anything.

Eden continues, "The way you described it, it sounds like you're pregnant."

"What? How could I be?" Sarah blows off the question. "That's impossible." Privately, Sarah is panicking at the thought. *Oh, God! No, no, no, it can't be true. But what if…?* "I have a stomach problem, that's all. When I have my stomach pain, that's the way I feel. I want to go to the clinic. Do you know someone?"

"Yes, I'll take you tomorrow."

The second coffee is ready to serve, and people are talking. Often in these settings, the conversation revolves around smugglers; which one is the best and what they charge. They also compare stories of the abuse they receive when they leave the compound.

***

Sarah has started with her new boss Ahmed, Eden's friend. He has four coffee shops. He shows Sarah the job, and also where his other stores are, in case she needs help or supplies. Sarah starts by cleaning all the glasses and preparing the cappuccino mix. She creates a blend out of sugar, Nescafe powder, and small amounts of hot water. She stirs the ingredients for about twenty minutes, adding small amounts of water as she goes until she has a thick, dark caramel-colored paste. A teaspoon of this paste will act as the base of every cappuccino she sells, and she makes enough in the one batch for the whole day. When she finishes, she sits behind the open door, out of view. A girl from one of Ahmed's other shops walks in. Sarah gets up and greets her in Amharic.

She looks at Sarah. "Are you new?"

"Yes, I just started today. Sorry, what is your name?"

"Kidist." Kidist is an Ethiopian who grew up in Eritrea. She's five feet and one-inch, curly black long hair, light brown skin, beautiful white teeth. And she is very caring and sweet.

"Sarah."

"Why do you hide? If you sit like that, you can't make any money. I know this is true because I used to sit like that."

"I don't want the men to come here because of me. I want them to come here to drink coffee, tea, soda, etc. But not for me. I'm not for sale."

"I know what you mean. I really feel the same way, but I don't blame them because our people make our bodies cheap for money."

"You mean the way our girls go out with these men for money?"

"Yes." Then she explains. A lot of Habesha women sell their bodies to get money to go to Italy. If they stay in Libya too long, they might get caught by the police and thrown in jail, or they might be killed in a racist attack. The women who are willing to go home with men from the coffee shops can cover the cost of their transportation to Italy in a single year. More traditional prostitutes can earn that money in just a few months, but without using sex, women are usually stuck in Crimea for years. Even women with husbands will sell themselves with their husbands' knowledge and support; that's how desperate they are to leave. Occasionally, a Habesha couple will pose as brother and sister, and the woman will tell the customer that her "brother" won't let her sleep around. Still, if the customer pays to send him to Italy, she will be free to remain and date the customer. When the customer fronts the money, the couple uses it to escape together. Or, if it's not enough money for both of them, he will leave and go to Italy where he's allowed to work and bring her the first chance he gets.

"That is ridiculous!"

"I know what you're feeling, Sarah, that's how I feel too."

"I don't care how long it takes; there is no way I could sell myself." Tears begin coming down her cheeks.

"Sarah, it's not a good place to show your tears." Then Kidist hags Sarah. "Let's go to my place. Let me show you around my shop." They walk to Kidist's coffee shop, which is roughly the same size and style as where Sarah works.

After a couple of minutes, Sarah walks to her place. Two Chadians watch Sarah as she moves between the shops and follow her in. They order coffee and tea. After she serves them, Sarah retreats to the small table behind the door and sits by herself. The men offer for her to sit with them, but she declines.

"Are you new?" they ask in Arabic.

She doesn't answer.

They chuckle with each other. "After a week, she will be the one wanting to sit next to us when she knows the business. Isn't she cute?"

Sarah doesn't understand what they are saying, and when they finish their drink, they give her money and walk out. She walks outside to give the change back, but they've left. Then she walks to Kidist's store.

"Two men left all their change."

"How much was it?"

"They gave me one-hundred Libyan dinar! I went to get changed, and when I came back, they were gone." She shows Kidist the money.

"They left it for you as a tip, which means they like you."

"Whatever." Sarah is disgusted. "Thanks for explaining." Then she walks back to work.

Liya, Sarah, Mazaa, and Aida talk about the behavior of the men on their trip home.

"God will help us to be strong, and he can protect us in this disgusting work," Liya says.

"I never believed it when people told me about Crimea," Aida agrees.

"We have to pray every day in the morning before we leave our house," Mazaa says.

"It doesn't matter how long it takes us; there is no way. We're not giving them a chance to talk to us, let alone to touch us," Sarah quietly says. "I met a girl today, her name is Kidist, and she's worked at Crimea for almost a year because she doesn't want to do the dirty work. I'm proud of her. There are a lot of girls that work hard to get the money." She looks at her friends resolutely. "Also, there are a lot of girls who like doing the shortcut, but for us, it doesn't matter how long it takes, in the end, we'll get there with God."

All the girls agree with her.

***

Sarah has been in Libya for almost five months. She keeps working, but her emotional struggles won't go away. After a long day, Sarah and her friends return home to Kaleb cooking dinner outside. The girls greet him and walk inside. Sarah walks to her bag to change her clothes and sees inside a letter and some new pairs of underwear. She is surprised, but not knowing who left the gift and why she tries to act normal and prevent her friends from noticing. She changes into her loose pajamas, subtly puts the letter in her pocket, and walks to the staircase to the open roof. She opens it and pulls out a letter. It's from Kaleb.

It reads, "Sari, I don't know where to start, but I know one thing, I can't deny I'm in love with you! I know you don't expect this from me." Sarah stops reading and looks around in frustration as tears form in her eyes. "Who can I believe?" She asks herself. "I thought he's looking at me like his sister, but I was wrong. Who can I trust? All men are the same. The only thing they think about is their feelings." Then she keeps reading, "The day I saw you, I was really into it. You are smart, easy to talk to; you have a great sense of humor, you're strong..." She smashes the paper into her hand, screams loudly, and drops to her knees, saying, "Who, can I trust?"

Liya runs up the stairs to the roof and sees her friend crying. She hugs Sarah, "What happened?"

"I'm fine!" Sarah pleads, "I just want to be by myself. Can you please leave me alone?"

"I see you are crying, and you say you are fine! I can't leave you like this." She looks at the letter in Sarah's hand and says, "What is it?" Liya tries to take the letter from Sarah, but Sarah holds it tight, and it rips into two pieces.

"Liya, I swear to God, if you try to read it, our friendship will end." Sarah is deadly serious, and Liya gives her back the torn section of the letter. Sarah says, "Thank you."

"Okay, I did what you said. Can you please stop crying? I'm here for you; you are my sister."

"Sister?" Sarah shoots back, bitingly. Then she laughs sarcastically.

"Are you okay? You're acting so different right now."

"I'm fine! If you care about me, can you leave me alone?" Liya agrees and walks back to the staircase. Sarah sits alone on the roof, her tears dripping onto her arm. "I have to find a place to live. I can't live with him." Then she looks at the sky and sees a big half-moon and a few stars. "If the moon wasn't out, I would see the stars clearly, but the moon outshines their light, and they don't show. You could almost forget they're there" A thought occurs to Sarah, and it seems important, like a sign. *I can't let the brightness of Kaleb's feelings for me make me forget the starlight of my friends' love. It's there, and it's important, I don't want to lose it.*

Then she goes quiet for a while and watches the sky with childlike wonder.

"Where is Sarah?" Mazaa asks Aida.

"I don't know. Do I look like her mom?" Aida responds.

"What's wrong with you? Why do you hate Sarah?"

"I don't like her, so what? I'm not her babysitter. And why do I have to like her? We're not alike, so what?"

Liya walks into the room. "Oh, no! You're not alike at all, because Sarah is beautiful, smart, and lovely," Liya says.

"If you love her so much, you can carry her on your back forever," Aida's voice rises.

"I'm glad Sarah is not like you," Mazaa says. "She is nice to you."

"She better be. Otherwise, I'll kick her out of this room. She doesn't have any place to go." Merely saying the words makes Aida feel powerful.

"That's it. I knew it, the day I met you. You're selfish. I never realized how small-minded you are until now," Mazaa says.

"You should respect me. I'm your elder!" Aida raises her hand.

"Being older isn't about the maturity of your body; it's about the maturity of the mind," Liya confirms.

Aida, angry and disgusted, storms from the room in search of Kaleb, who is outside.

"Can you ask your cousins why they are cursing me?"

"Liya, Mazaa, come here," Kaleb calls.

"Okay." Liya and Mazaa look at each other. "You see what she did? Why he's always looking after her? We're the closest relations to him." Then they walk out to the courtyard.

"Why are you guys abusing her? What is the reason behind it?" Kaleb asks.

"She just hates Sarah for no reason. I only asked her why," Mazaa responds.

"Yes, I don't like her," Aida responds.

"Why don't you like her?" Kaleb asks.

Aida laughs, "You're asking me why?" She settles into a very sarcastic smile.

"That's not an answer," Kaleb says.

"Say the reason so we can understand you, but don't just say 'I hate her,' that doesn't make sense," Liya says, with Mazaa nodding in approval.

"I don't think I have to tell my reasons to anyone."

"I get it now..." Liya realizes. "That's why Sarah went to the rooftop to cry."

"What?" Kaleb and Mazaa look at Liya, shocked.

"What happened?" Mazaa starts running toward the stairs.

"Come back!" Liya calls to Mazaa, "she doesn't want anyone to bother her!"

"Did she tell you what happened?" Kaleb asks with concern.

"No, she didn't. She's just crying non-stop and told me to leave her alone. And she was holding a letter." Kaleb's face sinks.

"Did you read it?"

"No. She absolutely forbade me."

Ignoring her cousins' objections, Mazaa climbs the stairs and finds her friend. Sarah is still looking at the stars.

Mazaa approaches her tentatively, "Sarah, what are you doing?"

Sarah looks at her and wipes her face. "I'm just like the weather. I'm looking at the moon and the stars." She pauses, seemingly distracted. "And the sky."

"But that's not the truth," Mazaa gently chides. "I see your eyes are swollen, and your face is wet. You're not a great liar."

"Nothing, I just miss my family." Sarah fights her tired mind to make up a small story about why her family is at the front of her mind.

***

After eight-months, Sarah has enough to pay a smuggler for passage to Italy. This time the smugglers are Habesha and Libyan. Sarah pays the Eritrean, along with several other people from the compound.

Smugglers sailing for Italy don't announce their departure dates; they expect you to be waiting at whatever time of the day or night they come. Several people have told her that it usually takes weeks before the smugglers have enough names to fill a boat, so she decides to finish her last day of work in Crimea. However, while she's there, the smugglers show up at her house to get her, and she isn't home. They move on to collect the rest of their passengers, ignoring Kaleb's explanation of where she is, and Sarah is left behind.

With no phones, Kaleb is powerless to call her and tells her everything when she gets home. The smugglers have left no contact information, and she has no idea if she will ever hear from them again. She sinks to the floor in shocking lament. "Why, God? Why is all of this happening to me? I'm not strong enough to handle all this. God, you know how hard I worked to make this money." After several moments, she rises wearily and walks outside.

Her neighbors have mixed reactions. One callously remarks, "They're not coming back," while others empathize with her position. "It is not easy making this money."

"I'm really sorry."

Eden hugs her. "Sari, I know it's hard; I've experienced it, but you're not in prison or dead. You can work hard. You're gonna make it. We can help each other."

Kaleb, Liya, and Mazaa each console her with hugs.

The next day after work, Sarah prepares coffee for her neighbors. People sit around the coffee ceremony talking about their friends who left with the smugglers the previous night, and how far they've gotten by now. One man has brought his television outside, and a football game plays in the background as the men sip their cups and talk.

There is a knock at the gate. One of the neighbors walks over and opens the door. It's the Eritrean smuggler! He asks for Sarah, and the neighbor calls to her and waves her over. Recognizing the man, Sarah's heart leaps, and she hurries over.

"I'm sorry about yesterday," He begins hurriedly. "Here is the money. Next time I will inform you ahead." He hands her back her money totaling $1,200 USA dollars. After a moment of pure shock, she bubbles over with expressions of thanks and offers him coffee, but the Eritrean is in a rush and declines. As suddenly as he arrived, he is gone.

Sarah turns back toward her coffee ceremony in amazement and disbelief. "Thank you," she exhales passionately to God. She walks back to the group of neighbors and explains what just happened. Everyone else is as surprised as she! People exclaim at her luck and go on excitedly about how rare it is for smugglers to return money—more than 99% of the time, once a smuggler gets his hands on your money, you will never see it again. Lies and scams are normal business.

Sarah looks at the thick stack of bills in her hand. "I worked for eight months to get this money." Then, suddenly coming to herself, she stuffs the bills in her pocket out of sight and puts a large kettle on the small burner to boil. Eden sits beside Sarah and puts her arm around her as they wait for the water. Finally, Sarah breaks the silence: "I had an awful dream the other day; I thought they were going to take my money."

161

"What was the dream about?"

"I saw myself hanging on the edge of a cliff. Below me was just... blackness. A deep abyss that I knew went underground, even though I couldn't really see it. Then a woman with chocolate skin grabbed my hand and said, 'your mom has been begging me to watch over you.' She pulled me up onto solid ground and sat me down. Then I woke up."

"Wow, that's so amazing! Your mom is praying for you for protection by angels."

The background noise of conversation starts to quieten, and someone turns the volume up on the television. A news program is playing in Arabic. Some of the neighbors understand the language, and many don't, but it's obviously a story of grave importance. An Ethiopian man translates for the Habesha, "A large boat of immigrants to Europe has sunk, killing all two-hundred-fifty passengers except for a two-year-old child. The passengers are listed as Ethiopian, Eritrean, Sudanese and Somalian."

Eden also translates the news to Sarah, and tears form in her eyes. "How long will our people die like this?" She laments to Sarah. Then a cry goes out from one of the neighbors at the sight of a recovered body. It's one of the men from Sarah's compound! Exclamations of surprise turn into shouting, and several more people run over to the television for a closer look.

Eden turns, wide-eyed, to Sarah. "Your dream! Your dream!"

"What happened?" Sarah asks. In the excitement, Eden has stopped translating.

"God protected you! This is your boat! Sarah, it's your boat!"

"What!?" Instantly Sarah's thoughts turn to her neighbors. "What about Alemayehu!?"

"I don't know! These people are saying they recognize the bodies! Everyone is dead except for a two-year-old baby."

"How did that happen?"

"It's a miracle! That is God's job. Wait..." She listens intently for several seconds to the excited Arabic pouring from the television. "It says the rescue workers found him asleep on a piece of debris.

They've only recovered half of the bodies. They think the others sank."

Sarah can't speak. Her thoughts roil and multiply and become confused. She starts feeling short of breath and sits for several minutes, trying to collect herself. Eden senses the heavy burden weighing on her friend and continues to sit with her and hold her.

As she sits with her friend, Eden continues listening to the broadcast. "It says every year, more than thirty-thousand people die this way. Why do we keep trying?"

Sarah shakes her head, looking at the ground. "If I knew this would happen when I was in Ethiopia, I wouldn't have even thought about it, but it's too late."

People approach Sarah in amazement. Some touch her shoulder, and others stand at a discreet distance.

"God loves you."

"Everything happens for a reason."

"Incredible!"

Sarah thanks the people one by one, trying to hold her emotions in check.

***

The next afternoon Libyan police come to Sarah's building, searching for illegal immigrants. With no oversight, and the immigrants having few legal rights, the real search is for money. The police use knives to tear open mattresses, break open television sets, and rifle through bags and suitcases, scattering people's clothes and belongings. Many residents are away working or running errands, but those in the compound are arrested and taken away.

Kaleb comes home from the store and sees the room in complete upheaval. He drops all his groceries on the floor and runs to his neighbors, but no one is home. He stands outside of his room, and he hears Eden's son crying inside her room. He bangs on her door. "Eden, it's me, Kaleb!"

Eden slowly opens her door. "Oh, they left. Thank God." She has a bruise on her face.

Kaleb gazes at her face. "Who did this!? What happened? Are you okay?"

Eden explains about the police, adding, "And they took all my money. Everything I saved for travel, but they didn't take me because of him." She points to her son and smiles weakly. "He saved me."

"Did they take people to jail??"

Eden nods. She was in the kitchen when the police arrived and witnessed the first few arrests before she was dragged to her own room. She recites the names of the people she knows were taken.

"Did they take your money too?" She asks Kaleb.

"I don't know; I didn't check."

"You should!"

A confused look replaces the urgency on his face. "I don't know where Sarah put it."

They walk to the room, and Eden feels sorry as soon as she sees the scene of upheaval. The police have been comprehensive. The foam mattresses have been entirely cut in half. Searching through the first mattress, they find a single one hundred USA dollar bill tucked inside a small incision, but all the rest of the incisions are empty. They check a second destroyed mattress, but there is nothing.

"They took it. I wish they'd hid it better. Somewhere. My sisters worked hard to save this money; we were so close. We were almost there!"

Eden tries to assure him. "I know it is not easy to save this money, but the most important thing is that we're safe, and we didn't end up in prison."

"But we will if we don't have the money to get out of here! They'll catch us sooner or later."

At this moment, the girls enter the room. "What happened?"

"The police came," Eden begins. "They came for our money."

Aida, Mazaa, and Liya all start asking if their money is gone.

"I think so; this is all I found," Kaleb responds. He shows them a hundred-dollar bill.

"Where did you find that?" Sarah asks. He shows her the tiny slit in the mattress.

Aida falls to her knees and begins digging her hands into small slits throughout the thick foam slab. "No! That's mine! No!" She sobs as she works.

"You're not the only person who lost. We all lost, but think about the people who ended up in prison! And the people yesterday who lost their lives. No one is dead; it's just money." Liya says.

Sarah notices the fan lying on its side, the blades still turning lazily inside the steel mesh. She walks over and carefully rights it. Kaleb notes Sarah's quietness and worries for his friend.

"Don't blame yourself, Sarah, it's not your fault."

Sarah now looks over at Eden, and for the first time, notices the bruise. "Eden, they hurt you?"

"I was at the kitchen cooking dinner, and six police officers entered the building. I literally peed into my pants when I saw them. They went to each room, and one of the officers came to the kitchen and slapped me in front of my son. I begged them, but they hit me over and over. Then they took me to my room and made me show them where my money was. Then they told me to sit inside the room until they were gone. I heard people screaming when they took them away."

Sarah hugs her. "I'm sorry."

Aida storms out of the room, and Mazaa and Liya wander out as well. People arrive back at the compound and sort through their rooms in shock and disappointment. The realization of friends and family transported to jail leaves several people distraught. Sarah softly closes the door behind Mazaa and Liya, and to Kaleb's surprise, locks it. Sarah unplugs the fan and begins unscrewing the motorized section from its stand. Kaleb watches her with growing interest. "What are you doing?"

Hearing the door lock behind her, Aida immediately starts back to the room and pounds on the door. "What's going on? Why did you lock the door?"

"Just give us a minute," Sarah calls back.

Aida glares at the door.

Inside, Sarah places the fan blades, and the motor on the floor turns the hollow stand upside down and shakes it vigorously. One small wrapped bundle of bills after another drop onto the floor. A look of delighted surprise overtakes Kaleb's face, and he throws his arms around her as she works.

"I thought you had hidden it in the mattress! I thought it was gone! I never ever thought you would put it here! How did you think to do this?"

She puts the stand down and steps out of his hug.

"I offered to hide Aida's too, but she said no. So, hers is gone. The rest is here. From now on, you can hide it whatever way you want." She pockets one of the wrapped bundles and gives the rest to Kaleb.

There is another urgent spate of knocks on the door, and Sarah opens it, annoyed. "What is wrong with you? I'm showing him something." Then she walks out without giving Aida a chance to respond. She pushes on toward Eden's room to play with her son.

Eden looks at Sarah with concern. "Are you okay? And to think after the miracle yesterday, it's heartbreaking. I'm sorry. It's not your fault."

"It's not about that. The police didn't find the money. I hid it in a place they never thought of."

"They didn't take your money?"

"No, it's here." She shows her the bundled wad and explains how she hid it.

Eden looks at her friend. "Okay, but if it's not the money bothering you, what's the problem?"

"It's Aida."

"Aida, what? What did she do?"

"I don't know what's going on with her, but she's driving me crazy. I want to leave the house. I can't stand her."

"Do you want me to talk to her?" Eden asks assuredly.

"No, don't worry, it's been going on for a long time, it's not new, but she's gotten worse lately."

166

"Do you think maybe you said something to her?"

"Not that I know of. But I saw something; maybe because of that."

"What?"

"I think Aida and Kaleb are in a relationship."

"What? They're cousins..."

Sarah shakes her head. "That's what I thought, but no."

Eden digests this a moment. "Okay, then what's the problem between you and her?"

Sarah takes a deep breath and lets it out. "A week ago, I woke up in the middle of the night to go to the restroom. I heard some movement, and I saw them in the middle of doing it."

Eden smiles dismissively. "Okay, that's not your problem. They're stupid and dirty."

"He is dirty. I live with them because of Liya and Mazaa."

Eden leans away from her friend in surprise. "I thought you were comfortable with them."

"No, I'm not, but I can't forget what they did for me. I'll always appreciate it. But what Kaleb said to me... and Aida's attitude... I can't stay with them."

"Don't worry about finding a place to stay; you can stay with Genet until you go to Italy. But please, tell me what he said to you?"

"It's between you and me. I knew Kaleb and Aida had something the day I met them. They didn't act like cousins. But Kaleb thought I didn't know, and he asked me to be his girl." Then she tears up and looks away. "Why is it all men just want me for sex? Why?"

Eden strokes her friend's arm. "Don't say that all men aren't the same, shame on him. Maybe that's why Aida doesn't like you. I thought he was a nice person; I respected him. But I was wrong."

"He is a nice person," Sarah concedes. "In many ways. I don't know. I'm just tired of it."

"If he's been nice to you, are you sure he just wants you for sex? What if he's serious?"

Sarah looks at her friend in the eye. "Eden, I just don't want it. I want to leave."

***

To Mazaa and Liya's confusion, Sarah moves into Genet's home with the help of her new roommate Malik. Sarah met Genet at a birthday party for Eden's son six months before, has visited many times, and the two get along easily. Genet's husband has already left for Italy, but their daughter is still home, and her husband's best friend Malik lives with Genet to help out and save money. Sarah looks up to Malik as a brother-figure, but the two squabble constantly. Sarah has unwittingly walked into another unrequited love situation that Malik kept secret from her during her previous visits. When his friends encourage him to tell her about his feelings, he always replies the same. "If I ask her, I'll lose her forever. At least this way I get to have her close by." He does care.

Their first evening together, Genet is exuberant. "I'm so happy about living with you."

"Me too," Sarah answers honestly.

Malik comes in, kicking off his shoes. "You guys okay, beautiful?"

Genet smirks without looking at him. "Thank you, Malik."

The rustle of plastic draws Genet's attention, and she looks over to see Malik putting down a small mountain of grocery bags. "Malik!" Genet exclaims. "This is too much!"

"But we have a guest! That's why."

Sarah laughs. "I'm not a guest; you guys are my family." Genet rolls her eyes at Malik.

Dinner is excellent, and the three adults talk and laugh late into the evening. As they prepare for nighttime, Malik gives his mattress to Sarah and spreads his sheets on the floor.

Sarah objects, "No, I can't do that. Keep the mattress; I'm happy on the floor."

Malik protests, but Sarah is adamant. "No. I will sleep over here." She sets up her bedding on the other side of the single-room apartment.

The first night goes well, but as they spend their days together, Malik's feelings continue to grow and sleeping in the same room as

Sarah becomes more and more difficult. He doesn't know what to do.

Genet is fully aware of the situation and encourages Malik. "How long will you keep this a secret? Just tell her."

But he won't. Instead, he leaks his love in small drips, washing her clothes by hand, and sorting and folding them while she's at work, always careful to lay the neatly folded clothes respectfully on top of her bag instead of opening it.

***

One day at the Crimea coffee shop, an Eritrean man enters and orders coffee. Without prompting, he tells Sarah, "I just finished a two-year prison sentence."

"I'm sorry to hear that. What was it like?"

The guy holds his coffee cup partway between the table and his mouth. "I don't know where to start, but I know one thing; it's the worst place on the Earth to live." Then he goes quiet for a while.

Sarah can't help tearing up as she looks at the broken, needy man.

The man looks at Sarah and says, "You know I was a doctor in my country when I used to live there. I never appreciated my life, I always thought I had the worst life, but I was so wrong. I used to complain about Eritrea. I was wrong. Now I need a way to go back home to my family and my country."

"But you're already here," Sarah says encouragingly. "You've passed the hardest part."

The guy looks up at her with a flash of anger. "What? I don't know about your life back home but trust me, our country is better than this life. All countries are the same. You are so young; you can go back to your country and study hard. You will change your life and your family's too. If we worked as hard in our own countries as we do in places like this, we would help our countries and ourselves."

"That is true," Sarah concedes. "But we realize it too late."

"Nothing's too late. If we want to change, tomorrow is a new day. Until we live like this, traveling country to country, looking for documents that no one will give us, learning new languages, getting called an immigrant, a foreigner treated like animals."

Sarah listens with admiration and growing confusion about the plans that have brought her this far.

"When did you start thinking like this?" She asks. "And can you tell me about your prison life?"

The guy says, "I'll answer both questions at once. I started thinking this way while I was in that ugly prison. Sometimes we didn't eat for days, or they gave us bathroom water to drink. There is nothing uglier than that place; it will make you curse the day you were born or the day you first thought about this road. You wish you were dead."

Then he screams, and Sarah jumps backward. He rages into a string of curse words, cursing everything, including the coffee cup in his hand, which Sarah is suddenly afraid he'll throw. The man gets up and starts walking back and forth.

Sarah moves to the doorway, watching the man. When his ranting has quieted to a rambling whisper, she finally addresses him softly, "Are you okay? That's the past. Today is another day."

The guy laughs loudly and jeers at her. "You don't have a problem because you're female. Some guy will give you money for your time. How many Sudanese boyfriends do you have?"

Sarah now feels a surge of anger in her chest, but he doesn't wait for an answer.

"Ten, twenty? More? Maybe you have a husband at home, and here you are selling your body! My wife does it too!"

Sarah asks him to leave, but he only descends into violent cursing and derisive laughter. She leaves and briskly walks to Kidist's coffee shop, telling her friend everything that happened.

"The man is not normal," Kidist confides. "He lost his mind, but everything he said is true." She is quiet for a moment, then says, "He got raped at the prison by the Libyan police."

Sarah's heart softens toward the man, and after a little more conversation, she fearfully returns to her store. The man is no longer there, and everything seems to have been left intact and unharmed.

She sits down and thinks about everything he said. She says to herself, "How many people have lost their minds doing this? We are all crazy. We're just not screaming or have proof from a doctor."

When Sarah comes back home, Genet wastes no time. "There is a boat going out this week! The boat owner has a good name; he is one of the biggest people in this business. He works with a police commissioner. That's why he never gets stopped."

"Did you buy a ticket?" Sarah asks.

"No, I was waiting for you to come back from work."

"Okay, we can buy, but where do we find them?"

Malik interjects, "They'll be here shortly."

Sarah looks at Malik. "Are you going too?"

Malik says, without thinking, "I can't stay here without you."

For a moment, Sarah betrays a knowing look, but quickly hides it and avoids eye contact with Malik. Malik immediately corrects himself. "I mean, what would I do here if you guys leave?" He smiles as casually as he possibly can.

"That's true," Sarah says as she puts down her handbag. "It would be hard." There is a knock at the door, and Sarah calls out, "Come in."

A neighbor sticks her head in, "The smuggler is here."

Genet takes over. "Okay, thanks."

The three collect their money and stride over toward the smuggler. He takes their money and gives them information.

Once again, no specific date is given.

A week later, the smuggler arrives around 9:00 p.m. giving them ten minutes to get ready. Everyone dresses and puts on big jackets, but suitcases and bags are forbidden, and there is nothing in their hands except their money, if they have any. Only Genet is allowed a handbag because of her baby. The smuggler comes back after ten minutes, and more than fifteen people wait in the courtyard. He has one van, and the people climb in one by one. The smuggler stands outside to keep watch. Once everyone is inside, the driver takes off fast. People talk excitedly but softly.

After twenty minutes, they arrive at a large home. There are a lot of people inside, perhaps two-hundred-fifty. Immediately, the smugglers begin organizing the first of several small groups to be guided on foot from the house to the waterfront. Sarah sees Kaleb, Liya, Aida, and Mazaa. Mazaa and Liya walk over to Sarah and hug her. Kaleb also walks over. "I didn't know you were going today."

"Me either," Sarah responds.

Kaleb sees Malik. "You're going with your lover?"

"What are you talking about? Who is my lover?"

"You think I don't know why you left us? I know about you two."

"What are you talking about?" Sarah fights back. "You know that's not why I left. This isn't the place to talk about it. But Kaleb, I never expected that from you."

Kaleb lowers his eyes, and Sarah walks away.

"What did you say to Kaleb?" Malik asks. "He looks so shocked."

"Nothing, it just a family thing."

"You still count them as family," Malik muses. "But he always liked you."

Sarah is resolute. "The only thing I know is that they are still my family. He can think the way he wants; he's a man."

"Please let me ask you one question?"

"Go ahead," Sarah says. "But, since when do you need my permission to ask questions?"

"Why do you hate men? I always hear you when you talk bad about us; sometimes, your tone is hard when you talk about men." Sarah becomes very quiet and stares at the floor. "I'm sorry I think I asked you the wrong question," Malik says.

She doesn't hear him.

He becomes worried. "Sarah, are you okay?"

Suddenly she starts, like someone waking from a deep sleep. "Sorry, what did you say?"

"What do you mean, you didn't hear me?"

"No, sorry. I heard some of it. Do you want to know the truth?"

"Yes," Malik says.

"I hate all the men on this planet."

Malik is taken aback. "What? All the men on the planet? We're not all the same. There are a lot of very nice men; you can't judge everyone. It will be good if you open your eyes, you can see it yourself. Also, you are too young to say that."

Sarah laughs it off. "Can we change the subject?"

"Yes, we can, but..."

The smuggler comes in and counts heads. He takes another group of people, and again, Sarah, Malik, and Genet are left behind. Sarah rises and walks to the bathroom.

Genet touches Malik's arm. "Did you tell her?"

"No, I didn't," Malik says resignedly. "It's not possible."

"Do you want me to tell her?"

"I don't think so, the way she talks about men..."

Genet interrupts him. "I know, but one day she'll change her mind. Trust me. If you wait too long, another man will come along and take her. I saw several men, the way they look at her."

"What do I have to do, tell me?" Malik asks, "I do love her."

Sarah returns from the bathroom and looks at them. "I thought you guys left me," she says, then laughs.

"You said you wanted to go to the restroom," Genet says to Malik. "Go before the smugglers come."

Malik is confused but walks out toward the restroom. His palms are sweating, and he's wringing and wiping his hands.

"I want to tell you something," Genet says to Sarah, "but please don't take it personally."

"Come on; we're friends. Tell me."

"Malik is in love with you, and you know him, he's a very nice man."

"I know that."

"You mean you know he's in love with you?"

"I knew on the first day."

"Wow... we were worried about it; he was scared to tell you."

"I know that, but I can't do anything."

"Why? Are you in love with some else?"

"Yes."

173

"Who? Do I know him?"

"I'm engaged."

"What are you talking about??" Genets bursts.

"I'm engaged with my dream. I made all this, made these sacrifices for my dream. Also, I'm never ever getting married. I hate men, all of them. All they want women for is sex, and to be their maids and their baby mamas."

"Don't think about today, you will get married one day. Until then, do you want to be single?"

"All my life. After my dreams come true, I can adopt as many children as I want. They'll be my kids. I can't give a man the power to give me orders about what I have to do, or to be constantly telling me what's good for me."

"If you want to be single your entire life, this is not the place to live. Go to one of the Ethiopian churches, and you can be a nun." She laughs.

"I don't have to be a nun to be single. Anyway, call Malik to come back. I know he's hiding, he told you to tell me, I know. I really feel sorry for him. I love him as a brother, but other than that, I'm not the right person for him."

The smuggler returns to collect another group of people. When he hears the smuggler's voice, Malik comes back, but the smuggler is already leaving with another small, anxious crowd. Malik is sweating from head to toe.

"Are you okay?" Sarah asks Malik, but he doesn't answer. She keeps talking. "You're sweating." He just keeps rubbing his fingers together, and she says to herself, "I wish I could help."

"I don't know!" Malik responds. "I think I'm scared about the journey." He takes a deep breath, and for the time being, all three find it easiest to let that explanation stand.

Finally, Sarah breaks the silence. "We will be fine." After that, the group sits in silence, awaiting their turn.

Finally, the four smugglers return and issue orders to the remaining travelers to follow them. This is the last group, and they walk outside. It's 2:00 a.m. and incredibly dark; as if to help, the moon has retreated behind clouds, and people can't even see each other in the pitch black. Two smugglers walk in front of the people, and two of them bring up the rear. The smugglers have guns and flashlights. The travelers walk in two long lines, and everyone is clutching the person in front with one hand, and the person beside with the other, to keep from getting lost. It's also tranquil, and nothing is moving. The smuggler's flashlights are weak and focused on the ground directly ahead, giving just enough light to avoid the rocks, mounds, and depressions that might trip people up.

Finally, they arrive at the shore of the Mediterranean, and a few meters out in the water bobs a fifteen-foot rubber dingy with just one crewmember. The stench of the shoreline is overwhelming. It smells like a dead animal, even worse than the water hole they experienced in the Libyan desert. Some people hold their noses as they wade out into the water up to their knees to get into the dingy. Sarah holds her nose tightly and tries not to vomit, but her stomach overrules.

Everyone climbs up the side of the craft and is pushed and pulled in, more than sixty in total for a vessel designed for ten to fifteen. Several, like Sarah, have stopped to be sick, and the smugglers wade over to them. One smuggler grabs Sarah's arm and shouts something Arabic in a thick, Libyan accent. She tries to pull away, but the man forcefully hauls her to the boat. Another smuggler inside the boat grabs her arms to pull her in, but she yanks them away. Behind her, the smuggler who dragged her to the boat puts both of his hands on her ass and roughly pushes her up and in. Sarah's body, already weakened by the intense odor, reacts with an aversion to the men, and she vomits again.

The sides of the dingy are weighed down to within inches of the waterline, and water continually splashes in, but as they get further from the shore, the terrible odor fades. After a short fifteen-minute ride, they arrive at a larger boat, where the rest of the travelers await. It's referred to as "the big boat" but is maybe thirty-five feet long. It would look crowded with forty people, let alone the two hundred people already on board, and sixty more who've just arrived. The Ethiopian and Eritrean immigrants cover the vessel like hedgehog quills.

Two of the smugglers jump into the water, which, surprisingly, is only chest-deep. They push the dingy up to the side of the big boat by hand. Many of the men climb on to the big boat using ropes that hang down, while the women are mostly pulled up from above or pushed up from below.

Once Sarah gets in the big boat, she tries to wipe the remaining vomit from her mouth with her hand, but her hand smells so much like the shoreline that it makes her gag. She finds a corner of her jacket that's still dry and uses that.

When everyone has gotten safely into the big boat, the lead smuggler yells, "Good luck, get there safely," from the dingy. Then the small boat turns and takes the smugglers off into the night.

Chapter Nine

On the big boat, there are two Libyan captains and one helper. The boat is a relatively small, single-tier vessel, with a large square, flat-roofed cabin covering most of the front half. Sarah sits near the nose of the boat where most of the children are. Seasickness has added to her stomach problems, and a woman sitting next to her gives her a plastic bag. Sarah vomits again, and when she's sure she's done, she ties the bag and throws it overboard.

She leans back against the gunwale and pulls her big jacket over her head. It's soaking wet and does nothing to negate the cold, but it does give her a pretense of solitude. It also blocks her view of the water just beside her, which has been filling her with unexpected dread and memories of the sinking ship she saw on the television, and it creates a small psychological barrier between her and the Libyan men commanding the ship. They can't lust over what they can't see.

Some people are talking, some sleep. Genet and the other women with babies and very young children sit in the middle of the boat behind the cabin, packed amid the hundreds of crammed travelers. Migrants cover every inch of the boat. Many men sit crowded on top of the cabin roof, while others sit up on the sides of the gunwale around the rear two-thirds of the ship.

Next to Malik, there is a young gentleman early twenty, medium height with light brown skin, curly hair, and big brown eyes. Malik looks at him and says, "I think I saw you before. What is your name?"

"Zahid. Yes, we saw each other at Eden's son's birthday."

"Exactly, that is where I saw you!"

"Sorry, what's your name?"

"Malik. How long have you lived in Libya?"

"A year and a half. What about you?"

"A year. I never tried to go before. This is my first time."

"You're lucky. I tried twice, but the smugglers stole my money both times. The first time we ended up in Tunisia. Then they put us in prison, and after a couple of months, we came back to Libya. I came here with my first cousin, but after we went through, and then seeing so many people lose their lives in the Mediterranean on TV, he chose to go back home."

"How?"

"He went back to Al Khufra. The Sudanese smugglers brought a load of people from Sudan, and when they drove back home, he went with them."

"Wow, I never heard of that."

"I know a lot of people who've done that. A couple of weeks ago, one guy went back to Sudan, then Ethiopia. He was in prison for ten months in Libya, and when he got out, his girlfriend had already left for Italy. He called her, but she didn't want to talk to him. He said 'I'm going back home because one day she'll come back. Then I know what I'm doing to her.' As in, he wanted to kill her."

"He's crazy! He came all that way and went back just for revenge?"

"We don't know, really. It's easy to judge, but it's hard to wear other people's shoes. The only way we can understand is by really wearing another person's shoes."

"That is true. I want to ask for some advice."

"Please, go ahead. If I can, I'll be happy to help."

"I'm in love with a girl, but I'm scared to ask her because she's looking at me as a brother. She doesn't know."

"Do you guys hang out together? Spend time together as friends?"

"Yes, we do."

"You've never tried to tell her?"

"No, I am scared."

"What's her personality like?"

"She is so full of life! Playful, smart. She loves studying people."

"Oh, okay. If she has all these qualities as you say, she probably already knows you're in love with her. She might have a reason why she wants you as a brother. A lot of the time, a woman will say 'you're my brother,' or 'my best friend' or 'family' for a reason."

"I don't know what the reason is. I wish she would tell me what she is thinking."

"She might tell you one day. Just give her time. Sorry, where is she?

"I hope so!"

Zahid presses to know who the woman is but gets deflected. Zahid changes the subject.

"Now, we have to think about ourselves and pray for safe passage to Italy."

"Let's pray."

The two men finish their prayers just as the first rays of sunrise are beginning to glow on the horizon. Malik looks up over the rail of the ship and observes the dawn with peace. "Alhamdulillah, it's a beautiful sun."

Zahid sits back, taking in the emerging glow of the sun. "Do you have family in Italy?"

"No, I don't." Malik answers. "But I have a friend; I count him as family. What about you?"

"I don't, no."

As though responding to the sun's glow, the glassy waters start to chop and froth. A pod of dolphins breaks the surface, swimming and leaping in front of the boat as though excitedly guiding the captain. Zahid looks at the dolphins with pure enjoyment.

Malik continually glances up to the front of the boat, where Sarah lays against the gunwale under her coat, entirely still. He starts to worry, not having seen her move since she first arrived.

Zahid is still watching the dolphins and points to them, "Look at the dolphins, how beautiful they are."

"They are so big; they look like they can turn the boat upside down."

"They do."

"Do you have a girlfriend?" Malik asks.

"Yes, but we never had anything real."

"What does that mean?"

"I had a girlfriend when I was in Ethiopia, but we never even kissed. I did see a girl in Libya. I was about to ask her, but Libya just isn't the right place to have a girlfriend. Most females here only care about whether you can get them money or get them out of that ugly place." Zahid takes a deep breath. "I don't judge them, what choice do they have? But still, you know?"

"They have a choice; they just want a shortcut to get what they want by using their body."

"I don't support it, but I understand it."

"What if your wife or girlfriend was going out with other men for money? What would you feel then?"

"I can't say, because I haven't been in that situation. Sorry, did you have a wife? Do you?"

"No! I'm glad I don't have. I would be crazy, or I would be in prison for life because, for sure, I would kill her."

"Don't say that you don't know that for sure."

"I'm sure you know how females treat us here; they don't look at us as men because we don't have money. It drives me crazy. I can imagine how I would feel if I was married to it."

"But Malik, do you know how many men beg their wives to do dark things for money? It's not easy to get money for two people. I know one girl, her fiancé, begged her to do it. She refused, then he asked his brother in the USA for money, and he left her there. Do you see? It goes both ways."

"Wow, I didn't know that."

Sarah wakes with a bad headache. She tries her best to get up, but she can't and lies back down—the woman sitting next to her looks at her and asks Sarah what happened. Sarah refuses to go into detail and merely repeats that she has a headache. The woman asks around for some medication, and finally, Genet hears. Genet checks to make sure her daughter's sleeping and covers her with her jacket and walks over to Sarah.

"What happened, Sari?"

"My head is killing me; I can't even get up."

"Don't worry; I will get you something," Genet asks a couple of people if they have some Tylenol, but no one does. As she walks toward the door of the captain's cabin, Malik sees her.

"What's happened?"

"She has a headache, and I'm looking for medication. I asked a lot of people, but no one has it."

Zahid reaches into his pocket and carefully removes two Tylenol pills from some plastic packaging. He gives them to Malik, who drops them into Genet's hand. Zahid also gives her a small package of cookies.

"It's not much, but give the cookies before the medicine. So, she has something in her stomach." Genet thanks Malik and hastens back to her friend.

Genet helps Sarah to sit, rests her against the edge of the boat. She feeds her the cookies and then gives her the medicine.

"Thank you, Geni."

"Don't worry about it." She rests her hand on Sarah's forehead. "You have a fever."

"Yes... I think, just let me sleep, I'm feeling dizzy." Sarah slides down the wall of the ship and wearily pulls the large jacket over face and feet.

"Sleep; you will be fine." Sarah doesn't need to be told and fades off in mere moments.

Zahid has been watching the exchange with surprise. As Sarah once again hides from sight under the jacket, he points at her turning to Malik, "Do you know that girl?"

"She is my best friend, like my sister."

"What is her name?"

"Do you know her?"

"I think so... is that Sarah?"

Malik's volume drops, and he answers almost reluctantly. "Yes, it is... do you know her?"

"She is Eden's childhood friend, and Eden's husband is my best friend. I saw Sarah when I was visiting Eden's house."

"Oh, you know Genet too?"

"Yes, I do, but I only saw her once, on Eden's son's birthday." Zahid changes the subject back to Sarah. "I went to Eden's home a month ago, but I didn't see Sarah at that time. I thought she went to Italy, because usually when I visited, she was there with her friends."

"Oh, you know a lot about her," Malik observes.

"Yes, she moved two months ago to Genet's home, that's why. But Sarah never mentioned you."

"We saw each other several times, but we never talked," Zahid explains. "She is very cold. And quiet. She would often leave as soon as I got there. Eden's the one who told me about her. She doesn't know me."

Zahid maintains a calm exterior or thinks he does and drops the subject. But internally, he can't help but breathe a prayer of thanks. *Oh, Allah, you heard my prayer! You put her in the same boat with me. Alhamdulillah.*

The next morning, clusters of people are talking and laughing, while many remain asleep like sardines packed in a can. Others stand leaning over the side, looking at the water. Sarah is still sleeping.

The waves gradually get higher and higher, and the boat starts rising and falling more precipitously. Conversations begin stopping one by one as people get distracted by the waves. The idle talk gives way to a concerning prayer. Land appears on the horizon, and word spreads through the boat's population that this is the island of Malta.

Suddenly a rush of men descends from the roof and converges on the cabin door. One of them brandishes a knife. They force the door open and push inside. A terrible ruckus of shouting erupts in the cabin, and there is a gunshot. The immigrants, outside, crane their necks to see what is happening, even as the women and children in the front of the boat scramble to the rear—men from all over the boat run to the cabin where the shouting continues.

Inside the cabin, the mob of immigrants has overpowered the Captain with the gun and hold him and his two cohort's hostages, demanding the ship dock at Malta.

"We don't want to die!" The immigrants keep shouting, and the Captain is yelling back in Arabic, seeming to agree to their request. The growing chorus of onlookers in the doorway shout at the mob inside.

"What are you doing??" "If we go to Malta, that is the end!" "We'll be trapped there!" The shouted argument rages back and forth.

"We'll die in this sea!"

"Then, we die! But we'll die in Malta too. At least this way, we die trying to reach out goal!"

More than forty men now crowd around the entrance to the cabin shouting at the four hijackers. A barefoot hijacker with no shirt levels the gun at the doorway with wide eyes.

"There are no bullets!" shouts one of the subdued captains.

"There was only one bullet. There's none left."

First one, then several, then a storm of men pour into the pitching cabin, and a violent fight ensues. The gun and knife are torn from the hostages and thrown out into the sea. The hijackers are battled down to the floor and held there by the pressing scrum of men. Then the counter-mob has a long and loud argument amongst itself about what to do with the mutineers.

Finally, they are dragged to the back of the boat, and the crowd threatens to throw them into the sea if they do anything like this again.

The captains yell angrily; the crowd is threatening aggressively, and the hijackers are apologizing loudly. Eventually, the men are released, and the angry mob begins to dissipate, seeming to take its cue from the crowd. The waves also lessen and begin to quell.

Genet walks to Sarah at the front of the boat and uncovers her face, but Sarah is still asleep. Genet touches the back of Sarah's neck; her fever appears to be gone. Then Genet picks her way back to her tiny spot amidst the carpet of humanity.

Malik looks back and forth at Sarah and Zahid. "She has been asleep for more than twenty-four hours."

Zahid is still looking back at Sarah. "She must be terribly tired."

"Usually, she doesn't sleep this much," Malik offers.

"Wow, you know her that well?"

"We lived together," Malik says plainly. Then he quickly explains, "Because I lived with Genet."

"Oh, okay." Zahid reflects on the woman he wanted to get to know but never could. "She always looks so tough."

"Yes, she is. Especially about men."

"What do you mean?"

"Always, she thinks all men are bad. I never heard her say one good thing about men."

"Did you ever ask her why?"

"I asked, many times, but when I ask her, she gets angry."

"How did you ask her?"

"I asked her why she hates men, but we start arguing."

"You see, that's why she gets angry. Sometimes girls don't like straight questions."

"You confuse me. If you asked her, how would you do it?"

"I would come at it from an angle that would get her talking."

"I don't understand what you mean?"

"I would say something she would agree with, about how awful some men can be, and see if she agrees and maybe it triggers her to begin talking about why she agrees. Maybe she would open up, and I'd find out what she's thinking."

"Why? If I tell her like that, she will think I'm bad too."

"I think that's where you're wrong. When you admit how bad some of the guys are out there, then she knows you're on the same page, and you're on the same team. She'll trust you more."

"Maybe that's why we fight a lot. I don't admit that to her because I don't want to encourage her."

That night the stars and moon come out clearly, and the waves are mild. The following day the dolphins return, the waves remain subdued, and for the first time, the crowded little boat passes other ships under a bright sun. Night returns, and Malik and Zahid talk late into the night, as the anticipation of landing in Italy builds.

It's almost 5:00 a.m., and the group has been traveling for three days and nights.

Zahid sees lights far off on the horizon and exclaims to Malik, "Look, the light! Oh, Allah, we've gotten to Italy."

Some of the other people notice the light and begin fervently expressing appreciation to their Gods. Peoples' faces beam with hope and happiness, but Sarah is still asleep.

Mazaa and Liya awaken to the excited murmurs of their shipmates and seeing the lights break out in smiles, but the lights are deceptively far away, and the sun is risen and well overhead before they near land.

Malik looks back at Sarah and says, "Ya Allah, what happened to her?"

"Who?"

"Sarah. She has been asleep for more than three days,"

"Maybe she's scared?"

"I don't know. I'm just worried."

"Malik, I'm sorry to ask," Zahid begins carefully. "Do you love her?"

"Yes, she's my best friend."

"Oh, okay." Zahid doesn't press but can't shake the feeling that Malik's feelings for Sarah are more than friendly. He suddenly recognizes that he may have revealed more of his feelings than he intended, creating an embarrassing situation with another man in the same position.

The big boat has crossed the nautical boundary of Sicily and is chugging toward the shore. The immigrants can see sparse crowds of vacationers dotting the distant recreational beach and talk more and more excitedly as land gets ever closer. Many of the people on shore stop their activities to watch the ship coming in, with its tell-tale overcrowding. Several vacationers scramble for their cell phones to call the authorities.

Sarah rouses herself, and for the first time in almost two days, she peels back the jacket, exposing her face to the sun. She pulls herself up stiffly and takes in the view of people swimming and sunbathing a kilometer or so away. "Oh, God, thanks for taking care of me." She spontaneously exclaims. "Thanks for saving me and for not letting me see any trouble." She folds her arms on the side of the boat and rests her head on them, staring at the beach. "Oh, it's a beautiful feeling, seeing people...seeing land. When I was in the desert, all I wanted was to see water and people. But after these past three days, all I want is to see land. God, make this the last stage of my journey. Don't allow me to wish for anything more. As soon as I get to Italy, I'll go to language school, then acting class, so my dreams come true, and I go back to my home, and I can make my mom proud."

Malik sees Sarah and waves his hand at her.

Sarah waves back. He approaches her, "Are you okay?"

"Yes, I just slept." Then she looks at Zahid, who is staring at her. Then she turns to the beach. "Why is he looking at me?" she asks. "Whatever. He's a man. Why do men always want females just for sex? Why don't they love her for any other reason? They just need our bodies, but they don't care for our minds." A sarcastic smile creeps across her face. "I don't think their minds are even capable of considering anything else."

When Zahid sees Sarah smile, his heart jumps at the idea that she's responding to the moment of their eyes meeting. "She smiled! I think she likes me. Ya Allah, she is the queen of my heart."

Sarah turns to look for Malik but sees Zahid still looking at her, and quickly turns back toward the beach. *He looks like he's never seen a girl in his lifetime*, Sarah thinks. *This is so weird. Oh, I wish there were a country to live in just for females. No men.*

Zahid's grin spreads from ear to ear. "She keeps looking at me. This is a good sign." He continues looking at her with admiration while she stays fixed on the people swimming.

Liya sees her and walks toward her, "Are you Okay, Sari? You were sleeping the whole time."

"I didn't feel well."

"What happened?"

Sarah pauses, then reveals the truth. "When we were getting on the small boat, and the Libyan smuggler grabbed my hand, I had a flashback to that awful night in the desert. I got a headache and felt very short of breath. Like it was happening all over again."

"Sarah, this thing happened so long ago... ten months have passed."

Sarah feels a surge of anger rise up inside her but tries her best to stay under control. "Ten months have happened, but nothing has passed," she laughs awkwardly. "I won't forget that night until I die." Deep, choking sobs take over her throat and chest.

Liya hugs her tightly. "Oh, Sarah! I'm sorry! I'm sorry! I didn't mean you would forget like that, so simply. But I want you to forget. It's not good for your future. Please, Sarah, think about your future. All Libyans are not bad. Somehow you have to get free."

"Tell me which Libyan is good!" Sarah shoots back bitingly. "The police who broke into our home? The kids who threw rocks at us on the road? Or the men who ruined thousands of women's lives? Tell me, which one? Forget it; you can't. And you can't understand my pain. You didn't experience it. It's easy to give advice, but living it is completely different. And you know that. So, stop saying it."

Liya stands silently beside her, angry, grieving friend. She lowers her eyes. "You are so strong, Sarah. I have never met a person like you. I wish I had your brains and personality." Then she cleans Sarah's face, which goes unnoticed by the throngs of travelers looking off the opposite bow towards the beach.

The boat's motors have been turned off, and the ship coasts to within a few dozen meters of the beach before grounding in thigh-deep water. The Red Cross has arrived, along with several police cruisers and a truck of border control officers. Many immigrants jump off the ship wading or swimming toward land, and officers wade out into the water to help the women and children reach the shore. Several police officers climb aboard the ship with guns drawn. They enter the cabin, but the smugglers aren't there; they abandoned ship far from shore and escaped.

Chapter Ten

Most of the immigrants obediently hike to the section of the beach pointed out by customs officers, but some, fearful of providing a fingerprint, try to swim or run down the shoreline to escape. Having a fingerprint on record can forever alter your chances of getting into another European country. Malik and Zahid help Genet, her daughter, Sarah, and some of the other females get off the boat and into the water. The women jump or lower themselves down into the outstretched arms of the men.

The police take the soaking wet immigrants to where the beach meets the road. They sit on the street as the Red Cross checks and helps each one. People are given simple sets of new clothes, and take turns holding up towels for each other to provide them with cover while they change.

Many of the immigrants are ill and malnourished from several days at sea without food. A series of ambulances arrive to get the sick people to nearby hospitals. People who are only dehydrated or suffering low blood sugar from not eating are herded aboard buses and taken to temporary detention for sustenance and basic first aid.

"The Libyans abused us, but here they take care of us. Wow." Sarah exclaims privately to Malik.

"That's true," Malik agrees. "That's why a lot of people come here."

"How do you feel now?" Genet asks Sarah.

"Oh, I forgot to ask you," Malik interrupts. "What happened? You slept for three days."

"I took sleeping medication. Also, I didn't feel like I was missing anything because I grew up next to the Blue Nile and Lake Tana." She smiles.

"Are you serious?" Malik says curiously. "Where did you get the medication?"

Sarah evades him playfully. "God gave it to me. I asked him; then, he made my wish come true." She keeps laughing. "But I saw everything that happened on the sea."

"How? You were asleep..."

"I saw it in my dream."

"When are you gonna give a straight answer?" Genet insists. "You joke, you laugh, but..."

Sarah goes quiet for a moment, "Life is short; we have to be happy." She starts thinking about her life, and this situation, and what she has discovered about herself and others. She whispers to herself, "People think when we laugh, make jokes, and smile, they think that person is happy. But people have a million reasons for acting that way. No one lives their inside thoughts. Everyone has two personalities; our outside says one thing, and our inside says something else. If we say what we feel, our true feelings will get judged. But we always lose what we want because we can't say what we want."

"Sarah, where did you go with your mind?" Genet asks.

"I had a flashback about Ethiopia. I do that sometimes."

Genet agrees. "Yeah, everyone does that, especially when we leave our countries."

While they are talking, they arrive at the detention center and get off the bus.

The place is one big office room, with five office tables. On the top of each table are paper forms, pens, a camera, and a fingerprint machine. There are a lot of immigration officers directing the immigrants and processing them at the tables.

The doctors start checking them one by one.

A doctor checks Sarah and discovers her blood sugar is dangerously low, and her heartbeat irregular. He mentions to an officer that she should have been taken by ambulance from the beach, and arrangements are made to get her to the hospital. Malik asks the doctor if he can go with her, but they refuse him. An ambulance arrives, and Sarah is taken aboard along with two police officers. Paramedics hook up an IV glucose drip, and the vehicle departs.

When Sarah arrives at the hospital, they take her to the emergency department, where they begin a full regimen of exams. Sarah is confused about what's going on. She says to herself, "Why have they brought me here? And how can I communicate with them? Maybe they speak English..." Feeling shy, she waits.

Following the tests, she is wheeled into a hospital room and transferred to a bed. Sometime later, a doctor arrives. "I speak English," she begins. "Are you speaking English?"

The doctor smiles.

"Yes, I do. But in these situations, you should speak your first language. We'll use an interpreter. Okay?" Without waiting, he picks up the phone beside her bed and dials a short number. Someone answers on the other end, and the two converse quickly in Italian. "Hi, I need help with an interpretation. The patient is Ethiopian."

The male voice, on the other end, asks, "What language does she speak? Ethiopia has more than eighty languages, but the TV national language is Amharic."

The doctor asks Sarah in English, "What is your first language?"

"Amharic."

The doctor repeats this over the phone, to the relief of the man on the other end. "Okay, yes, I can help you."

"Thanks. Please pass this on to her. She has several problems. First, her blood sugar is very low. More importantly, the right ventricle of her heart isn't receiving or pumping blood, and we're not sure why. She also has a bladder infection and RTS."

The doctor hands the phone to Sarah, who listens as the interpreter explains.

"I don't understand what RTS means?" She queries.

The interpreter asks to be given back to the doctor.

"It's both a physical and a psychological condition. Rape Trauma Syndrome. The psychological component is similar to post-traumatic stress disorder." The doctor explains. "Unfortunately, a lot of girls who come on this road face this. She is one of them; there are obvious signs of damage. Can you please ask her what happened?"

The interpreter's voice gets very soft when he explains to Sarah.

"I'm not crazy," Sarah protests, then bursts into tears.

The interpreter gently asks her what happened, but Sarah can't speak and continues crying. After a few moments, the interpreter tries again to coax her. "Please talk, it will help you. We're here to help you. You're not the only person to suffer from this; there are a lot of immigrant girls who've been hurt this way. The doctor only wants to help; this will help him know how to help you. Please, think about your future."

Sarah erupts and yells into the phone. "Which future? Also, don't treat me like I'm crazy! I'm not crazy!" Her sobs take over, and she refuses to talk further.

The interpreter explains what she said to the doctor.

The doctor says to him, "Let her know; we'll keep it secret. Nobody will know."

The interpreter explains to her, but she cannot be convinced and refuses to talk further. The doctor expresses his gratitude to the interpreter and hangs up the phone. In English, he says to Sarah, "You'll stay here for the night."

***

Malik and Genet are very worried about Sarah.

Liya looks around, but she doesn't see Sarah, and she walks toward to Genet, "Hey Genet, I saw Sarah earlier, but I haven't seen her for a couple of hours, where is she?"

"They took her to the hospital."

"Oh, good. She needs it."

"Why do you say that? Why does she need it?"

Liya suddenly realizes her mistake. "I mean, she was sick when we came. It's been a regular thing," she responds.

"That's true. She slept over seventy-five hours," Malik says, still in disbelief.

Liya finds a quick exit to the conversation and returns to Aida and her cousins. As she walks, she worries for her friend. "I wish they'd allow me to go and visit her because she needs someone. She may be crying by herself."

While she is walking, she notices a female immigration interpreter and decides to ask if it's possible. To Liya's happy surprise, the interpreter is an Ethiopian. "Do you have a moment? I want to talk to you for just a second…"

"How can I help you?"

"My friend went to the hospital, but she didn't come back. If she is staying there overnight, can I go to her?"

"I can ask, but we don't allow people to leave this facility."

"She really needs someone to be with her."

"Why do you say that?"

"She is very sensitive… and…" Liya struggles with how much to say. "Never mind. Can you please find out? Her name is Sarah Belay."

The interpreter inquires, and the supervisor eventually gets in touch with one of the police officers sent to watch Sarah in the hospital and hands the phone to the interpreter. The police officer mentions that Sarah has been crying non-stop. The interpreter asks them to ask the doctor what is wrong. The doctor is in the room, and they ask him. The doctor refuses to divulge the information but offers to take the phone.

"It's personal, I can't say." He begins. "But if she has a family, it would be good for her to have them here. She needs special treatment."

The interpreter pauses. "I will ask, but I doubt they'll allow it."

Hearing the interpreter's Ethiopian accent, the doctor decides to press. "If you care about your people, I will highly advise it. She really needs help."

"I will try." She hangs up the phone.

Liya, waiting with anxious patience, asks, "What did they say?" The interpreter reassuringly stops Liya with her hand as she walks over to the supervisor, who has left the desk. Liya begs her, "Please help us! Aren't you Habesha? She is your race!"

But the interpreter doesn't reply.

The supervisor turns and listens to the interpreter. "We have a problem at the hospital. The doctor says one of the women from this center is in real distress and needs a family member. She is crying nonstop. The doctor says the reasons can't be discussed by phone."

The supervisor's brow furrows. "I will talk to the doctor, but I can't send anyone. That's our law." He goes back to the desk and re-dials the officers in Sarah's room. They report to him the same things they witnessed to the interpreter. "But why is she crying?" The supervisor asks.

They're unable to explain, so the supervisor asks for the doctor.

"Give me his extension number," the doctor says. "I can call him." The doctor goes to his office to make the call and explains everything to the supervisor.

"But she has to leave by tomorrow morning," the supervisor insists. "They are changing camps."

"All the more reason to send family, then." The doctor responds. "It can only help her heal faster."

After the supervisor hangs up the phone, he gives Liya permission to go to the hospital. One of the police officers accompanies her to the hospital in a police car. When she arrives at the hospital, the police officer helps her find the room and places her in the charge of the attending officers.

Seeing Liya, Sarah tries to wipe her eyes.

"Sarah, what happened?" Liya asks. "Please stop crying." She cleans Sarah's face. "What did the doctor tell you?"

"I'm fine. I just had a headache, and they took me here, and then they started saying a lot of things."

"What did they say? Tell me."

"They said... my sugar is low and..." Then she looks down.

"Please tell me. You know I know everything about you. And please don't lie to them. You must tell them the truth; they will help you."

"It's not easy to tell. I wish I spoke the language here. But to tell the interpreter, hell no! I can't. Also, he's a man. There's no difference; they're all the same."

"Did he come here? The interpreter?"

"No, it was over the phone."

"Then it should be easy to tell... he doesn't know who you are. Please do it for your mom. You always said you love your mom, and you care for her. Do it for her. It would be her wish for you. You know you need help."

"You think I'm crazy? How dare you think that!"

"I didn't say that. I'm saying you have to tell them, and they can help you. Otherwise, it will be hard for you to get the right help. Or do you want me to tell them? I can tell them."

"This is not the time to talk about it. I will tell them one day in the future."

"When?" At that moment, the doctor walks in. Liya looks at her friend and says, "Tell him, it is the right time."

The doctor asks Sarah how she's feeling?

"Better."

"Tell the truth," Liya says.

"Do you know anything about her? You can help her as a family member."

Sarah looks at Liya. "I can tell him, but I don't need an interpreter, I can try my best to explain to him in English."

195

"It will be easier for you in your first language," the doctor cautions. "But yes, you can tell me."

Sarah turns back and looks at Liya. "Liya, do you mind leaving us for a moment?"

Liya agrees and leaves the room.

Sarah takes a breath and recounts the trip.

The doctor asks her to be specific.

"Eleven months ago, I was the happiest person. I always laughed, made jokes, had fun. I was focused on my dream and how I would make it happen."

"What is your dream?"

"To be a Hollywood actor, and build the Ethiopian film industry, but..." She starts to cry.

"You're young; you'll make it." The doctor assures her. "Just be strong. You're not the first woman to have this kind of dark experience; you must be strong. You must be open. I don't mean to suggest that this is easy. But you're too young to give up on your dream. Trust me; if you are strong, you'll make it. Some of our famous artists here in Italy, they've had experiences like yours. Some people get raped by their family members, but even they face the fact head-on, and they make their dreams come true."

"I will try," She looks out the window to avoid eye contact with him.

"Say, you will do it. Also, I will refer you to the psychologist; they'll help you to find your way forward. But for now, tell me everything that's going on. I've already seen your medical results, but I want to hear it from you."

Sarah tries her best to tell the story. She looks around, searching for an answer.

The doctor continues watching her, and finally, she makes eye contact with him. "Ten months ago, I was raped by three men."

The doctor nods slowly, and his eyes get misty.

Sarah's tears come down, but she continues, "I remember the first two guys, but the last one, I don't really remember. It was like a dream that I only partly remember. A Sudanese doctor helped me the next day. After two months, I felt sick and went to the doctor, and he told me that I was pregnant. That day I was about to kill myself, but the doctor said, 'Don't worry, I will help you.' Then he gave me two days to relax; then, I had an abortion. I feel so guilty because I killed an innocent child."

The room is quiet for a moment, then the doctor says. "I'm really sorry about this, Sarah. But don't feel guilty because it wasn't your fault. You did the right thing. Thank you for telling me." He leans back in his chair a bit. "What did you feel when a man gets physically close to you, or when men talk to you?"

"When I see Libyans, and when I hear their language, I want to murder them. I want to bite them."

The doctor listens patiently.

"But it's not just Libyans. I'm sorry to say this, but all men are the same. They don't have the same parents, maybe or come from the same place or have the same skin color. But they are the same." Then she gets lost for a moment.

"No, all men are not the same. Think about your father, your brother, or your cousin. There are a lot of nice guys. The human species is imperfect. There are bad people of both genders and nice people of both genders. Being a male and female doesn't determine who's nice; it's strictly to define biology and gender."

"I don't think there are good men. I'm sorry," Sarah argues. "Because all the men I meet just want me for sex, that's all. For example, I met a guy on the road; I looked at him as my brother, and he saw what happened to me, but he says he loves me while he has a secret girlfriend. How? It's a lie. Men are liars."

"Try to think more positively. You will help yourself more than a doctor can by doing something that makes you happy; by thinking about your dreams, your future, the good things that have happened in your life. The people who think positively always receive positivity from the universe. If you think this, you will be strong, and you can go further in the direction of your dreams. Also, every morning when you wake up, think about your dream, and tell yourself, 'You can do it! You are so strong.' Do this exercise before you do anything else.

Also, by making your dream come true, you will help a lot of girls like you; you can speak for them. A lot of artists use their life experience to help others."

"I will." She says. The two sit in therapeutic silence. Then Sarah asks, "How is my health? Am I in danger?"

"If you take your medication on schedule, you'll get better. And quite soon. Also, I'll send your information to the camp, and they will help you with everything. Don't worry about it, we will keep the information secret, and I'll try to find you a therapist. Do you have any other questions?"

"No, thanks."

The doctor stands. "Be strong," he says, and walks out, leaving the door open behind him. Liya pokes her head in and enters. "I'm proud of you. You did it."

"I tried my best, but it was hard."

"I know. It is."

***

At the temporary camp, the immigrants have all finished their check-ups and received initial medical attention. Everyone is now being fingerprinted and filling out paperwork.

"This is how Italians keep us detained," Malik says, "To keep us from escaping anywhere."

"They're smart," Genet agrees, "They keep us here for menial labor. I wish I could have escaped before I gave the fingerprint, but it's too late."

"I don't want to leave," Malik says.

Genet laughs. "Oh, sorry, I forgot, you don't want to leave your secret love."

Zahid hears her laugh and walks toward them.

"Where have you been?" Malik asks Zahid.

"I was in the bathroom," Zahid responds and looks at Genet. "What made you laugh so loud?"

"Malik makes me laugh."

Malik winks at her in a warning.

Genet feigns ignorance. "What?"

198

"Nothing," Malik responds profoundly. He looks at Zahid and says. "Why didn't you escape?"

"Anywhere in Europe is the same," Zahid responds. "I don't have a plan to escape anywhere."

While they talk, the officer points his finger at Genet, Malik, and Zahid, and waves them over. They get up and walk toward him. One by one, they stand in front of the camera and get their pictures taken. Then they tell their information to agents filling in the paperwork and get fingerprinted. The process of getting everybody processed has taken the full day. Finally, after the last person is fingerprinted, the immigrants line up single file to receive a packaged dinner of rice, chicken, black beans, and an apple. A veggie option substitutes collard greens for the chicken.

As they sit on the floor to eat their meals, Malik looks over at Genet. "Sarah is taking a long time at the hospital; what happened to her?" He eats a bite and continues. "She said she is Okay."

"That's what Sarah always says," Genet replies.

"She has a positive mind," Malik says, shaking his head in admiration.

"Sometimes, you can't tell if she is happy or not," Genet says.

"Those kinds of people, it's hard to read their minds," Zahid responds.

While everyone eats and talks, an officer approaches with the interpreter. She speaks for him, as he hands them four thin mattresses and some blankets.

"When you've finished eating, you can go and sleep. Tomorrow morning you will be transferred to a new facility."

"Oh no," Genet blurts out. "What if Sarah doesn't come back in time?"

"We can tell the officer," Zahid responds, "and ask them if we can stay here until she comes back."

"Don't worry; you can go," Malik says. "We can wait here for her."

"I'll wait with you guys. We're family," Zahid says, "I can't leave you now."

"Let me ask the officer." Genet gets up, but Zahid rests his hand on her arm. "Don't worry. Go ahead and rest. I'll go and talk to them."

"Okay," Malik takes Genet's baby while she prepares the beds.

***

Sarah holds Liya's hand. "Thanks so much. You mean so much to me. I won't forget your kindness in my life. You're always there for me. If you weren't there for me, my life would be so much harder; I can't even imagine."

"You are my sister. Even though we are not blood."

"Yes, we are." Liya sits close to Sarah's bed, and they hold hands for a moment in quiet solidarity.

"Where are you going to sleep?" Sarah asks.

"I will sleep on the couch."

"I'm sorry, I sleep on the bed while you are sleeping there."

"Sari, don't forget where we used to sleep." Liya smiles.

"If you forget where you come from, you don't know where you go," Sarah says. "I heard that somewhere."

After a while, Sarah drifts off to sleep.

Liya ponders her friend. *I wish I knew what she's thinking and what she needs*, she thinks to herself. *I could help her.* Liya closes her eyes, and tears come down her cheeks. *I wish I could tell her about my experience, but it's so hard.*

Memories return to her of her overwhelming shame and depression, and her suicide attempt. *If I could tell her, maybe she'd grow stronger, but how can I? How could I live if people knew I got raped by my first cousin? Oh no, it's Impossible! I don't even want to think about it.*

She releases Sarah's hand but continues to look at her. *If I hadn't experienced the same thing, I wouldn't be able to empathize with her. It's good. But I can't burden her; she has so much pain and anger already. This thing, it must die with me. Oh God, please help me not to think about it.*

Sarah squirms in her bed but doesn't wake.

***

Zahid comes back from the officer's desk to tell Malik and Genet about Sarah. She will be staying at the hospital for the night and returning tomorrow. Then he walks to his air mattress. After three hungry and exposed nights on the open sea, the combination of a meal, soft bedding, and the first real sense of protection leads many of the two-hundred-twenty immigrants to have their best sleep in months.

Early in the morning, Sarah and Liya return from the hospital, and everybody is preparing to leave. Sarah hugs Genet and Malik and kisses Genet's baby. Everyone takes a packaged breakfast and walks to the waiting buses, long and white, with blue striping along the base, and thin slit windows near the roof. After a three-hour drive, the buses pass a checkpoint and rumble onto a large ferry boat in Borgo Del Ringo, which connects Sicily to the toe of the Italian boot. Many of the immigrants are confused, not realizing Sicily is an island.

Sarah turns to her friends and half-jokingly says what many of the immigrants are fearfully thinking. "What if they are taking us back to Libya? That would be funny."

"Sarah, this is not a joke!" Malik almost shouts.

"They are taking us to the Cortona detention center," Zahid assures them.

"How do you know that?" Sarah asks.

"I have a lot of friends who've been there," Zahid responds, and points back to where they've come from. "This part of Italy is an island." Then he points forward. "But that's Italy too. This happens to everyone."

"Are you sure?" asks Liya nervously.

"Yes. Absolutely. All of my friends went through this."

"Oh, my God, I'm glad to hear that," Genet says with an exhalation.

The buses rumble from one end of Italy to the other. Twelve hours later, as the final glow of twilight loses its power, the long milky vehicles chug through a mechanical gate into the Cortona camp.

The officers divide the immigrants by families and assign them to small RV trailers—Sarah rooms with Genet and her child. Zahid and Malik get placed together. As they make their way through the massive grounds, the friends are amazed at the astounding size of the camp. There are thousands of immigrants here. At least eight hundred Habesha reside at Cortona, making them the largest ethnic group in the camp.

"I never saw a car house with my own eyes," Sarah says, absorbing the inside of the small RV. "Except in films. It's nice; I like it better than the house."

"I prefer the house. My baby can move around," Genet says.

"She can play outside." There is a knock on the door. "Come in."

Zahid pushes the thin door open, and Malik also sticks his head in. They tell the girls that dinner is ready, and people are already in line.

"In line, for what?"

"For food," Malik answers. Having been in the hospital the two days previously, Sarah has never stood in line for food in her life.

"Come in; I'm just changing the baby," Genet says.

The men step inside, and Sarah walks over to close the door. She sees the big line, hundreds of people long. Her hand goes to her head in amazement. "What are we doing?" She blurts out loud. "How long do we choose this banishment from our beloved county? We did this by choice; no one forced us. Why are we paying all this sacrifice? For what?"

Malik walks closer to Sarah, but she doesn't see him and continues talking. He stands there for a while, wanting to say something comforting.

She turns back, and her shocked reaction to seeing him so close sends her tumbling through the door and down onto the ground outside.

Malik jumps out of the RV. "I'm sorry! Are you okay?"

Zahid and Genet run to the doorway and jump down. "What happened?"

Sarah sits up from the ground and hits Malik. "He scared me!" They take her arms and help her up.

Genet is trying not to laugh, "Are you okay?"

"I think I'm fine." She glares at Malik. "You scared me!"

"I said, sorry."

"The line is getting smaller," Zahid says. "Let's get our dinner before the food truck leaves."

Together they walk to the truck. There are two options, one vegan and one meat. Sarah chooses the vegan; the others pick the meat. The chef gives them the packed food with a pear and a bottle of water. Sarah has never seen a pear. It looks very much like the small, and highly toxic, Ethiopian calabash gourd, and she's surprised to see people bite into it.

Zahid can't help but smile at the concerned look on her face.

The two men step aside to say their evening prayers. Genet and Sarah open their packages and start to eat. Genet asks Sarah how she feels.

"Good," Sarah answers simply. She looks over at Zahid, "You know Geni, Zahid looks like my older brother."

"That is how love starts," Genet answers puckishly and laughs. "Do you like him?"

Sarah gets mad. Her face and voice change. "How could you think that?" She gets up with her food and walks to the car, puts her food on the shelf, and goes straight to bed. Genet is confused and wonders how a simple joke could have made her so angry. Genet turns her attention to her daughter. As she feeds her a tiny spoonful, Malik and Zahid come to join her. They ask about Sarah, and Genet says only that she's gone to bed early.

"Ya Allah, did she get hurt when she fell?" Malik gets up in a fit of worry, but Genet pulls him down to sit.

"I made a joke, and she got offended. But she is fine."

After dinner, Liya and Mazaa come by to visit. They share a modified shipping container with their cousins in the opposite corner of the camp.

"Where is Sarah?" Liya asks.

"She's inside," Genet says and points to the ground. "Have a seat."

"Let me check her." Liya walks inside, and Mazaa follows her.

Sarah has pulled her blanket up over her head.

Mazaa uncovers Sarah's face, but Sarah acts like she's asleep. Mazaa replaces the blanket, and the two cousins walk out of the small trailer.

"She's asleep," Liya says. "I'll come tomorrow. Good night."

The two groups bid each other farewell, and the cousins depart.

After they finish eating, Zahid and Malik also wish Genet a good night and leave.

The next morning at 6:00 a.m., the loud horn of the food truck announces breakfast. This is the closest thing to an alarm clock most of the camp inhabitants have, and a line begins to form. After breakfast, a new interpreter comes to Sarah's trailer to tell her she needs to get ready to go to the hospital. Very soon, an ambulance arrives, and Sarah is taken away.

"Why did they take her to the hospital again?" Zahid asks Malik. "I hope she feels better soon. We have to pray for her."

"Let's pray together," Malik suggests.

The four cousins arrive to say hello to Sarah and learn about the mysterious hospital visit. Liya, Genet, Mazaa, Aida, Kaleb, Zahid, and Malik all pray together. Their religions are different, but they believe that praying together brings strength. They talk all morning about their lives and dreams. The conversation then returns to Sarah.

The camp residents all spend most of the day outdoors, but there is precious little to do. A large fence and plenty of guards make sure that no one leaves, though a rumor persists that some of the men escaped long enough to purchase a few cases of alcohol and smuggle them back into camp. Some of the immigrants do exercises or jog, many sit and visit, and some do each other's hair. Many lay down, sleeping on the ground.

Genet walks back into her trailer to put her daughter to bed, but Zahid and Malik remain talking outside.

"The girl you love, where does she live?" Malik asks.

"She's not far; she lives near me," Zahid responds. "But she doesn't know me, I can see her, but she doesn't see me."

"This is complicated, but I understand."

"Let's talk about yours."

"Mine is even more complicated. I made a big mistake at the beginning. I wish I told her before she started to see me as a brother, but now it's too late."

"Sorry to hear that," Zahid doesn't take his gaze off Malik. "Are you talking about Sarah?"

"Oh, no!" Malik protests a little too loudly. "She is my sister. Why would you say that??"

"I'm just guessing, that's all. I'm really sorry. For suggesting it was Sarah, but also just that you have to go through it."

***

Sarah has begun sessions with her psychologist at the hospital and has her own room. She was relieved to learn that her therapist is female and surprised to hear in their first session that the therapist had been raped herself repeatedly at the age of eight by her stepfather. The process of overcoming that tragedy had led her to choose to help other struggling women.

Her doctor leaves after the second session, and Sarah watches her walk to her car through the hospital window.

"She is so strong when she talks about it; she doesn't cry; she smiled when she told me. Is she faking it, or is this for real? It seems real; she is so strong. But one thing I don't understand; her stepfather raised her since she was only eleven months old. He should look at her like she's his daughter."

Sarah gets increasingly angry as she thinks about it. "Men are animals; I don't think they have any humanity at all." Eventually, she falls asleep.

Sarah stays in the hospital for a week, then prepares to leave. She gives a hug to her doctor and nurse, and the doctor reminds her about her weekly follow up. Sarah is driven back to the camp.

***

For the first week after arriving back at the camp, Sarah stays in her small trailer all day long. Zahid visits every single day and spends most of his time with her, but they are never alone. Malik is always hovering with offers of help, and Genet stays nearby as well. Still, Sarah and Zahid have many long conversations that Sarah finds herself enjoying very much.

After a week, Sarah begins venturing outside and walking around with her friends. One day she is walking around the courtyard with Zahid, and they start talking about their dreams. His dream is to go back to school for computer engineering; he went to a private school back home and was one of the top students in his school. He asks her, but she evades his question.

"I guess I'll figure it out when I get there."

Malik sees them and runs over to them. There is plenty of room between Zahid and Sarah, and Malik steps in between them. He playfully takes Sarah's arm as they walk, but she pulls back.

"I told you a million times; I don't like it when people touch me."

"I'm sorry, I always forget," Malik responds.

"What's wrong with it?" Zahid asks Sarah. "He sees you as a sister."

"It doesn't matter who it is; I don't like it when men touch me. That is all."

Zahid apologizes, and they keep walking.

Women are sitting on the ground in small groups throughout the compound. One of the girls looks at Zahid, Sarah, and Malik and says, "What is that girl's name?" She points her finger at Sarah.

A twenty-year-old Habesha in jeans cleans under her nails with a sturdy blade of grass. She glances in the direction of the pointing finger. "Her name is Sarah," she says and goes back to her nails.

A third woman stops unbraiding her hair and stares at the woman in jeans. "Is that the girl who steals everyone's boyfriends? She goes out with one guy after another after another."

A fourth woman in a navy-blue blouse and long, flowered skirt and jean jacket jumps to her feet. "She slept with my boyfriend last night! I saw him leaving her room this morning." Without warning, she runs toward Sarah as the other women watch.

Sarah, Malik, and Zahid hear footsteps running up behind them, and realizing the woman is coming toward them, and they stop to wait for her. The woman runs right up to a stop in front of Sarah and slaps her hard across the face. Sarah falls backward, completely stunned. The girl tries to kick Sarah, but before she can land any blows, Zahid grabs her from behind and pulls her back.

"What are you doing?" Sarah exclaims at the distraught woman.

"You slut! You slept with my Kidus last night!"

Malik and Zahid look at each other in confusion. Sarah starts laughing at the girl, which only infuriates her further. She kicks wildly, trying to wrench free from Zahid's grabs, but he holds her tight.

"You're mixed up! You've mixed her up with another person; she was homesick all this week." Zahid says commandingly.

"Her name is Sarah, yeah?"

"Yes," Malik says.

"Yeah," Zahid responds questioningly.

Malik stands in front of Sarah to protect her. Sarah is confused; she looks at the girl and back at them.

Zahid asks the girl, "Why do you think this is the girl who slept with your boyfriend? I'm telling you; this is the first time she's left our trailer."

"Everyone knows the whore, in this prison is named Sarah! She lives over there!" And the woman points to a row of small structures nearly a hundred yards away.

"You fool, this woman lives with our friend, over there!" Malik exclaims, pointing back at Genet's trailer.

"You think there's only one Sarah in the place?" Zahid demands. "Did you even see her?"

The woman doesn't answer, but her struggling becomes less violent and more indignant.

A police officer and interpreter come toward them and ask what happened. Zahid explains the last few moments to them, and the woman interjects with protests. They write down the information and then walk away with the woman.

"Oh, wow; I'm speechless," Sarah says. "I really feel sorry for her; she's fighting other girls because of a man. The mistake is her man, not the other girl. If I were her, I would dump him, not fight with other girls. Secondly, if her man is going around with another woman, he was never really hers. And third, how could she believe a man in this world in the first place? Because all men have two belief systems, one is sex, and the other is money. That's all."

Zahid looks at her with growing concern.

"Why do you say that?" Malik asks, "You always look for reasons to talk bad about us."

"I wasn't talking about you; I'm saying this about other men. If you feel that way, I'm sorry, but I didn't mean to hurt your feelings."

* * *

Since meeting with her doctor, Sarah has become more relaxed. She's also become closer with Zahid. Every morning he wakes her up for breakfast, and they go and stand in line together. They talk, and invariably he makes her laugh; he's the only man to do that since the trauma consistently. Sometimes he reminds her of her older brother, the way he respects and takes care of her; he always checks to make sure she's eaten and carries her leftovers back to the trailer for her. On the days where Zahid stays home to rest or get something done, she finds herself sitting outside the little RV, looking blankly at the road.

At one point, Genet mentions Zahid and Sarah's growing relationship with Malik to see how he's handling it.

"Don't worry, he is in love with another girl," Malik says, based on his and Zahid's earlier conversation. "Also, you know Sarah. She can't look at a man as more than a brother." Genet disagrees but decides not to push it.

The next day, as most of the camp stands in line for dinner, fixed speakers around the detention center crackle to life, and a voice booms over the public address system. "These people will meet in front of the office at ten tonight."

Fifty names are read aloud over the loudspeakers, and the four friends look at each other in surprise when Sarah's name is announced. They wait in silence as the rest of the names are spoken, but Genet, Zahid, and Malik are not mentioned. Sadness mingles with joy as the friend's hug Sarah and rejoice at her good fortune.

After dinner, Sarah slips away and walks by herself through the camp, talking to herself. "Where am I going? I don't even know anyone." She gets down on her knees in the middle of the camp, puts her hands together, and holds them up to the sky as she prays to God. Zahid sees this and walks toward her. He watches her with admiration until she finishes praying. When she gets up, she sees him, and they walk back to her trailer together. She packs her meager belongings into a single plastic bag, and the two sit there mostly in silence until the bus comes.

Over the loudspeakers, an interpreter calls the listed immigrants.

"Everyone whose name was called this evening, please come. The bus is ready."

Sarah gets up and kisses Genet and her baby on the cheek. She gives hugs to Malik and Zahid, and the whole group walks with her to the bus. After another round of hugs and many tears, she goes to board the bus.

An immigration officer standing outside the bus takes her name and gives her a plain, white envelope. She puts it in her plastic bag and finds a seat near the back. It takes longer than expected to get all the passengers aboard, and the driver is summoned out of the bus to speak with officials.

More than forty minutes later, the bus finally chugs to life and makes a wide turn to leave the camp.

Sarah's friends remain outside watching, and she waves at them. As the bus heads towards the gate, Zahid bravely smiles and waves goodbye.

The bus pulls through the gate. It closes behind them, and the last twenty-two days of Sarah's life begin to dissipate like a strange dream. She wonders if she will ever see her friends again.

After a short hour and a half bus ride, they arrive at a train station. The officers guide them into the station, and the group of anxious travelers wait for what seems like an eternity for a train.

The group is mostly Eritreans and Ethiopians, about forty out of fifty. They talk with muted excitement about the day and what their reactions were to be heard, their names, and what's next, but the guards are tight-lipped about what awaits them or where they're going. Eventually, the train comes, and the group is split into two smaller groups. The first, including Sarah, is put on the arriving train, and the rest are told they are traveling somewhere else. Sarah's group boards the train, apprehensively.

Once everyone is seated, the guards leave the train, which seems strange. There has still been no conversation about where this trip ends, and the travelers are confused about who will guide them where to go next? Seated on the train, Sarah remembers the envelope. Can she open it, or is it supposed to be given to whoever is waiting to receive them? As the train lurches and rolls out of the station, she decides to look inside. There is an immigration paper of some sort written in Italian and two hundred and thirty euros.

They ride through the night and arrive in Rome the next morning. The weary travelers step out of the train and into the terminal station tentative, confused, and free.

Chapter Eleven

The immigrants talk amongst themselves, taking in the massive and cavernous terminal. One wing of the group, all men, begin to move in the direction of the bus station, and Sarah is unclear if someone is leading the group or if they're just following the general flow of traffic. The group stretches like it's made of elastic, and then the rear of the group conforms to the new direction and its globs back into an irregular oval. Some people are only now learning about the contents of their envelopes. They board a bus. Sarah doesn't have any idea where they are going.

On the bus, it becomes clear one of the men has a contact that he is hoping can provide shelter to the travelers. When they stop the bus from getting off, Sarah follows, and waiting is Kidist! Sarah can't believe her eyes. She runs to Kidist and hugs her. Kidist's eyes are huge.

"Sarah?! When did you come?"

"I just got here. What are you doing here?"

"I live here!" Kidist points to the large dilapidated glass building behind her. "You know, sometimes you don't have a choice. When you are going to other European countries, they give you shelter, food, clothes, and money. Here, they don't give you anything. After we got here, they left us at the terminal station, that is why people started doing this. They break into old buildings to live. We think this used to be a hospital. We don't have a choice."

211

"It's true," Sarah muses. "I was worried about where to go because the only thing they gave me was these two hundred and thirty euros. What do I do with this money? The only thing I can be is homeless."

Kidist abandons the bus and takes Sarah into the building. It's big, with seven floors. The wide hallways and occasional countered station do indeed resemble a hospital interior. The building is entirely inhabited by Habesha, with larger concentrations of people on the lower floors because the elevators are offline.

Sarah is amused. "How did they think they would get away with breaking into a building this big?"

"If you don't have a choice in life, you can do anything to survive."

Kidist and Sarah climb the stairs up to the seventh floor to find a place for Sarah. After checking a few rooms, they find one that will work. Sarah's face brightens with relief; then, she hugs Kidist and thanks her friend. Kidist asks her if she's hungry, and Sarah nods yes.

Kidist takes Sarah on a journey to a charity shelter that serves warm meals to immigrants with documentation. Italian buses allow people to enter through a rear door with an honor system for payment, and Sarah is alarmed to see that Kidist walks past without contributing. Sarah goes to put a euro into the metal receptacle, but Kidist grabs her hand.

"How will you replace that euro?" She asks Sarah. Sarah is startled by the seriousness in Kidist's eyes.

"We'll work..."

Kidist looks dismissively at Sarah and pulls her into the bus. Sarah reluctantly pushes the coin back into her pocket.

As they settle into their seats, Kidist looks intently at her naïve friend.

"That paper they gave you on the camp is worthless." She says matter-of-factly. "It says you're not allowed to work in Italy."

"What?" Sarah can't hide the alarm on her face. "How do we live?"

"You leave for somewhere else. That's what they want."

At the train station, Kidist ducks under the turnstile and gestures to Sarah to do the same.

They arrive at the charity place; there are people from all over the world, especially Africans and Arabs. Sarah and Kidist get into line. The place is big and has more than a hundred chairs, but it's still not enough. People eat fast and move on to give a place for others standing in line and outside.

After lunch, Kidist and Sarah walk around the city. Sarah buys a small, cheap flip phone with ten euros of phoning credit. Later in the evening, they go to a different church-run charity for dinner. Some places offer lunch, others dinner, some of them provide groceries and other's clothes. The trick is to learn, which offers what, when, and where.

Sarah sees some of the people from the detention center at the dinner charity and greets them with a hug. The meal is simple but warm, and they eat it gratefully. Afterward, they take the bus back home.

Kidist walks Sarah up to her room, but they see Sarah's belongings sitting outside the room in the hallway. Sarah opens the door slowly, and a circle of people inside the room looks over toward her. She begins to try to explain to them that this is her room, but they overrule her with objections, claiming that the room is actually theirs and was only temporarily vacant while they were out of the city for two days. Sarah apologizes, and at Kidist's urging, she picks up her plastic bag and follows her friend to spend the night with her and her boyfriend.

The next day she finds another room on the fifth floor and stays a couple of nights there by herself. All the beds and furniture have been removed from the rooms, and she has nothing to sleep on. She sleeps on the floor, with half the blanket underneath her, and half-covering her body. The room is too cold for her small blanket. It's now November, the floor is concrete, and there is no heat. On her second day, loneliness starts to overcome her, and she uses her new phone to call one of the few people she met in the detention center who had a phone.

Sarah convinces her to take the phone to Zahid's trailer in the evening, and that night she calls him. Zahid sounds delighted when he answers the phone, and Genet and Malik are with him. She talks to all three but shares most of her news with Zahid. She tells him about the trip, the building, the charities, and Kidist.

After three days, she finds a large box in an alley and is overjoyed. She takes it to her room and pulls the box apart into a long cardboard slab that she can sleep on. It's not a mattress, but it does mute the coldness of the floor somewhat.

Five days after leaving the camp, she travels to dinner at the charity. While she's eating, someone touches her shoulder. Startled, she jumps up to face her attacker, but it's Zahid! "You scared me! How did you get here!?" She sees a newly purchased flip phone in his hand. "You have a phone!? Why didn't you call me?" She embraces him.

"I wanted to surprise you. Did it work?"

"Yes! Where's Genet? Is she here? What about Malik?

Zahid doesn't try to hide his broad grin, "Genet is in Palermo. The government gave her a home to stay in there because she has a child. Malik was sent somewhere else; he got on board a different train at the first station. How are you, Sarah?"

"I'm… oh gosh, go get your dinner before they finish! The other day I traveled all the way here and then had to go home and sleep without dinner because the food was gone."

Zahid walks to get his dinner, and Sarah watches him intently as he goes through the line. He comes back with a single chicken leg on his plate.

Sarah looks at his plate, "What happened?"

"That's all that's left!" Sarah offers to share her plate, and he accepts. They eat together, and he tells her about his trip. When they finish, they take the bus to the building.

As they arrive, Sarah points it out, "Look at how big it is."

"When you told me, I didn't believe it."

They pass through the front doors. "I think my friends are here in this building, looking for a place. Let me call them and see what they found." He grabs his phone and calls them, but they reply that they couldn't find anything and are downstairs at the restaurant. He hangs up and looks at Sarah. "Where's the restaurant?"

She points to one corner of the building, a larger room that she has never actually gone inside. The small restaurant is owned by immigrants and is non-permitted. It's only for people who live in the building and serves Ethiopian food. The food isn't the best, but it suffices when people are missing the comforts of home.

Walking in, Zahid sees his friend, and they greet each other with hugs. When they see Sarah, they are surprised and ask Zahid, "Where did you meet her?"

"The camp," he responds.

Suddenly Sarah recognizes the men, remembering them and the endless meals of spaghetti in the house where they were abandoned in Al Kufrah. With an exclamation, she hugs them.

"When did you get to Italy?" They explain to her that they were at another camp and met Zahid on the train to Rome. She invites them all to her home for the night, and they trudge upstairs to Sarah's empty room, furnished only with her cardboard sheet and blanket.

"I'm sorry, it's not much." Sarah apologizes.

They thank her genuinely for the place to stay. The men all sleep together on one side of the room, and Sarah sleeps in the corner, furthest away.

Zahid takes off his jacket, offers it to Sarah to use as a pillow. She refuses at first, but he insists, and she eventually gives in.

Early in the morning, they awaken to the sound of shouting and footsteps running down the hall. A voice yells that police are in the building.

Zahid steps out into the hallway to find out what's going on, and a neighbor says that water and electricity have been cut off to the building, and the police are on the lower floors clearing the occupants.

People in the hallway are frantically stuffing their belongings into bags and running to the stairwell to get to the roof.

In the room, Sarah starts to notice a smell like vinegar. Zahid comes back in and tells everyone to pack up their belongings. Very quickly, the group is moving up the stairs to the rooftop emergency exit. Sarah's eyes are starting to water, and she can feel a scratchy sensation in her eyes and throat.

On the roof, they look down at the chaotic scene playing out below. The street glitters with the flashing lights of a long line of police vehicles. A small crowd of building inhabitants on the street confronting police are fleeing from clouds of tear gas, abandoning a rudimentary barricade going up in front of the main entrance. A police spokesman on a bullhorn orders people to leave the building, as more officers enter the main front doors with batons and gas masks. The derelict hospital sits in an industrial area on the outskirts of town, and employees from the beer distillery, sponge, and plastic factories nearby huddle in their front entrances, watching the scene. The friends on the roof can also see clouds of white tear gas streaming out of various windows on the hospital's first three floors.

About four hundred immigrants are gathered on the roof when the first police officers come through the rooftop doorway. A chorus of shouting goes up from the Habesha, and dozens of men step forward with lighters and the small propane gas tanks from their kitchen stoves, threatening to use them as makeshift bombs.

"Let's die together!" they yell at the police.

Caught off guard by the large numbers and ferocity of the crowd, the police back up and begin looking to each other for guidance. Emboldened crowd members throw gravel at them, and anything else they can find, and soon the police are retreating through the small door from which they emerged.

Inexplicably, the police in the street all begin returning to their vehicles and driving away. In a very short time, they are gone, and the crowd on the roof descends to the street to join the protesters.

The water and electricity remain, turned off, and the roiling confusion and frustration of over a six hundred Habesha in the street turn into a protest. The street is clogged with shouting men and women, traffic is stopped, and the employees of the surrounding

216

buildings have retreated inside and locked their doors for fear of violence. Frantic phone calls go from the business owners to various police and government offices, but no police return.

The street protest continues all day, and finally, as twilight approaches, two city municipal vehicles arrive, and construction workers step out to turn the water and power back on.

Great cheers go up from the crowd, and in no time at all, the workers are back in the trucks and go. Lights begin flickering on in the building, but the lingering acrid smell of tear gas still causes coughing fits and prevents most people from returning to their rooms. With nowhere else to go, the protest turns into a late-night street party.

Sarah turns to Zahid, "What is their plan? To kill us? If they don't want us here, why did they fingerprint us and give us papers and money?"

Zahid watches the people singing and milling about on the street.

"The Italian government uses us as income. Other countries and the Red Cross give them millions and millions and millions of dollars for refugees, and the government pockets most of the money."

Darkness falls, and most of the people haven't eaten all day. As the temperature goes down, people finally begin venturing into the building. A loose form of government has evolved over the day, and it is decided that the building should have guards at the front and rear door, to give people a warning if another raid occurs. By 9:00 p.m., the street is clear, and the building is filled with people coughing throughout the night, like a scourge of unearthly crickets.

A week later, Sarah once again finds her and her friends' belongings put out in the hallway. A spirited argument ensues between Zahid and his friends, and the new occupants of the fifth-floor room who claim to have just returned from a trip to France. Both sides are tenacious, but eventually, Sarah and her crew are looking for a new place to stay. Hoping that people have left the building because of the tear gas, Zahid's friends decide to look for a space of their own.

Sarah and Zahid walk up and down the hallways of the building and come across a small electrical storage room right next to Kidist's room on the sixth floor, not much larger than a walk-in closet.

"It's small, but for now, it's not that bad. We can use this until we find something else," Zahid says as he considers it.

"If we clean all this junk out, then at least we know it's ours," she says with a smile. "And no one can tell us they were away on a trip," Zahid laughs.

While they're talking, Kidist arrives at her apartment with her boyfriend, Elias. Sarah embraces her and introduces Zahid. "This is Zahid; he is my brother."

He reaches his hand out to them, looking back and forth between Kidist and Elias, who Kidist then introduces.

"What are you doing here?" Kidist asks.

Sarah explains her room situation, and Kidist looks approvingly at the storage room.

"Why don't you take this room? Elias and I can help you to clean it."

Sarah remarks about how small it is, but Kidist shakes her head. "It's big enough for two. And it's really not that much smaller than my place."

Sarah remembers her night spent in Kidist's place, which was like the bedroom of a small child.

"Oh yeah, I forgot." She laughs.

The room is piled high with loose mechanical trinkets and stacks of boxes, and the shelves crowded with trays and boxes of wire and all manner of metal objects. They clean up the room, taking armload after armload of boxes and junk downstairs and behind the building. When the room is finally empty and swept clean, they go back to the fifth floor to retrieve their belongings and move them into the storage room. Tired but relieved, they leave for lunch.

As they walk to the bus stop, Sarah notices a large sheet of foam in the alley beside the sponge factory. She points it out excitedly, and they hurry over to it. It's thick and soft, and they immediately grab it and take it up to their room.

After lunch, they head to the terminal to get coffee from a vending machine. Inside the train station, they run like children, hug, and laugh without reason.

"Why can't we work? I mean, really, why can't we?" Sarah asks as the two recline on a terminal bench.

"Because a piece of paper says so?"

"Do normal people really care about that paper?"

"I don't know," Zahid muses. "I guess they can always say no. It wouldn't hurt to ask." They decide to start job hunting the next day.

Before the week is over, they both have jobs for the same newspaper company. In the crisp winter air, they position themselves at intersections so drivers can wave them over to buy papers while they wait for the lights. About two and a half hours into the workday, Sarah walks up to one row of cars to call out her sales pitch but loses her grip on the papers, and they fall to the ground. She tries to catch them as they fall, but her hands are shaking and already becoming numb from the cold. She bends over to pick them up and is frustrated at how thick and lifeless her fingers feel, making something as simple as picking up a newspaper difficult. One of the drivers gets out of his idling car and helps her collect her merchandise. She thanks him, and he gives her a ten-euro tip but doesn't make a purchase. Sarah looks at him with curiosity. They work from 4:30 a.m. to 10 a.m. and begin their trip to the charity for lunch. As they walk, they hold hands.

Zahid and Sarah seem like a couple, but neither of them ever admits it, to the amusement of their friends. One day one of Zahid's friends decides to check on them in the middle of the night to see what their sleeping arrangement really is. In the wee hours of the morning, he slowly opens their unlocked door and is surprised by what he sees. They only have one mattress, but they each sleep on a different end of it, facing away from each other, with a large gap between them. They each have their own blanket wrapped around themselves. Zahid has a gray color blanket, and Sarah has a red color blanket.

The man quietly shuts the door and leaves, but he and his friends come back several nights in a row to quietly have a look. They never see any evidence of anything other than a platonic family relationship and eventually stop checking. One of Zahid's friends can't help, ultimately suggesting to him that he get a lock for his door, and Zahid does.

When people see Sarah working on the street, they look twice, because of all the newspaper salesmen on the streets of Rome, she's the only female. People from her country are especially surprised. The work is laborious, carrying the papers up and down the street and running from car to car, and the weather is bitingly cold, especially for Sarah, who doesn't have a proper jacket.

After working a week, she buys some groceries and a knife. She's tired of the charity kitchens and wants to prepare food in her own home. As the weeks turn into months, she slowly stocks her little kitchen with utensils, bowls, and small items.

Zahid grows more and more in love with Sarah with each passing week. As beautiful as she is, her personality and character draw him even more. She's a tenacious worker and gracefully determined, but though he senses she likes him back, he also feels resistance to the idea of a relationship and doesn't know how to bring their feelings into the light.

Ramadan season comes and goes, and on the final day, Sarah returns home from work early to create a small celebration for Zahid. When he comes home, she surprises him with a warm meal cooked on Kidist's small stove, some soda, and a bowl of popcorn sweetened with sugar.

"Thanks so much, this means a lot to me." He says, surveying the spread.

"If it were my holiday, you would do the same for me. I wish I could do more; this is nothing. Next year we'll do something bigger."

Then she becomes quiet for a moment, and says, "You know when I grew up, we had Muslim friends and neighbors. On their holidays, they invited my family over, and on our holidays, we invited them. Ethiopia is the best place when it comes to religion. Everyone respects each other."

"Exactly. I miss that life." Then he grows silent, wondering if this is the right time to tell her. He decides against it for fear of ruining the beautiful moment. Zahid knows he has to tell her eventually but worries she may only love him as a brother. "I know one thing. She doesn't hate me," he says to himself. "And for now, that is enough."

Sarah notices his distraction and, misinterpreting, wakes him out of his thoughts with an apology.

"I'm sorry, I'm not trying to bring up memories. I know holidays make a person miss their family. But don't worry, I'm here for you," Zahid's face brightens, and Sarah continues, "I will be there for you anytime, I promise you. I will be your sister." The word "sister" wounds Zahid, but he masks his feelings and excuses himself to the bathroom.

***

After living together for three-months, Zahid decides to tell Sarah about his feelings. Sarah now has a job at a hair salon, and usually, by the time she gets home Zahid is already there, but today he isn't. She sits on the bed, withdraws her phone from her bag, and looks at the screen. Zahid has called several times.

Sarah calls him back, "Hey, sorry, I see you called me; I didn't see it as my phone was on silent. Where are you?"

"I'm with my friend; I called you because I wanted to tell you..."

"What?"

On the other end of the call, Zahid starts sweating, and his hand becomes shaky. His tone diminishes to a mumble, and he says, "Never mind." He hangs up.

"If you can't tell her, I'll tell her," his friend says. "I don't want to see you suffer more like this."

"It is not easy; she sees me as a brother."

"That's how all the girls talk. She might know that you are in love with her; that is why she is playing with your mind. Don't forget that she was in Libya; she's not that special."

"What does *that* mean?"

"We all know. All the girls who come on that road, we know how they make a living there."

Zahid rises in anger, "You don't know her, you can't say that. I don't need your help."

Zahid walks out of his friend's room and goes up to the roof of the building.

Sarah is momentarily confused by Zahid but realizes what's happening. Her own emotions and thoughts begin to buzz. *I wish I could tell him what I'm thinking. I know he loves me, I love him too, but I can't sleep with him. When I think about sleeping with him and having sex, I feel repulsed. Like I hate him. I wish we could love each other without having sex, but if I tell him how much I love him, then we'll have to have sex because we're in a relationship. No, I don't want to think of him that way. If I say no sex, he'll have to find someone else. But I will love him for the rest of my life even though he isn't mine. He's so different from other guys. I wish he could understand me without me saying a word.* Her phone rings again. It's him.

"I'm sorry, it was my battery... it died."

She rolls her head at the proud little lie but doesn't push it, "Oh, Okay. Are you okay?"

"Yes. Why do you ask?"

"I just want to make sure, because of how your voice was."

"You became a police detective today? What happened to my voice?"

"Never mind, forget my question. Come, I'm here by myself. I'm bored and getting hungry. Come home."

Zahid puts his phone away, takes one last look at the cityscape, and walks towards the roof exit to the stairwell. Very shortly, he opens his own door, and Sarah is waiting for him with a smile. It seems he has only closed the door for a minute when there is a knock. Zahid steps back to the door and opens it, and it's Malik, with luggage in hand. Sarah jumps off the bed in surprise and runs to hug him.

"Malik! What are you doing here?"

222

The three had already been in touch by phone, and both Sarah and Zahid knew the basics of Malik's story after leaving the camp: how he was sent to Firenze by train, fell in with friends from the camp. Bringing his bags into the small room, Malik tells them about his struggles to find work in Firenze. After making enough money to travel to Rome, he hopes he can find a job as they have. He also plainly says that if he can find a job, he hopes Zahid and Sarah will let him stay with them.

After long hours of talking and catching up, they eat dinner and go to bed. Malik sleeps in between Zahid and Sarah, sharing Zahid's blanket.

Malik stays with them for two months. During his stay, the small home begins to take shape. Modest furnishings start to appear as money or chance allows: a tiny dresser, a small refrigerator, on top of the fridge and even more miniature TV, an actual bed with a frame, and their own small propane stove. What these accouterments add in comfort, they sacrifice in floor space, and there is little room to stand except for a small area just inside the door and to the left.

After two months, Malik's situation hasn't changed much, and he decides to try to go to the UK. He asks Sarah and Zahid if they want to go with him, but they're tired of traveling from country to country and don't want to go anywhere. Sarah asks Malik how he plans to get there, and Malik explains, "Travel from Rome to Milan and Milan to France is easy. Getting from France to England is more complicated and requires smugglers. There is a garbage dump outside of Dunkirk where people camp and sleep until enough travelers are gathered for the smugglers to make a profitable trip."

"Where do you sleep in a garbage dump?" Sarah asks.

"I have friends who've done it. You just sleep on the ground or find a thing. One slept on a metal beehive frame."

"Why would you do that? You are so crazy!"

"It is better than living here," Malik responds. "At least after I make all that sacrifice, the government can send me to school. What do I get here? Only working all day in the street selling clothes for somebody and getting thirty euros per day, that is not my dream. I could get that in my country before I ever travel this road. I will leave tomorrow morning. If you guys change your mind, let me know." With that, he lies down on the mattress and pulls Zahid's blanket over himself.

"Never ever," Sarah declares. "I'm not changing my mind. For the rest of my life, this will be my last destination. Also, you don't have any guarantee you'll be able to stay there. If they get your fingerprints, they'll send you back here. You know how many people come back from all over Europe because the government finds these Italian fingerprints? All European countries have an agreement that if an immigrant has registered fingerprints in Italy, they get sent back to Italy. Be aware of that too."

Malik sits up. "Not all people get turned back, depends on the luck. Also, someone showed me how to take off my fingerprints. Don't worry; I will be fine."

"Take off your fingerprints? Okay. I'm just giving you my opinion as your sister. Also, how do you travel after getting into the UK?"

"As a sister?" Malik laughs sarcastically.

Zahid speaks up. "I know people who've tried this. People traveling from the border of France don't even know for sure where they're going most of the time. These smugglers don't use their own trucks; they sneak people into the backs of semi-trucks, and the drivers don't even know they're there. They might be put on a truck going to a completely different country. And they also don't know how long they're going to be locked in the back. They can starve to death back there. All they can do is bang on the walls of the truck to let the driver know they're there, but then he might call the police and get them arrested. Or he might let them out, but they don't even know where they are."

"Is this true?" Sarah asks her balding friend. Malik shrugs, tellingly. "You are crazy! How could you think of trying something like this? You could spend all this money and not have any idea where you're gonna end up? Wow."

"You can work here, and you can go to school," Zahid offers.

"Which school? The language one? Tell me which one. I thought you are so smart. Never mind, thanks for all the advice, let's go to sleep." Malik lies down and turns away from the two friends.

In the morning, Malik stubbornly goes to the train station and waits for his train to Milan. Zahid and Sarah go along to say goodbye to their friend. When the train comes, Malik hugs them. He hugs Sarah tightly and whispers into her ear. "I love you so much. I never loved someone like you in my life; I will always love you."

Sarah doesn't say anything for a moment. When Malik starts walking to the train, she says to him, "I know Malik. I'm sorry."

He looks at her from the doorway of the train, but she turns and leaves.

***

Easter Sunday comes, and Sarah goes to church to celebrate with Kidist. When she returns, Zahid has made her a surprise. He has cleaned their small home, cut the grass behind the building by hand, and spread it out on the floor of their apartment as though to make it feel like outside. He has also borrowed or found all the equipment for an Ethiopian coffee ceremony, which sits prepared and ready for use. He wears bright, clean traditional clothes.

When Sarah sees the house, she smiles, "I'm blessed to have you in my life." She says and hugs him.

"Wow, where did you find the grass?" Kidist asks, "This reminds me of back home."

"Call your Elias," Zahid invites her, "there's plenty for everyone." They invite some neighbors. Everyone sits on the bed, and Sarah puts a big plate of Ethiopian food in the middle for everyone to eat from together.

"Your house is small, but this is as lovely a feast as I've had," one guest says.

Sarah smiles. "The most important thing is love. It doesn't matter where you live or what you have if you have a love, and you share what you have, life is good. There are people with big houses but no love, and they feel lonely and empty. The only thing in this world that makes you full is love. It doesn't matter what you have; it matters who you have. Money and stuff don't buy your happiness."

"That is true."

"In this world, the most important thing is that we have to love each other without worrying about race or tribe or creed."

"I wish everyone thought like Sarah," Kidist declares in admiration. "We would be one Ethiopia, even one world! Look at us; we are different races; Eritrean, Ethiopian, Sudanese, Moroccan, and Italian, and different religions; Muslim and Christian. Sarah is our friend. She doesn't care where we're from or what kind of religion we have. That is a blessing." Everyone agrees with Kidist. When Sarah finishes eating, she gets up to perform the Ethiopian coffee ceremony.

***

Sarah and Zahid have lived together in the same house, and the same bed, as brother and sister for more than six months. He's tried to tell her several times about his feelings but continually shrinks back in fear.

Zahid receives a phone call from a friend in the UK, and who had lived with her and Zahid.

"Hello, how are you?" Zahid asks.

"I'm good. Did you tell her or not?"

Zahid admits that he hasn't, and likely won't soon. The voice on the other end takes on an urgent tone.

"When are you coming to the UK? You can have a lot of opportunities here. Don't play the love joke; you didn't leave your country because of her. Don't forget why you come down this road. Think about this. You're wasting your time and money because of this girl, and she doesn't even know it. If you can't tell her by tomorrow, I will call her, I swear to God."

"I wish you could understand my pain, how much I love her, but if I tell her, I'm afraid I'll lose her forever."

"Also think about your religion, and hers," the voice insists. "It's not the same. You guys can't get married anyway. Think of the future, not only for today. I've heard love is blind, and it's true I see it on you. Tell her. Don't forget, I'm calling her tomorrow." His friend hangs up the phone.

Zahid tries calling back several times, but his friend doesn't pick up.

***

While Sarah cooks dinner, her phone rings. It's her sister Meron. They talk about family and work and men. Sarah has upgraded her phone and sees an incoming call from Zahid but dismisses it to continue her chat with Meron. Several more calls from Zahid come in, but she waits to speak to him until her conversation with Meron is completed almost an hour later.

"Sorry, I had a long conversation with Meron."

"It's fine." He lies. He's angry. "I wanted to talk to you about something important; please listen to me, okay?"

"Okay..."

"I don't know where to start. But I know one thing, I love you," Zahid says. "I've been holding my feelings in all of this time, but now I can't anymore."

He gets quiet. Sarah rises from her sitting position, then sits back down on the edge of the bed, then she stands up and paces with one hand on her waist.

Zahid is waiting for her to say something. Anything. "Please don't be quiet. I can't stand it anymore."

Sarah can't speak and keeps moving around the room. Then she smells something. She looks at her small propane cooker and realizes the onions are burning. She runs over to take it off the flame and makes a mistake she never makes. She grabs the metal handle without protection and burns her hand. The pot and phone both fall with a clatter to the floor, and the smoking black onions spill everywhere. Zahid hears the clamor and Sarah's small yelp of pain.

"Are you okay?"

Sarah stands holding her hand and calls down to the phone on the ground. "I burned my hand."

"Sorry! It was my fault, put some oil on your hand."

227

Sarah picks the phone up from the ground, "Don't worry, I'm fine. Come home; we can talk about it."

"I'm sorry to say this, Sari, because you don't expect this from me, but if you don't give me an answer, I'm not coming home."

Sarah's forehead furrows in disbelief. "What do you mean you're not coming home? What about me? Are you going to leave me here by myself? Where are you going? You know that I can't live without you."

"I know, but what about me? I'm at the station, and I'll go to the UK tonight. I'm taking the overnight train."

He stands at the train station with his bag, and a tear streaks down his face. "Sari, remember this; I have been in love with you since the day I saw you at Eden's baby's birthday. You wore a long burgundy dress with high heels. Your hair was up. I remember it like it was yesterday, but it's been more than a year."

Sarah's eyes fill with tears, and she gets emotional, but she doesn't say a word.

"Sarah, tell me the truth, do you love me?"

She frantically tries to decide what to say, but Zahid hears only silence. "I'll take that as a no then. So, I'm going to leave. But you will always be my love; it doesn't matter what your answer is."

Sarah can only listen in disbelief, and words fail her.

Zahid checks the schedule; the train is leaving in roughly an hour. Still holding the phone, he begins putting euros into the ticket machine and types in the information with his other hand. The machine spits out a small, pale blue ticket. "I've got my ticket; I'm going. Don't wait for me, Sari. I have my bag with me. I'll leave straight from here."

Sarah walks to the bed and bends down to look. His bag is not there. She cries out loudly, "I thought you loved me, but I was so wrong! I thought you knew how much I love you! But you don't. I thought you were different from other guys, but you're not. I trusted you more than I trust anyone. I allowed you in my life as I've never allowed anyone, but it's too late. I forgot my pain because you were next to me. I realized all men weren't the same because of you. You taught me so much! You were my teacher, my best friend, and my brother, but now everything is gone!" She cries violently, falling on her belly onto the bed, still holding the phone.

Zahid goes quiet, and his tears start to flow.

"Good luck," Sarah says through her sobs. "I wish you all the best. I will pray for you that you'll be safe wherever you want to go. But remember one thing, my heart and my door will always be open for you. Any time you want to come back, I will wait for you. It doesn't matter when you come; I'll wait for you for the rest of my life. My love for you is endless." She cries loudly for a few moments, then says, "Bye. Go take your train. Be strong, I will be with you anywhere you go, in your heart." Then she hangs up the phone and turns it off. Then she drops to bended knee and begins praying passionately.

"God, wasn't he meant to be mine? I thought you gave him to me to heal my pain! To help me forget everything. I did forget, but now I feel more pain than ever." She can't continue to pray. She drops to the floor and cries from deep in her heart.

Zahid sits on the ground of the train station, emotions racing, tears trickling, waiting for his train.

At one in the morning, Sarah is still disconsolate on her bed. The door softly opens, and she sits up. The room and hallway are dark; she can't see who stands in the doorway and is scared to ask who it is. Her breathing quickens. The person steps inside and leans against the wall. Sarah goes to speak, but her voice is gone. She swallows hard several times and tries again.

"Who is it? What do you want?" The person at the door turns on the light. It is Zahid. She doesn't move, and he realizes her eyes are closed.

"It's me," Zahid says. He walks to the bed and hugs her. Many emotions swirl around Sarah's mind, but she sits still, not even able to return the hug. "I'm really sorry about everything."

"Thank you," is all she can say. "Thank you. Thank you."

They hold each other for several minutes. Then Zahid wordlessly prepares for bed, and they go to sleep in their usual manner.

For the next little while, they continue as they always have, but a week after Zahid's return, they have their first kiss. The following week Zahid prepares a wonderful meal for her, and the relationship becomes intimate, but Sarah doesn't feel as good after sex. She gets dizzy, vomits, and one time even falls unconscious. Zahid gets worried.

Sarah assures him that she'll be fine, but he becomes very conscious of her reactions and begins asking how she's feeling not only after their intimate encounters but even during the act itself. Worried for his feelings, she can't bring herself to tell him the truth, and finally, secretly, begins seeking out a psychologist and a gynecologist for advice.

***

Sarah and Zahid's home is full of people. They celebrate Eid Al-Adha as well as the Ethiopian new year. Sarah wears a hijab to make Zahid happy and cooks several Ethiopian traditional dishes. Everyone eats, talks, and laughs. People reminisce about people and holidays past in their respective homes. Some of them pay tribute to Sarah and Zahid's love for each other and respect each other's religion.

***

The first year in Italy passes, and then the second. Sarah's visa is enhanced, and she receives the right to work legally and even travel. A third-year pass. Later in her and Zahid's fourth year together, she receives word that her sister Meron has passed away. Sarah buys a plane ticket and, for the first time since leaving, returns to Ethiopia. The loss overshadows the trip, and everywhere she goes, reminds Sarah of her sister. Her mother takes Sarah to a church outside of the city and rents a small private, adjoining cottage. They stay for a week, going into the church to pray, and taking the holy water. Her mother knows Sarah has a Muslim boyfriend, but she never brings it up.

***

Zahid waits for his lover at Fiumicino airport in Italy. He holds a lovely bouquet of red roses and white baby's breath in his hand, his hair is cut, and he is nicely dressed. Sarah finally comes through the gate

230

with her luggage, and he walks to her; he gives her the flowers, and they embrace, then head for home.

* * *

Sarah's phone buzzes and rings on the floor beside the bed, and she shimmies over to pick it up. It's Liya.

"Hi, Liya, how are you? It's been so long…"

Liya's voice returns, small and distorted by the phone, but unmistakable. "Sorry, Sari, I've been so busy."

"Are you still working in the same home?"

"Yes, but I'm tired of it."

"I know, being a maid is tough work."

"You're lucky; you never have to work like the rest of us."

"Umm, it's not the same job, but it's still pretty hard."

"Sari don't even compare it. At least after work, you can go home. Me, I stay in Signora's house six days a week. Only one day do I have a break. Cleaning the whole house, cooking, laundry…"

"I know it's not easy. I'm sorry, Liya, but you'll get through it. How is everyone? Did Aida get to the UK safely?"

"Mazaa is working. Also, as a maid. She stays most of the time at her workplace. We spend most of our break days together. Kaleb works at an ice plant. They freeze and bag ice. Every day he gets sick from the cold; it's terrible. He tried several times to go to the UK, but they turned him back because of his fingerprints. He went to Germany, the same thing. This road is a block. Aida had an exceedingly difficult time getting into the UK."

"I'm really sorry to hear that. What happed to Aida? Is she okay?"

"It's between you and me, but when she left Italy, she was three months pregnant."

"Oh, no! Really? That must have been so hard."

"When she got Calais, she stayed in the house of an old man. A lot of immigrants go to this town, and this man is known for taking in pregnant women and women with small children. He doesn't feed them; he just gives them a place to sleep. Charities help him with money and packed food, but Aida said he often ate food himself and

231

didn't give any to the women, and he simply pocketed the money. When Aida was in that awful man's house, there were more than ten pregnant women and five women with newborn children. Some of the pregnant women delivered their babies right there while they were waiting for the smugglers. If they went to the hospital, the French government take your babies and give them up for adoption. There are a lot of moms who lost their kids that way. They can't fight it because they don't have documents. They don't even know who ended up with their kids."

"That's awful!" Sarah gasps into the small phone.

"I know. It's terrible. It's terrible for the people without kids too. The women and men without children have to sleep in the jungle outside of town. Some people get bitten by snakes."

"Oh, my God!" Sarah almost puts the phone down and brings her hand to her face.

"Aida stayed with the old man for four months. Many days she only ate one tomato with salt the whole day. The smugglers came to the house and took her money three times, but two of those times, they were caught and went to jail before they could come and get her.

"At the beginning of her pregnancy, a lot of the immigrants and smugglers were good to her, helping her into cars and things, but after her belly started to really show, no one wanted to travel with her because she couldn't run as well, and they didn't want to get caught because of her. She was abandoned by everyone. After her smugglers got caught by the police, she started trying by herself. Every night at two in the morning, she would walk by herself to the truck stop where smugglers sneak people into the backs of semis while the drivers sleep or make purchases. And every night, they would send her away because no one wanted to travel with her. While she was at the old man's house, one of the pregnant women went to the hospital to give birth, but the baby got taken. She came home without her baby, and Aida freaked out. She was almost seven months. She said she cried day and night."

"So..." Sarah interrupted. "What happened? Did she get to the UK? Is she still in that awful place?"

"Listen to this. After all that, one night, she goes to the truck stop and actually convinces the smuggler to put her on a truck with eight Arab guys. She asks them for help up onto a pile of boxes in the truck, but instead, they threw her out the back, down to the road."

"What?"

"She is lucky she landed on some boxes. The smuggler saw it, barked at the Arabs, and helped her back in. He closed the door, but the Arab guys started yelling through the door that they didn't want to travel with a pregnant woman, and while they're yelling, the driver came back and heard them and caught them. But he didn't see Aida, who was up on top of the boxes!"

"What? So, she made it!?"

"Yes! She rode the whole way by herself. She said it was very uncomfortable, and she was hungry. But by God's help, she got into the UK. When the driver found her in the back the next day and saw how pregnant she was, he felt sorry for her, and he bought her lunch." Liya laughs.

"How is she now?"

"She was in the hospital for a month, but after all of that sacrifice, she gave birth to a healthy, beautiful daughter."

"God has mercy. Can you please send me her number? I want to call her."

"I will, and I will send you the baby picture." Liya pauses. "After all that she did to you, you still care about her."

"I don't blame her for anything. She was in love."

"Wow, Okay." Impressed, Liya's lower lip sticks out a bit as she nods. "I didn't find out about Aida and Kaleb's relationship until after you left, but they never admitted it by mouth. Only by stomach."

***

After returning from Ethiopia, Sarah attends church regularly. She also starts talking about religion. Zahid notices the change but doesn't want to say anything. One day as they prepare the evening meal at home, Sarah asks him a question.

"When we have a baby, what will his or her name be?"

"I never thought about it," Zahid responds, "but if she's a girl, I like the name Sofia."

"Ahh, a Muslim name," Sarah says quietly. "Do you want our kids to become Muslim?"

"I didn't mean to give a Muslim name; I just love the name. It's my mother's name. But they can choose what they want to be."

"My kids have to be Christian," she says with resolve.

"Don't worry about it. When the time comes, it will figure itself out. We're too young to think about kids now." Then he hugs her and holds her tight.

Sarah and Zahid finish their fourth year in Italy, and Sarah begins feeling that she's caught in a loop. There is nothing new in her life. She works, she goes home, she goes back to work, goes back home. The routine never changes.

One day she is sitting in the park by herself and turns her phone off.

"What is my life?" She asks herself. "Is this my future? More of this? Become a housewife? Raise kids? Have my expenses paid by him? Oh, God, I can't. I'm not born for this. I must go back to school, but how? Maybe it's impossible. But I didn't make all those sacrifices for this."

She decides to take steps toward her longtime dream of being an actress and starts seeking information about acting schools. She doesn't know how Zahid will respond to her desire to act. In all their talk of dreams and ambitions, she never mentioned this one.

"It's my dream; he must support me," she tells herself. "Otherwise, I will choose my dream." She gets up and walks a little bit, and then she sits again. "But I love him. I can't do that." She stays at the park, thinking for some time. Finally, she decides that Zahid must come first, but she can't bring herself to head home. She stays and procrastinates, watching the people walking and playing.

***

Zahid finishes cleaning their room, then does laundry in some small machines owned by people on a lower floor. He brings the clean clothes back upstairs and starts to fold them on the bed.

Kidist walks in.

"Where is Sari?"

"I think she's still at work."

"Wow, she works long days. She's the strongest girl I ever met."

"She is." He smiles. "I'm the luckiest guy on earth."

"You're nice, too; she's so lucky. You clean the room; you cook, you do laundry. Most Habesha men can't do any of this."

"She works hard; I must help her. I care for her."

"A lot of people talk about you guys. Everyone is so jealous."

"Why?"

"The way you guys treat each other, respecting each other, everything you guys do; you are an example of a good couple. You're meant to be with each other."

"Thanks, that's why I said I'm lucky. Before I had her, I was honestly nothing, but after finding her, my life changed. She forces me to go to school! If it wasn't for her, I couldn't do it. She influences my energy, the way I view the world; she makes me a stronger man. Now I feel like I'm full. She's my other half. My soulmate."

"They say 'behind every successful man is a strong woman.'" Kidist smiles.

"That's one hundred percent true, but this kind of woman, ya Allah, they are few. The men who find them are the lucky ones. Alhamdulillah, I'm one of them."

"That is nice of you, saying all the good thing about her."

"I could go on and on."

"You said it well. Oh, my gosh. I forgot why I came here. Do you have oil?"

"Since when do you have to ask? Come in and get whatever you want. This is your home."

"I'm not asking if I can take it," she laughs, "I'm just asking if you have it. I always feel like it's my home. Sarah makes that very clear.

Always when she needs something, she comes over. She doesn't even ask me if I have it, she just comes and gets it."

"She's always doing crazy things, that's why I love her. If she loves you, that's who she is," Zahid places the oil before Kidist, and she takes it and leaves.

Zahid finishes folding all the clothes and prepares dinner. By 9:00 p.m., she still hasn't arrived, and dinner is getting cold. He calls her, but her phone is off. "What's going on?" He starts to wonder. "Did something happen to her? I hope she's okay."

***

Sarah is still sitting in the park, watching the different people walking by. Some people walk their dogs, some of them are couples, and sometimes whole families pass by. She watches them but isn't really watching them.

***

Zahid finishes eating his portion of the dinner, turns on the TV, and lays down on the bed. He flips the TV channel always, as though playing a game that requires it.

Kidist lets herself in to return the oil bottle and puts it down.

"Thanks." The mood in the room has changed, and she regards Zahid on the bed. "Sarah's not come home yet. Is she okay?"

Zahid swivels lazily and sits up on the side of the bed. "I called her several times, but her phone is off."

"I hope she's fine. Maybe she got kept late at work? You know their work is crazy if she has late customers."

"Yeah, but she's never been late like this."

"Maybe the train is broke, like usual?"

"Oh yeah, I forgot about that. Italian trains." His smile isn't entirely convincing. "Yeah, that's probably it. Thank you."

***

Sarah turns on her phone to look at the time, and when she sees it, she gets up and runs like a child, typing in Zahid's number.

"Amore, I'm sorry!"

"Amore, are you okay?"

"Yes, I will tell you when I come."

"Okay. Get home safe."

While she is on the train, Sarah calls her coworker Anna and speaks to her in Italian.

"Anna, do you know of any acting schools here?"

"Acting school? Why do you need an acting school?" Anna responds sarcastically.

"You know what, never mind."

"Sarah, are you okay? You seem upset."

Sarah doesn't answer.

"What's wrong with you, is there a problem? Tell me. You were quiet at work today."

"It's personal, thanks for asking."

"Are you with someone? If you can't talk, text me. Please, Sarah."

"No, I'm by myself on the train."

"From where? You left early."

"Yes." Sarah's thoughts feel like a balloon about to burst in her chest, and she pours it all out to Anna over the phone, including her many isolated hours at the park. "I don't know how to tell him."

"I know you love him, but don't throw your dreams away, just tell him. He will help you and encourage you. You're scared because you love him, and I understand that. But let me tell you the truth about the film industry here, Sarah; here almost all the stories are made for us White people. For people of color, it's very hard."

Sarah's quivers with unexpected emotion. "You mean my complexion won't allow me to work in the Italian film industry?" She collects herself with a joke. "I'll cover myself with white paint. They'll never know."

"Unfortunately, it's the truth, Sarah; I'm not making a joke. I want to let you know ahead of time. I mean, even at the salon, you know how some of the older women treat you. Forget the film industry."

"Oh, my God, that lady last week," Sarah recalls with annoyance. The woman had booked an appointment over the phone, assuming Sarah was Italian because of her name. Upon walking in the door and seeing her, she had brazenly declared that she didn't want to be touched by a Negro. Sarah's co-workers were horrified, and after a pitched debate, the woman was eventually asked to leave.

"I'm sorry about that. How are you doing? We all felt awful for you, but I never asked you how you're doing?"

"I'm fine. I'm used to it. I don't care what people think. If they hate my skin color so much, why do they all go to the beach to look more like me?" Anna laughs.

"The old women don't like my color, and the young men like it too much," Sarah says, cleverly referencing the catcalls and whistles that are a regular part of her commute to work. "So, I guess it balances out."

"You have a beautiful color; I wish I had your tone."

"Go to a church in Ethiopia. God will bless you. Your heart will get lighter, and your skin will get darker," Sarah starts laughing loudly before she even finishes the sentence. People on the train turn and look at her, but she doesn't notice them.

"You know, Sarah; I miss your jokes on my days off. You were born to be an artist, not a hairstylist

"Being a hairstylist is a type of art, too. But thanks."

"Don't forget, just tell your lover, as I said. Be honest. Also, I have honest suggestion. If you want to be an actress, America is the right place for you. In that country, an all-encompassing story is written. Go there. Why do you get tired of all this effort and stumble over something? Tell him and he will support you. Love works when you talk openly about everything. Dream alone cannot be realized, it takes effort, so you must strive to make them come true."

"Thanks for your advice. I'll think about it, but I don't know."

"Think about it and tell him."

***

Sarah opens the door and sees her portion of dinner laid out on a blanket, along with two candles that have long since been blown out. She goes to him and kisses him.

"Thank you so much, *amore mio*. I was so hungry."

She pours some water over her hands and into a bucket to clean them.

Zahid watches her, "Since when do you eat dinner without changing your clothes?"

"*Amore*, I'm so tired and hungry."

Sarah brings her food onto the bed, and they both lay back to watch TV. Zahid strokes her hair, and Sarah tentatively begins to speak.

"I want to tell you something, but if it's too late, I understand. It can wait."

"*Amore*, you can tell me anything you want." He kisses her. "Please. Tell me."

"It is okay; let's sleep."

Zahid hugs her tight and kisses her. "*Amore mia*. I've been waiting all evening to find out what's going on. Please, tell me."

She stays quiet.

Suddenly he jumps off the bed and gets on his knees beside her, startling her with his enthusiasm. He brings his head close to her belly. "Oh, ya Allah, are you pregnant? Please tell me, yes. I'll be the happiest man on earth! Please tell me, don't worry. I'll try my best to make you happy. And I'll be a great daddy!"

Sarah remains quiet, and her eyes begin to glisten. Only six months earlier, she had discovered she *was* pregnant, but her gynecologist warned her there might be complications because of scar tissue from the abortion. She had waited, not wanting to hurt Zahid, and sure enough, the baby miscarried in the second month. She couldn't bring herself to tell him.

Zahid looks at her, quizzingly, "Are you crying? *Amore*, please don't confuse me, tell me."

She's not able to speak, and he realizes something serious is going on. He stands up and leans on the bed. "I'm really sorry. Look, forget it. If you don't want to talk, forget it. No problem. It can wait." He climbs back onto the bed and lies down beside her with a long embrace.

Sarah begins visiting acting schools to see them and learn about them. It's thrilling to be in the environments and feel the energy of the places, but they're all vastly out of her price range. And whenever she tells her friends, they poke fun at her. "Are you out of your mind? Do you want to be an actress? You should see a psychiatrist." A lot of people tell her to warn her that it's a bad choice.

She becomes frustrated. "Why do they say that? They don't know whether I have any talent. And they don't know my drive."

Getting into an Italian acting school becomes a dream for Sarah, but it feels like an impassable wall stands between her and it. She becomes frustrated and starts to get uncharacteristically grouchy. Even at the salon, people ask her if there's a problem, but she doesn't know how to answer them.

Finally, she knocks on her boss's door and approaches him about taking time off for a vacation to Mexico. She also asks for an employer letter to the Mexican embassy as part of her tourist visa application. He is surprised but agrees.

Later at her hair station, a call comes in from Zahid. "*Amore,* I don't feel well, can you come home?"

"*Amore*, I will be there as soon as possible. Is there someone around to help till I get there?"

"No one is around, and I feel short of breath."

"Let me call emergency."

"No, there's no need. I can wait until you come. Don't worry; I will be fine."

Not wanting to take the long circuitous path home by train and bus, Sarah asks around if anyone can give her a ride. Her boss comes over.

"Don't worry; I'll call you a taxi. On me."

"Thanks."

She climbs into the car and calls Zahid again. He doesn't answer. She keeps trying but nothing. She calls Zahid's cousin Hammed, who has been staying with them, but he also doesn't answer. Sarah begins to panic and urges the driver to go faster.

Arriving at the building, she runs up the stairs and down the hall to her home. She fumbles with her key in the lock and pauses to breathe and collect herself. "Please, God," she asks, "let him be okay." She twists the key and throws open the door, then stops. The room is filled with flowers and candles. An Ethiopian love song plays over the TV, which is connected by a short cord to a cell phone. On the bed is non-alcoholic champagne with two glasses. But there is no one there. *Am I dreaming?* Then she turns back to the hallway and calls out, "*Amore*, where are you?"

From inside the room, Zahid's voice says, "Happy anniversary, *amore mia*."

She whips back around, and Zahid finishes crawling out from underneath the bed.

Sarah stands there, taking it in, him, and the whole room. "Oh, my gosh, *amore*, I was so scared! I didn't know if you were alive or dead or what!" She hugs him tight and says, "I don't know what to say."

He hugs her back, being careful not to crush the one flower he holds in his hand.

"Thanks so much, the same to you, my love." Then she kisses him.

"I'm sorry for scaring you; the whole thing was a set-up," Zahid beams. "I called your boss and told him what I was about to do. I ordered the taxi too, and he agreed to pretend he did it. The driver was already outside when I called."

"You are *so* bad! I can't believe you did this to me." She pulls him in tight. "This time, you got me. But our anniversary is next week."

"Yes, but we have to go to that wedding in Venice, did you forget that?"

"Oh, shit, I totally forgot."

241

"And that reminds me," Zahid says, holding out the flower. "This is for you."

She takes the flower fondly, but something catches her eye. Wrapped around the stem of the rose is a white gold ring with a small diamond. Her eyes get wide, and she looks up at him.

"Will you marry me?" He asks and laughs.

The look on her face only adds to the humor.

Zahid drops to one knee. "Will you marry me, *amore mia*?"

"Are you sure you want me?" She asks. In answer, he pulls her in close. "Yes. Yes, *amore*," is all Sarah can manage, as she pulls the ring gently on to her finger and sinks into his embrace.

They hold each other for a long time. When they finally release their embrace, he guides her to the bed, and she sits down to collect herself. A hand grabs her foot from underneath.

"CONGRATULATIONS!" She jumps up in fright and scampers to the door. Hammed's head appears like a newborn baby, and he climbs out from under the bed, followed by Kidist.

"Oh, my God! You guys are so crazy!" Sarah shouts.

"And happy anniversary!" Kidist adds.

"You're the one who taught us to be crazy. -" Hammad retorts. "You think you are the only one who knows how to make a surprise?"

"Yes, we got you!" Kidist says.

"How many people are under there??" Sarah demands, grinning from ear to ear.

"Just us, I promise."

Sarah bends down and scans under the bed to make sure.

"At least you guys could have answered my calls. I thought you weren't home. I thought he'd died." Then she looks back at Zahid. "Amore, you know how much I love you; why did you do this to me? You could have just said something simple. I swear to God I was so scared; I couldn't even bring myself to open the door! I was praying when I put the key in the lock." She took them all in. "But you guys just wait, I will pay you back big for this, don't forget that. You guys got me today."

Kidist closes in on her and looks at the ring with joy. The two ogle it extensively. Then Sarah hugs Zahid again, and he kisses her in front of the guests, which makes her shy. She glances at Hammed and Kidist with embarrassment.

"They know we're a couple," he says, and smiles. "Your mind still thinks like it's in Ethiopia. But even there, young people kiss each other outside. We're in the west now."

"It doesn't matter how long I live here; I'll always love my culture. It's about respecting other peoples' feelings too. Think about poor Hammad here." Now everyone laughs. "And poor lonely Kidist who's man won't be home for hours."

"Sarah knows the real traditional way; you're the right one sister," Hammad says. "Because we have a good culture, but we are adapting to this western culture and losing what we have."

"It's true; we're lost." Kidist agrees.

Zahid shakes his head, "I believe that way too about most things, but sometimes we have rules that aren't necessary. Everyone knows we kiss when we get home. Who does it hurt?"

Sarah points out that, "Our culture is wonderful. And unique. It should be protected. We should appreciate it. Who else has thirteen months in the year? What have other nations in Africa that never been colonized? Who else has more than eighty dialect, and beautiful places like Axum and Lalibela."

"If Sarah starts talking about her country, no one can stop her," Zahid chides. "Let's celebrate."

***

In Venice, Sarah's skills are put to good use. She finishes a long morning of freestyling by doing the bride's hair and make-up, as friends and family gather at a nearby facility. More than three hundred people have arrived, but it's a small gathering by Habesha standards, where five hundred or more guests are considered standard. The older women wear traditional Ethiopian outfits. The young ones wear formal western dresses. Sarah wears a dark blue, long dress with black, high heel shoes.

After Sarah finishes the bride's hair, Zahid walks inside. *"Amore,* you've gotta be tired, that was a lot."

"Amore, I'll be fine; I love doing it."

The bride looks back and forth between her mirror and Sarah, "Sari, it means a lot to me that you flew from Rome to make me this pretty. And you won't let me pay you! You really are a good friend."

"Please don't make it a big deal, it's nothing." Sarah looks at Zahid, "Amore, let's go for a walk."

Zahid and Sarah hold each other's hands and walk for a little bit. They pass a coffee shop and step in. Sarah orders an espresso; Zahid orders a cappuccino. Zahid looks over at his fiancé with a wrinkled brow.

"Amore, since when do you drink espresso?"

Sarah smiles. "This is my last week in Italy. I don't want to miss it."

"Oh, my God, just one week, I'm gonna miss you." He takes their cups, and the couple moves to a small, comfortable table.

"Amore, me too."

"Oh, I forgot to tell you. Earlier I called Daniel in Mexico. He invites you to visit Acapulco."

She strokes his hand. "Thanks, my love, if it weren't for you, I wouldn't be able to do it."

"We need each other. I want to support you. We've already traveled a long road, why stop now? I don't want you to give up on your dream for anything. I'll be there for you for the rest of my life."

"Oh, *Amore,*" she gets up and hugs him. "I'm glad your flight is so soon after mine."

"Oh, Ya Allah, yes. I can't imagine that house without you." Then he grows quiet. Emotion begins to grip him.

"Amore, I can stay; I don't want you to be sad."

"No, don't even think about it, be strong. I'm not pretending it doesn't hurt. I'm hurting. But this isn't me saying 'don't go.' You're doing the right thing. And it hurts. That's all."

Sarah's eyes brim tears, "After you come back from Ethiopia, think about moving to another city." Then she takes his hand and sits next to him. She looks into his eyes.

Zahid looks back at her and sees her emotions brewing and roiling. He hugs her tight. "Amore, think positive. We'll be fine; it's just for a couple of years until you get your green card."

"Hopefully, they won't take long. I'll come back the day I get my paper, we can get married in the court. I'll wear a long white bridal dress with my hair all done up, and I will walk to you." She takes his left arm in both of hers. "And give my word to be the best wife ever, for the rest of my life. Oh, mi Amore, you'll be such a handsome groom."

Sarah's phone buzzes, and Zahid's phone plays a little tune immediately afterward. Sarah's phone buzzes again, and she glances down at the messages popping up on the screen. The wedding! They suddenly realize they're missing the event they traveled five hours to see. The two lovers scramble to their feet, rush out the door and down the street to the ballroom.

Chapter Twelve

Z ahid lays on the bed. He puts the pillow on top of his face, and his tears soak into the fabric. Hammad sits outside in the hallway by himself, leaning against the wall. Kidist's boyfriend, Elias, passes Zahid's room on his way home and sees Hammad in the hallway. He says, "Hey," but Hammad says nothing. He walks into his room and notices his girlfriend sitting on the floor, grieving.

"What happened in this building today? I said 'hey' to Hammad, but he didn't answer me, and you are here crying. What happened?"

Kidist is silent. He insists his girlfriend answers, "I'm asking you!"

"Sarah," she says simply, then covers her eyes with a tissue.

"Sarah, what?"

"She left."

This makes no sense to Elias, and he looks at his girlfriend. "I don't understand what you're talking about?" She is slow to speak. "You know what..." With a backhanded wave of his hand, he heads out of his own home toward Zahid's room.

Kidist gets up and calls him. "Please come back. I will tell you. He's not in a good mood, please don't bother him. She went to

Mexico. I don't think she's going to come back; she might go to the USA."

"Why do you say that? Did she tell you?"

"I'm just thinking. A lot of people when they go to Mexico, they don't come back."

"Sarah loves Zahid; she is not going. She is not like other girls. She will be back; she went maybe for a vacation. Also, she has the best-paid job, a generous fiancé, and us; she has a good life. She even told me once she has a plan to open a hair salon here."

He steps back into his own home and closes the door.

Kidist doesn't answer.

Zahid holds a letter in his hand, and with his other hand, he cleans his face. There is a knock on the door, but each rap feels like another knife in Zahid's chest.

"Can you please leave me for a while? I want to be by myself."

Hammad steps away from the door and goes back to his seat in the hallway.

Zahid opens the envelope Sarah gave him at the Fiumicino airport. "*Amore*, you know how much I love you; I don't even think of life without you for a second. It doesn't matter where life takes me. My soul is with you anywhere you go. I will be with you for the rest of my life. Do you remember when we were last week in Venice at the wedding what I told you, I want to be your bride one day with a beautiful long dress? I'm your queen, and you are my king; it doesn't matter how long we stay apart. I believe in you, and I trust you more than I trust myself. No one can take your place on this Earth; I promise you in the name of God.

"After five years here, we have almost the same life as the first month we arrived in Italy. We're not living our dreams here; we're building someone else's dream. As soon as I get my green card in the USA, I will come back to marry you; then we can start our life there. Our life. I will continue my education, and you're going to continue too. I want to see your smile when we make our dreams come true.

"We made a lot of sacrifices to get here, to pursue our desires, and honor our dreams. We must be determined and strong;

otherwise, why come this far? I appreciate you supporting me more than you'll ever know. With God, I'll be fine. Just pray for me. I'm lucky to have you in my life. I love you more than any word can express. Nothing can describe my feelings toward you. You're my life, my everything. I'll see you soon. Also, I forgot, have fun on your trip back home tomorrow and say hi to all the family. I've already packed your luggage. I'll call you when I get to my hotel. Check your black jacket pocket. Goodbye, my precious, precious love. Your queen."

He holds the paper with two hands and pulls it into his face, pressing it against his skin. He kisses the paper, then moves off the bed to check his jacket pocket, as instructed. He finds a wallet with their picture printed on the side. His tear-stained cheeks smile broadly, and he looks intently at the wallet for some time. Then he opens the door.

Hammad gets up, "Can I come in now?" Without speaking, Zahid waves him in. Hammad enters respectfully, watching his cousin. He looks at the wallet, which Zahid doesn't seem to know what to do with. "Can I see it?" Zahid pauses, then hands it across to him. Hammad turns it over and peers at the image. "Wow, how did she print the picture right on to the leather? It is a nice picture."

"That was our first week as a real couple, one of our first kisses. She took it on her phone. That was four years ago, can you believe it?" He takes the wallet back and looks deeply into the picture of his love. "She is such a sweet person, so different from other women. I don't know how to live in this house without her. I'm glad my flight's tomorrow."

"You should go to a different city; otherwise, it will be hard for you."

"Yeah, that's my plan too. And Sarah's. She said the same thing. She told me not to stay in Rome because I'll see reminders of her everywhere I go. But even if I move, anywhere I go, the hardest part will be not having her around until I go to be with her.

***

Sarah disembarks from the plane in Mexico City airport and heads for the baggage area and pick up. A driver waits for her holding a large card with her first and last name.

In the taxi, Sarah gets right to work, asking the driver questions about the city, beginning with safety considerations. When they arrive at the hotel, Sarah marvels at how drastically her living situation is changing. From a small closet to a four-star hotel room. From no running water to a large bathroom with a creamy white tub and a separate stand-alone shower. She enjoys the luxury of a bath and then heads downstairs to find a phone with which she can make an international call.

After her conversations with Zahid, she pushes away her fatigue and heads out to find something to eat. Nearby is a small local restaurant, and she walks in and takes a seat. The restaurant is an authentic, traditional Mexican place, and most of the items on the menu are entirely foreign to her. There is a tourist section on the menu containing the word "pizza." It's the only word she recognizes, and she orders one.

There are a lot of tourists sitting in the restaurant, large groups, and couples, but Sarah is the only person sitting by herself. She people-watches and takes in all the little decorating details in the colorful room. After several minutes, the server brings the pizza and puts it on the table. Sarah looks at it. Unlike the thin-crust pizzas Sarah is used to in Rome, this crust is incredibly thick and covered with loads of cheese and sauce. She cuts into it, and the small pools of oil atop the pizza trickles down over the uncooked dough, sliding back and forth beneath her knife. Five years in Italy reveal their stamp on Sarah's life, and she calls the server over to order something else.

The next day, Sarah walks around Mexico City. The city is crowded and enormous. The streets are congested. People sell and consume all manner of food in the streets, tacos, burritos, corn, sweets, and drinks. Sarah is surprised to see people eating in the street; it's a major social faux pas in Ethiopia, especially for females, and it wasn't something she saw commonly in Italy either. She also sees people selling jewelry and approaches one of the tables. She purchases a small necklace with a circular pendant of the Virgin Mary's face and slips it over her head. "Santa Maria, help me," she quietly breathes.

Sarah spends several days walking around and looking at Mexico City, but the experience fails to help shake her lonesomeness for her fiancé, and her phone calls to Zahid increase to three per day. She finds herself resenting her expectations and the city's failure to meet them.

***

At the end of her first week in Mexico, Sarah travels to Acapulco to meet her friend Daniel. Daniel had met Zahid first, and the two became friends in a school eighty kilometers from Bahir Dar. Then Daniel's family moved to the city, and he met Sarah in school. It had been a most unexpected and pleasant surprise when he learned the two were engaged. He had been the first in their circle of acquaintances to leave Ethiopia and has lived in Acapulco for eight years. A friendly smile crosses his face as he greets her at the airport.

"I can't believe it. It was always my dream to visit Acapulco," Sarah sighs.

"But why?"

"Do you remember the TV show 'Acapulco'?"

"Yes, I think so. Kind of."

"That TV series made me dream about Acapulco. I always wanted to come here. I used to think Acapulco was one of the most beautiful cities on the earth," she laughs. "It was everything to me. I thought Hollywood was in Acapulco."

At that, Daniel lets out a full laugh. "When we're kids, our imagination is so powerful."

As they drive, Sarah absorbs the road, the palm trees, the mountains, and the clean, blue Pacific coast. It looks very much like she imagined, and the combination of gorgeous scenery and pleasant company lifts her spirits. Daniel lives in the mountains and can see both the city and the ocean from his home.

They turn into a long driveway, lined with trees.

"You live here?" Sarah asks.

Daniel smiles and continues looking ahead.

The driveway leads past an impressive swimming pool, up to a large creamy white Spanish-style villa, with large windows, rounded archways, and a red, ceramic tile roof.

"Daniel, you have a beautiful house! It looks so expensive."

"It's not bad."

After they rest for a couple of hours, Daniel takes her back into the city for a whirlwind trip through the tourist areas, and past the best restaurants, hotels, clubs, and stores. They park the car at the ocean and get out to walk. The weather is beautiful and hot, with a cool breeze coming in off the ocean. Sarah sees a couple walking together, holding hands, and immediately her heart and mind are in Rome with Zahid.

Daniel is speaking but may as well be in a different country. Sarah feels his hand touch her arm.

"Sarah?"

"Oh, sorry... I was a bit lost in my head."

"What are you thinking about?"

"A lot of things. Reminders of home if I'm honest."

Daniel looks over at the couple holding hands.

"Are you all right here by yourself? It must be hard."

"I'm fine," Sarah says believably.

"I hope the reminders are good," he laughs. "I didn't bring you here to depress you."

Sarah agrees with a measured laugh. Sarah meets several of Daniel's friends and explores Mexican culture with him. He takes her to a friend's child's birthday party, and the drive takes them past some beautiful resorts, palm trees, and beachside properties.

Daniel notices Sarah's rapt attention and glowing nostalgia.

"Remind you of Bahir Dar?" Sarah hasn't seen palm trees since leaving Ethiopia, except for the one time in Libya, Sudan, and here in Acapulco.

"Yes," she says dreamily, lost in memories of watching the beautiful trees lining the streets of St. George from the backseat of her father's car.

As they near the birthday home, Sarah notices the beautiful cars arriving for the party. Daniel parks his car in front of the house, and they are ushered to the backyard. The family's home is even bigger than Daniel's, and the backyard goes right down to the beach. The many guests come and go from the house to the beach in swimsuits and towels, passing through and around the centerpiece of the backyard: a giant, ivory-colored tent giving shade to long tables festooned with colorful drapery, balloons, and trays of food. The ceiling of the tent is also decorated with balloons, and right in the center hangs a large horse-shaped pinata, which Sarah assumes is strictly decorative.

Daniel approaches the parents of the birthday boy in the tent, and Sarah follows. Their son looks like a little angel, dressed all in white with silver sparkles, sparkly silver shoes, and a white and silver sombrero. Daniel introduces Sarah, and they welcome her warmly. The mother offers them two creamy beverages. Daniel takes them and offers one to Sarah.

"I'm so sorry; I don't drink alcohol," Sarah says in Italian.

Daniel responds in Spanish.

"There's no alcohol in this. It's a traditional Mexican drink called Horchata. It is homemade. A mix of creamy rice and cinnamon flavor and water and vanilla."

Sarah takes the drink and looks at him. Then to satisfy his sparkling eyes, she takes a sip. It's very sweet, and the cinnamon gives it a delicate flavor.

They approach the food tables, and Daniel offers Sarah a plate. Ahead of them stretches a marvelous assortment of tacos, carnitas, pozole, quesadillas, chilaquiles, huarache, nachos, guacamole, molote, sopapillas; it seems endless. A nearby beverage table sports large clear containers of pink, brown, red, lemon, green, white, and cream-colored beverages. Next to that is a table splendiferously arrayed with a cornucopia of desserts, all arranged around a large, work-of-art of a cake.

Sarah takes a tiny portion from every item on the dinner table and sits with Daniel, awash in new friends and tastes.

At one point, the children are assembled to take down the pinata, and Sarah watches the event with almost childlike fascination. Against her protests, family members pull her out of her chair, blindfold her, and hand her the stick for a turn. She carefully uses the stick like a blind man's cane to find the rope above the paper Mache animal, then brings it crashing down on the pinata from the top down. The innovation elicits an enormous cheer from the laughing crowd and joyful applause.

At the end of the day, they head home. Daniel is driving, and Sarah sits in the passenger seat, resting her head against the window.

"Thanks, Dani, for bringing me here, to this beautiful place. Oh my God, this has been a wonderful day."

"Mexicans have a very authentic culture," Daniel responds, "rooted in kindness and simple pleasures. It's hard not to fall in love with it. Of course, there's trouble and hardship here too, but you can see for yourself. My travel to the West ended. Why would I want anything different from this?"

There is silence in the car as Sarah considers this.

"I'm so glad your schedule was free to show me around these last few days. When do you go back to work? Will you be at the house tomorrow?"

"I will be, yes."

Sarah turns her head so that her back rests on the window, and she can see Daniel.

"Daniel, what do you do? It must be a good job."

Daniel says nothing, and an uncharacteristically severe expression masks any indication of an answer.

"We'll be home at any moment. You must be exhausted."

***

Zahid is finishing his first week in Ethiopia in eight years. Born in a small town, he was the fourth of eight siblings, with three brothers and four sisters. He is surprised at how much the town has changed. New buildings, new roads, the whole lifestyle of the city seems different. It's like everyone secretly waited for him to leave to reveal their embrace of modernity.

Right away, Zahid asked for information about his friends. A lot of the young men aren't living in town anymore. Some changed cities, some went to South Africa, some followed him on the "Libyan road," and some got married. Zahid feels pangs of pity for the friends named to him who left Ethiopia, knowing all too well the price of discontent.

On his first full day back, Zahid's father had asked about his life and if he had plans to marry. Zahid had evaded with an explanation of the hardship and scarcity of immigration.

"Son, you should marry, you can grow up and build a life together." The father had urged.

Zahid had grown quiet and replied respectfully, absolutely avoiding any mention of Sarah. His parents' rigid devotion to Islam would mean total rejection from the family if his engagement was discovered. Her persistent phone calls from Mexico had led to some close calls, and they had taken to speaking only in Italian, with Zahid explaining to his parents that these were calls from his friends in Rome.

Now, Zahid's father sits on a couch, observing his son. "Zahid, I want to see your kids before I die."

"I'm sorry, Dad, but I'm just not ready to marry now. I have to be focused on my dreams."

"You can do it at the same time, son. And your wife can help you to pursue your dream."

"Marriage is a prison, Dad; just give me more time."

"Look at me." Zahid glances over at his dad. "I'm old. I want you to marry soon. I've chosen a beautiful girl for you, and she's a good Muslim too. She can remind you to pray. She comes from a strong family."

Zahid looks at his father, and panicked energy begins circling in his chest. His younger brother Abdu, sitting next to him, looks up at Zahid. They can sense his alarm.

"I want you to get engaged before you go back to Italy. I've already asked the girl's family, and they say yes. They want to know when we are doing the engagement party. I'm not asking your permission, I'm telling you."

The father rises and walks out. Zahid sits in shock. His brother quietly asks, "Why don't you just tell him you have a fiancé?"

"I don't want to disappoint him. I respect him. But..." Zahid can't decide what to share.

"...Then marry the girl."

"You don't understand how much I love Sarah."

"Okay, so what do you want to do? You don't want to disappoint Dad, and you don't want to lose your heathen fiancé. But you have to choose one."

"It's not easy, Abdu. It's easy to give advice, but..." Zahid lets out a troubled sigh.

***

Sarah stays a week in Acapulco, meeting Daniel's friends and enjoying his social circle. Mexicans love Sarah's easy manner and embrace her fully. She's surprised at how little of a language barrier there is, and how similar Italian is to Mexican Spanish. One of Daniel's friend's wives takes a keen liking to Sarah's hair color, which leads to a conversation about Sarah's work at the salon, which leads to an invitation. Sarah comes to the woman's house and spends five hours cutting and coloring her hair. The couple is enthusiastic about the result, and the husband buys a beautiful gold bracelet that they drop off for Sarah at Daniel's house the next day. Sarah can't deny a burgeoning love for this place, its people, and its ways.

Daniel has made good on an earlier promise to connect Sarah to reliable smugglers who can help her cross the American border.

"These are reliable men. Professionals." Daniel's friend assures him. "Very good at what they do. I'll have them call you."

***

Daniel receives word that Sarah is to travel to the Mexican border city of Reynosa with no more than one handbag, where she will meet her escorts. A photo of her in her travel clothes is requested. There is no information provided beyond that. After a heartfelt farewell to her gracious host at the Acapulco airport, she turns to walk towards the departure gate.

"Wait, Sarah, one more thing." Sarah turns back to Daniel, whose facial expression has taken on a serious thoughtfulness.

"Yes? What?"

"When you arrive at the airport, do what they say, but don't speak. Be a listener, but don't speak."

"Why?"

"The fewer people know about you up there, the better. Let others talk. You listen. Okay?"

Sarah is curious but decides to agree and let it go. She and Daniel hug, and then she walks to the security checkpoint. The next stage of Sarah's journey begins.

***

When she reaches the baggage claim of the Reynosa airport, two men approach her. "Sarah?" She nods at the sound of her name but says nothing. They compare her again to a picture on the taller man's phone, and they beckon her to follow them. Outside they usher her into a parked car and, to Sarah's thinking, drive away with conspicuous speed. One of the men drives, the other sits in the passenger seat, and Sarah sits in the back. She notes the clicking sound of her door locking and resists the urge to test whether the unlock button is disabled.

The two men discuss in Spanish while the driver inspects Sarah in the rearview mirror. "Let's take her to the radio shop."

The other man looks back at her. "Why?"

Sarah listens while looking out the window as casually as she can.

"What do you mean, why?"

"But we know who sent her."

"What do I care?"

The second man's eyes dart back to Sarah and then to the driver. His voice quietens. "She might…" he mouths, pointing up to his ear. The first man laughs.

"Look at her," the second mocks, "does she look Spanish to you? You can smell the jungle on her."

The second man looks back at Sarah.

The first man continues, "If you don't want to, that's up to you. But we can share if you want."

"Okay, but…"

"Did you see her ass when she got in the car?"

Sarah stifles a reaction and continues her listless act.

"That's the only thing I look at. Big tits, no tits, I don't care. She can be a man from the waist up. I don't care. But when they have a nice ass, ooohhh…"

The second man looks back at Sarah again, searching her face for any understanding of the conversation.

"Relax." The driver says jovially. "She'd be kicking the window out by now if she understood this."

Suddenly a cell phone rings, and the driver shifts his weight and his shoulders to keep the car moving straight as he digs into his pocket. He pulls out his phone, and a quick scan of the screen results in a loud curse. "The boss needs us. Let's drop her with the group, and we can get her later."

Sarah's heart is pounding so loud she can hear it in her ears, but she carefully maintains her casual pretense of watching the passing scenery. She suddenly becomes aware of her hand squeezing and rubbing the small religious ornament hanging from her neck, and she slowly softens her grip.

After thirty minutes of driving, they arrive at a large house, the smaller man in the passenger seat exits to open the gate, and the driver parks the car inside the fence. More than fifty immigrants are sitting on the floor of the house in groups. Sarah walks toward a corner and finds a small empty space to sit by herself. She glances around the room, seeing many Latin Americans, but no Habesha.

The driver turns to the passenger and gestures to Sarah. "You see? If she spoke the language, she would sit with them." The passenger looks Sarah over one more time as the two men leave.

The two smugglers arrive at their boss's office, and he walks to the car. The passenger holds open the back door for him, and when he is comfortably seated, the three men drive to a restaurant. They eat and drink together for a couple of hours, then drive back to the house where Sarah and the other immigrants wait.

***

The immigrants are eating a sparse dinner provided by the smugglers and talking to each other. One of the Spanish women talks about the road, and Sarah listens quietly.

The woman says, "I came down this road four more times, every time I see a new smuggler, and we take new roads."

Another woman looks at her, "Why are you making all of this sacrifice?"

"I want to give a better life to my kids. And their father is in love with another woman."

"Where are you from?

"Guatemala. What about you?"

"Salvador."

Something grabs Sarah's attention; another group is talking about a pregnant woman who lost her life on the American border—eaten by a giant snake. Sarah's face involuntarily puckers. She catches herself and lets her face go blank.

The people sitting in the middle of the room talk about how many women get raped on the road by smugglers. How many people lost their money on the road? How many people got killed?

Sarah's anxiety begins to spike, and she feels the dark shadow of depression returning.

Why am I putting myself through this again? She asks herself pointedly. Every cluster of people in the room is talking about the dangers and horrors of the trip. Some of them talk about their worry about being caught by American immigration officers. Sarah says to herself; *I hope the border police catch me before I get killed or something worse.* Then she heads to the restroom.

The three smugglers arrive at the fence and park their car. The two drivers stand behind the boss smuggler in the doorway. The boss smuggler walks inside and brazenly looks at the women. A lot of the women are old and weathered. He is about to step out of the room when he sees two young women emerge from the bathroom. He points his finger at the two women and signals the drivers to take them with him. They march up to Sarah and a young Mexican lady. The smugglers grab each of them, take them out to the car, and drive off. The two women sit in the backseat beside the boss. He tries to talk to the women, but they don't respond. Their fear is palpable.

The driver looks back at the boss through the rearview mirror. "She doesn't speak Spanish. But I think the other one is local."

The two women don't say a word. They look desperate and hopeless.

"I don't care if they want to talk to me or not, just that they're so sweet." The driver looks at his boss and turns back to look at the other smuggler.

Sarah is very quiet, but inwardly she is talking non-stop, *God, please don't give them this power over me. If you let this happen to me, I'll deny you! You can't exist if you would let this happen. My mom prays to you so much! If I'm your child, help me! Help me, and I will be your child for the rest of my life. Don't let them use me as a toy. I will kill myself.*

They arrive at the small storefront office. Sarah is taken inside, and the departing men lock the front door.

For a time, she stands still in the dark room, wondering if the men will re-enter with the second woman, but they don't. After several minutes she begins to look around. It's a used electronics store with cell phones, computers, radios, power bars, outlet covers, and phone cases. Sarah walks around the room slowly and searching for the light switch, which she finds and turns on. She walks around searching for a window, but all she can see is a small window set reasonably high up the rear wall and covered with a grate. Beneath it sits a very out of place bed, with old faded and musty sheets.

She opens her bag to search for something but can't find it. There is a small desk behind the store's counter and on it a computer. Hoping against hope, she approaches it and taps the keyboard. The screen blinks to life, and to her amazement, there is no password protection. She attacks the keyboard, scrolling and typing, and very quickly accesses her emails. She opens a document and presses "print," not knowing if a printer is even hooked up to this computer, and if it is, where it is. She waits, not breathing. Then she hears a clicking sound and the noise of a small motor whirring to life off to her right. She runs to the sound and yanks open a small cabinet door. As soon as the page finishes printing, she snatches it, wipes the counter with both sides of it, scrunches up a corner of it, then folds it and places it in her handbag.

She fishes a small dark red lipstick tube out of her bag and steps inside a dingy, closet-sized bathroom behind the counter. Moments later, she emerges, not having applied the lipstick. She drops into the padded office chair behind the counter and breathes deeply. Then she prays, "Please, God, help me. You are my only hope. But if you don't and something happens to me today, don't judge me for taking my life. God, I believe in you, you can do anything in this world, please give me hope. Please help me. Please make this work."

Around 10:00 p.m., the sound of keys jangle in the outside lock, and the boss smuggler opens the door. He walks in and sees Sarah sitting in the chair. Locking the door behind him, he walks to the rear of the store and places some food and drink on the counter for Sarah to eat. She breathes a prayer of protection and consumes the food. The man removes his pants and sits on the bed, then motions for her to take her clothes off.

Sarah sits on the bed and addresses him in Spanish. "I'm sorry, sir, but before you do anything, I want to tell you something; then you can do anything you want."

He slaps her hard across the face and barks at her to get undressed. "I'm HIV positive, and I'm on my period!" She exclaims.

The man stops moving and looks at her as disbelief spreads across his face. He grabs her and slaps her again.

"You're a liar! You want to be smart? You don't know who I am! You don't know who you're talking too!" He slaps her defending hands and throws her off the bed to the floor. Then he stomps his foot down hard on hers and aims to do it again.

Sarah scrambles to her knees and pleads with the man. "I swear to God I'm not lying! I can show you!" She unbuttons her pants and yanks them partway down her thighs and pulls her pad partially out of her underwear. It is splotched and streaked with dark red. The man winces and looks away.

"My diagnosis letter is in my bag. From my doctor. It's right there, sir!" She gestures emphatically at the bag.

The man climbs off the bed and grabs her bag, dumping the contents on the ground. He picks up the letter and flips it open. His eyes dart back and forth over the Italian script.

Sarah still sits on the floor, waiting.

"Why did you tell me this?" He asks suspiciously.

"To save your life. I don't want to kill another human being. I can save others, even if I'm already dead."

He drops the letter to the ground and reaches to grab his pants. Sarah seizes the moment.

"I left my country because of this. Everyone pointing fingers at me, laughing at me. My life will end, but not surrounded by those people; it will end in freedom." Her emotions swell, and she can't contain the sobs that begin to pour out. The man pulls his pants on.

"There is a medication for this in the USA; you will be fine. Now, get up, and let's get you to the other location. But why did you act like you don't speak Spanish?"

"When I'm with other people, I'm shy. I don't want them to know I'm positive."

The boss considers Sarah, and something resembling appreciation crosses his face. He goes to the door and calls the driver. They come right away, and he orders them to take Sarah back to the house. "She will leave tomorrow with the rest." He says.

"What happened?" The boss tells them everything that happened and orders them to bring the Mexican girl back to him, this time in the office.

An overwhelming mix of relief for herself and horror for the young Mexican woman causes Sarah to stagger as she walks back to the car. She feels deep sorrow for the woman trapped in the office. "She's from Mexico; she could be their cousin. Oh, God, help her."

As the smuggler handles her into the car, she silently gives thanks. "Thank you, God, for saving me. I don't know how to thank you. I feel like I've been born again. Thank you!"

Sarah doesn't sleep the whole night. She sits in her little corner of the house as everyone else sleeps. She keeps looking at the door hoping the Mexican girl will come walking through. She never does. Around 4:00 a.m., the smugglers come to the house and wake them, passing them each a small yogurt cup.

By 5:00 a.m., all the immigrants from the house arrive at a river outside of Reynosa, on the American border. The smugglers have brought several large tire tubes and a rubber raft. A rope stretches across the swiftly moving river, tied to a boulder on the other side. People are placed onto the tubes and rafts and begin pulling themselves across the river using the rope. One smuggler is also on each tube, and two are in the raft. When they reach the other side, the immigrants are dropped off, and the smugglers pull the tubes back to the starting point to pick up another load.

After thirty minutes, the whole group is across. The smugglers give some quiet instructions to the group and begin moving them like a small herd across the mesa. Three of the smugglers walk ahead of the group, and three behind.

Sarah walks near the back of the group. The smuggler keeps telling everyone to run, but the movement is hard through this terrain. There is no path, only dense, prickly shrubs, spiny bushes, and stones of all sizes and shapes.

After forty-five minutes, the sound of car engines can be heard far off, and the smuggler orders the group to move faster. "Run fast! Before the Americans come! Our cars are waiting up ahead!"

Sarah struggles to run, not understanding whose car engines she's hearing. Exhausted from stress, hunger, and her sleepless night, she begins to lose ground. One of the men beside her offers to hold her bag, and she gives it to him. But even freed from that burden, she falls further and further behind.

Up ahead, the immigrants are frantically pushing into the waiting vehicles, including the man with her bag! Doors slam and one car after another speeds off in a cloud of dust.

"No! Wait!" Sarah cries out as the doors bang shut on the final vehicle. As she stumbles towards the meeting spot, the car peels out and drives away. "No! NO! NOOO! NOOO!" She falls to her knees in the dust. Three other women and a man also sit or stand panting, watching their escape disappear.

Two white border patrol jeeps pull up beside the exhausted immigrants, and officers pour out, yelling a din of orders no one understands.

Chapter Thirteen

Sarah and the four others are handcuffed, examined, and led toward the white border patrol jeeps. In faltering English, Sarah asks her guard, "Is this America?"

"Yes, ma'am, it is."

Sarah breathes a deep breath.

"Thank God." The officer glances over at the handcuffed woman and shakes his head.

Sarah tries to watch the dry terrain speed past, but there really isn't much to look at.

"Wow," she asks herself, "Is this America? Where are all the buildings I saw in the movies? Or am I still in Mexico? But the policeman told me we were in the USA. Also, I saw the American flag on their uniform. Maybe their countryside is the same as Ethiopia."

The Mexican woman next to Sarah sputters in indignation.

"Why do they cuff our hands? We didn't kill anyone; we didn't steal."

After a short but bumpy twenty-five-minute drive, they arrive at a compound and pass through three different gates. The jeeps lurch to a stop outside a large white building. The officers let the immigrants out of the vehicles and remove their cuffs.

Inside the immigration office, there are immigrants from all over the world - Latin America, Africa, Asia, Europe, and the Middle East. Sarah looks with amusement at all the ethnicities represented in the giant room.

"I thought only Africans were immigrants, but I was so wrong. Why are there European here?"

The immigrants are interviewed one by one by immigration officers. When an officer determines what language they speak, they call an interpreter to help them.

Sarah gets called up to an interview desk, and she takes her seat across from a male officer.

The desk is covered with stacks of files. He opens a file with several empty forms and begins asking questions.

"What is your full name and nationality, please? And what's your first language?" He holds a phone in his left hand and a pen in his right.

"My name is Sarah Belay. I'm Ethiopian. My first language is Amharic, but I do speak English too."

Sarah's accent is thick. The officer's eyes squint as he tries to understand her, then he dials a phone number. An interpreter walks over to them and sits down beside the officer.

When Sarah finishes her deposition, she is escorted to temporary detention. The guard opens the door and guides her in.

The room is wide and drab, with few lights in it. There are more than sixty women in the room with nothing to sit or sleep on, except a large concrete bench that runs along the wall. The floor is also concrete, the air conditioning is on, and the room feels like a deep freeze. All the women sit with their knees tucked into their chests, trying to stay warm.

Sarah absorbs everyone in the room. The cold washes over her and through her as she steps inside. She wears only jeans, a light T-shirt, and sneakers. Her jacket was in the handbag she lost in the scramble towards the escape vehicles.

After a couple of hours, the officer opens the door and brings small lunches with a ham sandwich to the detainees. Sarah peels open the bread.

"Is there pork in it?" She asks the guard.

"Yes, ma'am, there is."

Sarah can't eat pork. Most Ethiopians consider pork distasteful; it's quite ingrained in the culture. Sarah puts the sandwich aside and leans back against the cold wall. Her stomach is empty, the cold is getting into her bones, and she becomes aware of pain emitting from her knee. She tries to sleep but can't. Around midnight the pain in her knee is becoming excruciating, and she realizes she can barely move her leg.

"My leg, my leg!" Other immigrants begin knocking on the door, and the officer opens it and asks what happened. They all point towards Sarah.

"Something is wrong. She is sick."

The officer walks over to her. "What happened?"

"My leg, I do not know. It's very painful. And my stomach."

Two officers take Sarah to the nearest hospital. The temperature is much warmer in the hospital, and she falls asleep on a gurney. A doctor wakes her, and she is examined. She has a badly wrenched knee, which somehow was masked by the adrenaline until a long time after the fact. Her knee is iced and wrapped, and she is given pain killers and anti-inflammatories.

When she gets back to the detention facility, it's not long before she's shaking violently from the cold and gets sick to her stomach. Her stomach pain becomes acute, and it's not long before she's taken back to the hospital. The doctor gives her another round of pain medication, but she can't keep it down because of her weak and empty stomach. It's been forty-eight hours since she ate.

A few days later, she's in the hospital again when her knee locks up and causes incredible pain. This time she's kept overnight, fed, and given crutches.

The doctor tells her guards, "It should heal, but the cold in that room is stiffening her muscles and making things worse. She needs heat."

***

An officer walks with a paper file toward the large detention room. He opens the door and begins calling out names. As people step forward in response to their names, offices, approach them and put them in handcuffs and leg-chains. Sarah hears her name called and hobbles forward on her crutches to be processed. The detainees shuffle in a line outside to a waiting van. Two officers hold Sarah's crutches for her and help her into a van.

After one hour, they arrive at a massive prison-like building, and the guards empty the van. The detainees are marched into the building and taken to rooms where they receive full medical exams. A female doctor sees Sarah and looks over her documentation from the first detention center.

"How do you feel now, Ms. Belay?"

"I feel pain in my stomach, and my leg it hurts."

"I see that in your results, yes. Take this medication, and we'll see. If it's not getting better in the next couple of days, I'll send you back to the hospital, okay?"

"Thanks."

When Sarah finishes her medical exam, the officers fingerprint and photograph the detainees and have them change into prison uniforms. There are three different colors of uniform; blue, orange, and red. Sarah is given a blue uniform, and most of the Hispanic detainees are given orange. A few people are given red. Sarah is the only one in blue and wonders why.

The newly clad prisoners are taken to giant rooms filled with hundreds of bunk beds.

Sarah follows a female officer into a room crowded with female inmates.

Male officers escort male prisoners into their own barracks-style rooms and stand guard inside.

267

Sarah is given a lower bunk because of her leg. The barracks are equipped with bathrooms, showers, and three wall-mounted public phones. The immigrants can't leave this room except to talk to their lawyers.

Sarah heads straight to the phones and calls her first cousin, Rosa, who has been living in the US for a year. Sarah grew up with Rosa and had visited with her only a year earlier in a trip back to Ethiopia, shortly before Rosa had won a visa lottery. They are like sisters.

"Hi Rosa, this is Sarah."

"I recognize your voice, silly. How are you?"

"I'm good. I'm so sorry. I didn't tell you about coming to the USA because I knew you would say no."

"What are you talking about?"

"I'm in detention in Texas. I need a lawyer to get out of here, Rosa. I need your help."

"What? Are you out of your mind? Does Mom know this? What about Daddy? Oh, God! You're here!"

"Nobody knows except you and Zahid. Please don't tell them. They'll freak out. Just help me to get out, please? Also, I need some money because they took my money away at the other facility. They said they'd give it back when we leave, but I need money here for phone calls and some snacks."

"Send me the address and the facility's name. I'll call the lawyer right now. I'll see if she can come this week to visit you. Do you need clothes?"

"No, thanks. They gave us prison uniforms. I feel like I've committed a crime."

"Sweetheart… you have," laughs Rosa. "Don't worry about it now. I'll try everything I can."

"Thanks, sis."

***

At this facility, breakfast is served at 6:00 a.m., lunch at 12:00 p.m., and dinner at 6:00 p.m. The food is not bad. Chicken, vegetables, and water are staples, with different starches and the occasional different entrée. Sarah rarely awake in time for breakfast.

The next morning a lot of the Latin American prisoners are deported, and Sarah starts to worry. She asks a woman near her. "Why are they deporting them?"

"A lot of these people have crossed more than three or four times. Their cases are known, and they're sent back where they came from. If it's your first time, they take you to a review and figure out who you are."

"Sorry to ask, where are you from?"

"Guatemala. I've lived here for more than twenty years, built my family here, but I never had the right documents. The police caught me one day during a traffic stop. That's why I'm here."

"Oh, my God, I'm really sorry. What about your family?"

"My kids are American, they were born here, but I'm getting deported."

"What about them?"

"I'll come back soon, but they are grown. My son is twenty, and my daughter is eighteen. My husband is here still, and he is with them. Our house is even paid off."

"I'm really sorry."

Sarah hears her name called.

"Ms. Belay? Your lawyer is here."

***

Zahid and his brother take their luggage to the bus station for a visit to Sarah's family. Sarah's family lives in Bahir Dar, about eighty kilometers away.

"How many hours take to get there?" Zahid asks his brother.

"Three hours."

"Really? Back when I was here, it took six or seven."

"Yeah, but now all the roads are fixed. Ethiopia isn't how it was back in the day. Everything's changed."

"It's true, I see it, all the new buildings, new roads. And even just people's lifestyles, it's so great. I'm happy to see this."

"A lot of the younger generation are educated now, that changed things. Work opportunities are better than before."

"I wish we worked as hard to make our own country great as we work for other places. Africa has such rich resources, but we never use them. They get sucked up by other countries, and Africa is called the poor. All over the world, they say, 'Africa is starving,' and they use these ugly old images and pictures. They act like they're helping us by giving us wheat, or sugar, or some kind of loan. But then they use our resources to fill their own pockets and build their own countries."

"Exactly."

Three hours later, they arrive in Bahir Dar and disembark from the bus before it crosses the bridge over the Blue Nile. Sarah's family's home is just over the bridge, and the young men would rather walk over it than drive to enjoy the view. Then they walk along the bank, enjoying the gorgeous view of where the Blue Nile broadens into Lake Tana. You can watch the lighter, creamier water of the Nile traveling around both sides of the deeper blue water of the lake. In the middle of the Lake is a small forested island with a church.

Zahid points his finger to the Island church, "You know, Sarah's sister Meron got baptized in that church."

"It's gorgeous."

After one hour, Zahid's brother, Abdu, senses that Zahid might be stalling.

"Brother, let's go; you look like you want to stay here."

"Oh, sorry. The nature kind of captures me." He pauses. "I really miss my country."

"Then why don't you stay here?"

"Not now. But I'm sure I'll be back. One day."

They walk to catch a taxi and ride to Sarah's home. As they drive, Abdu looks at Zahid.

"Does Sarah's family know you?"

"No. I've never talked to them, but I think they know my name." He smiles. "At least they know you."

Abdu laughs, "Sarah has a good family. I met them when she came last time. She gave me a tour of the city with her brother."

"You guys had a good time. I could see it in the pictures."

"What do you think, how are they going to feel about you and Sarah?"

"I don't know for sure, but they can't be happy about it. It's normal. I can understand that."

"That's exactly what Sarah said when I asked her."

"We're both aware, but we love each other. Love is bigger than hate." He pauses as they walk. The cool winds of the Nile breeze across their faces. "After I visit Sarah's family, I'm going back to Italy as soon as possible I can't stay here anymore."

"What are you talking about? You came here for two-months; you just got here three weeks ago."

"I can't stay anymore. I'm going nuts here."

"Hey, take it easy. Relax."

"My life is so damn complicated. I came here to have a good time and relax, but it became a disaster. Nobody understands. Dad's trying to marry me to... somebody. No one understands the way I love Sarah. I love her more than my own life. I'd die for her. And I'll die without her."

Abdu processes this. Then he ventures a thought. "Do you think Sarah loves you the way you love her?"

"She loves me more! She sacrifices so much for me. She sent me to school before she went herself. She's unique; no one can love me the way she loves me. Also, she put her own dreams aside for five years to not hurt my feelings. Sarah's a very determined person, but she did that for me."

"How do you know that? Did she tell you? Females take your dreams from you; they don't leave their dreams for you. Trust me. She might tell you all this to get you to love her, but in reality, she doesn't know. I hope you're not foolish or blind."

"She never told me."

"What do you mean? You're confusing me."

271

"She never talked about her dream. She never brought it up. But one night, she was talking about it in her sleep. It sounded like she was talking to a girlfriend. 'I don't want to disappoint him. I want to be an actor. How do I leave him? You know I love him! As you said, if I go to USA, I can study acting, but it's hard to tell him.' I asked her in the morning, and she told me everything. That's why I support this trip of hers to the USA. Sarah lives for me. She's lived for me for five years. Now, I'm living for her. I love Dad; I respect him. I respect all my family and my religion..."

"Okay, then marry the girl Dad chose for you." Zahid just shakes his head in disgust.

"I love you guys, but not to the point where I'll marry someone; I don't even like to make you happy. I have the right to choose my own wife."

They arrive at Sarah's family's house. They knock on the outer gate, and a little girl playing in the yard runs over to open it for them.

"Who are you?" She asks.

Zahid looks her over.

"Are you Sarah's sister Betty?"

"Yes, come in, my mom is home." She holds the door and looks at Abdu.

"Do you know me?" Abdu asks,

"Yes, I saw you with Sarah. Is that Zahid?"

Zahid smiles and gives her a little hug. "Yes, it's me, how do you know me?"

"I saw your picture in Sarah's album." She opens the door wide and takes them into the house. "Mom is inside."

Zahid and Abdu walk inside, where Sarah's mother, Tsehay, sits on the couch drinking coffee.

"Hey," Zahid begins pleasantly but tentatively. According to custom, Zahid bends low and kisses Tsehay's knee as she sits. Then she reaches up, takes Zahid's face in her hands, and kisses both of his cheeks. Then she kisses his brother too.

"Welcome to your home country." She says.

The maid brings them superbly aromatic coffee and popcorn. Abdu looks at Zahid and whispers, "I think she knows you."

Tsehay gets up from her couch.

"How is your family, Zahid? Are they well?"

"Yes, Mom, they're well and in good health."

"And how's my beautiful child? After she lost her sister, she didn't call us like she used to. I haven't heard from her in almost a month. Is she okay?" She looks at Zahid.

"She is fine," Zahid says concisely and reaches over for the bag. "She sends this for you." He puts the bag in front of her.

"We need her, not her stuff," Tsehay fusses. "She always sends us things. We don't need things from her. We miss her. I wish she would come. Did she start school?"

"No, not yet, but she'll start soon. She's looking for the right school."

Tsehay gets up and prepares some food. The maid brings water for them to wash their hands. They wash their hands, and the maid shows them to the dining table. There are several bowls of different vegetable dishes, a plate of injera, and a small stack of dinner plates on the table. Zahid looks at the plates, then at his brother and Tsehay.

"Are you okay?" Tsehay asks.

"I never eat individually like this," Zahid says gently. "We always eat together."

"Oh, sorry. I thought you had maybe gotten used to western culture."

"Sarah doesn't allow me," he says with a smile.

Tsehay looks at him knowingly, and Zahid catches himself and blushes. The maid brings a traditional big plate, and they eat off the same plate together.

When they've finished, Zahid's phone rings.

"Hello?"

"*Amore*, it is me," Sarah speaks to him in Italian.

Zahid responds in Italian. "How are you? How's the prison treating you?"

"It's not a prison; it's detention even though I wear a uniform. When you say prison, I feel like I'm a criminal, or I did something wrong."

"You did. You've been committing a crime your entire life," he laughs. "You cross the borders illegally; you marry a Muslim; you don't do anything legally."

Sarah laughs loudly, "I absolutely did. I got you legally. You gave me permission to have your heart."

"Oh, sure *I* did, but my family didn't give you permission."

"Oh yeah? So, when did my family give you permission?" She teases.

"Well, you'll never guess where I am..."

"Somewhere on the earth, I don't know." She laughs. "Don't tell me, I'll guess. You're in Bahir Dar."

"Yes, in your family house as we speak."

"Really? Oh, wow, thanks for visiting my family! How are they? You didn't tell them I'm in detention, did you?"

"Don't worry; I didn't tell them. And I didn't even tell them who I am, but when they saw me, they already knew. Including your sister Betty."

"Did they say something bad to you? Please tell me."

"No. They've made me feel welcome."

"Oh, I'm glad to hear that. I wish I'd sent them something."

"Don't worry, Amore, I brought them a bag of gifts, but I told your mom they were from you."

"Oh, thanks so much, my love, it means a lot to me."

"They're my family too. You did the same for mine, even though you didn't tell me about it."

"Can I talk with Mom for a second?" Zahid passes the phone to Tsehay.

"It's Sarah." Tsehay leaves the brothers and walks outside with the phone. The secretiveness causes Zahid and Abdu to look at each other.

"Hey Mom, how are you? Sorry I haven't called. I've been super busy with work."

"I'm good, my baby, how about you? I was worried about you! I didn't hear from you in almost a month. You usually call twice a week."

"Mom, I'm really sorry. That is why I told you I might be busy; just pray for me. I'm good. I love you."

"Seeing Zahid makes me feel better."

"Do you know him?"

"I saw his picture in your album. I know everything." Tsehay takes a deep breath. Her forehead furrows as she shakes her head. "Thanks for sending us all this stuff, but we don't need all of this. This is too much. The only thing I want is for you to follow your dream and make me proud. Don't forget how much sacrifice you've made. I'm always proud of you. But please go to church every Sunday."

"Okay, Mom, I won't forget. Also, I didn't send anything. Zahid brought it all."

"Oh…"

"Mom, talk to me. I'm sorry. I didn't tell you he was coming. I didn't even know he would; he surprised me. But please, Mom, treat him well. I know that you're not happy with our relationship. I know I disappointed you. You don't deserve this. I'm really, really, sorry. But I love him. If you love me and care about me, please accept him. For me. He loves me so much; I don't want his feelings getting hurt."

"Don't worry, my child. Even though I'm not happy about it, I can pretend. But I never expected this from you…"

"…I'm sorry, Mom, for making you disappointed. I hope you understand me."

"Don't worry. Have a great day." Tsehay turned to head back into the house. "Do you need anything? What can I send you?"

"Thanks, Mom. No, I still have everything you sent me two months ago. I love you."

"I love you too, darling."

Tsehay passes the phone to Zahid, and he says in Italian, "I'm sorry, Amore, did your mom get mad at you?"

"Not really. But just so you know, I told her you're the one that bought the stuff."

"Okay. I miss you."

"Me too. I always talk about you with the girls I meet in detention."

"Tell me what you talk about. I want to hear it. I'd enjoy that."

Sarah tells him about a conversation with a Habesha woman she met in the detention facility. She recounts their conversation about Sarah's plans to get a green card and travel to Italy to marry her soulmate and start a family.

"You are so sweet," Zahid says. "That makes me feel good. I was in a bad mood yesterday."

"What happened, Amore? Please tell me?"

"It's a family thing. Don't worry about it; it'll be fixed soon."

"Is this about me?"

"No, my parents don't know about you. But my father wants me to marry another girl."

"Go ahead and marry her. You will be enough for both of us. Muslims marry so many wives." She laughs.

"I can't even handle you. You're crazy. I'm trying to talk to you about a serious issue, and you gotta make jokes."

"I'm trying to make you laugh. Don't worry. We'll be fine because our love is so strong."

"I miss your craziness."

"My card is running out, my love. I love you from the bottom of my heart." The phone abruptly disconnects.

After spending a couple more hours with Sarah's family, Zahid says, "We have to go, or the bus will leave without us. I wish I could stay longer, but I didn't tell my family I'm here."

Tsehay asks them to stay, but they insist. They hug Sarah's family members and walk out into the night.

***

Once again, Sarah gets transferred to a new detention facility. This place does not use uniforms, and Sarah can wear her own clothes, which Rosa happily sends. This building has a computer room, gym, an outdoor fenced yard, a school, handicraft classes, a store, and a cafeteria area where the detainees eat together. There are no barracks-style sleeping quarters—just small individual rooms for two detainees each, with bunk beds and a small closet-sized bathroom. Showers are in a shared room down the hall.

Sarah likes the new facility; it feels much freer and more civilized than the other places she's been. She spends most of her time in the computer room, handicraft classes, and at the school. She uses the computer to email her lawyer and watches films. At the craft classes, she learns how to make scarves and hats. At school, she takes ESL. Most of the immigrants spend the bulk of their time in the yard. Talking, or playing soccer, or throwing baseballs.

When Sarah sees people running outside, she gets frustrated. She's still dependent on crutches and can barely walk without them, let alone run. When she goes to the dining room for meals, other Habesha girls help hold her food as she works through the cafeteria line. The food is excellent, and they can choose what they want to eat.

Sarah shares her room with another Habesha woman, and they keep it very clean.

Sarah's lawyer visits her every week.

***

Zahid arrives in Rome, and Hammad is at the airport to help him with his bags.

"Thanks for coming. I don't know how I'm going to stay in that room without her."

"That's why I took a break to come here."

"How's the new city treating you?"

"Work-wise, it's very good, but I like Rome better."

"I love it too, but honestly, I want to leave as soon as possible. I don't want to be here without her."

"I got a job for you. Oh, sorry I forgot, how's the family? And Ethiopia? Thanks for visiting my folks."

"Everyone is fine. They say hi."

"How was it with *your* family?"

"Not good. They told me if I don't marry the girl Dad chose for me; I'll be rejected from the family."

"I told you it would be that way. Does Sarah know about this?"

"I told her, but you know her, she says 'don't worry, we'll be fine.' But she has no clue how bad the situation is." He goes on to tell Hammad about a terrible incident that may change everything.

"One morning, while I was still in bed, my mom walked into my room with a picture of Sarah and me in her hand, asking, 'who is this?' I was shocked! I didn't know how to respond because the picture says everything. I couldn't figure out where she got it from. So, Mom tells me that when Sarah visited, it fell out of her wallet when she was getting some money. It fell on the ground, but she didn't notice it, and Abdu saw it and asked her if he could keep it. He already knows about us, and I guess he made a big deal about it, so she said yes. I don't know what she was thinking. Then later, a maid found it in Abdu's pockets when she was doing laundry and gave it to my mom."

"Oh, no. So maybe that's why they want you to marry that girl?"

"You know what Mom told me?" She said, "Before I knew Sarah was your girl, I liked her. She came all the way here to visit me. But then I find out she is your girl? Did she come here as my daughter-in-law?"

"But Sarah visited my family too. She visits a lot of our friends' families because she's such a sweet girl. As well as that, when she visits them, she gives them some presents. Or money."

"She loves doing that. When she likes a person, she considers them family."

"How's she now?"

"She's in detention." Then he lowers his head. "I'm there having fun, visiting my family, and eating what I want, but she's in prison."

"She'll be fine. She's a smart one."

"There's no doubt about that. Oh, Ya Allah, I didn't tell you what she did in Mexico!"

"What?"

"Before she left here, she went to her doctor and begged him to give her paperwork for a fake HIV diagnosis. I don't know how she got him to do it, but he did. Then she scanned it and kept the image in her email."

"For what? Why does she need that?"

"No, wait, let me finish." Hammad nods and puts his hands up in mock surrender. "And she bought red food coloring and dark red lipstick, and some feminine pads." Hammad looks at him with puzzlement.

"You're confusing me, Zahid. I don't know what you are talking about; food coloring, paper, pads, blah, blah, I don't get it."

"You didn't give me a chance to explain. She has all of this in case of an emergency. In case some guy wants to rape her. So, it happened to her in Mexico. She put the lipstick and the red food color on the pad and wore it, and she printed the HIV positive paperwork and pulled it out of her purse as if she carries it around. They believed her, and it saved her life."

"What!? That's amazing! How did she even know to do that? It's unbelievable."

"It is."

***

Sarah has been in the third detention facility for two months now and has made friends from all over; Spanish, Chinese, Habesha, and European. Most people find Sarah entertaining and positive. Every morning when she wakes up, she prays before she gets out of bed.

Sarah sits on the bed and looks out of the window in her door at the rest of the complex. "Oh God, thank you for everything you've done for me. I wish I could bend my legs to bow and pray, but I'm not complaining." Then she rises from her bed unsteadily, but without her crutch.

An immigration officer walking past with a stack of papers says, "Hey Sarah, how do you feel? Your lawyer paid the bond. You're leaving tomorrow. If you have a family tell them to send you a ticket."

"Oh, that's wonderful! That's great news! Thank you! And thanks, I feel better. I'll call about the ticket!"

Sarah hobbles hurriedly to the phone station and calls Rosa.

"Hi, Rosa, thanks for everything! And thank you so much for raising the bond money. The lawyer made the payment. I leave tomorrow! Can you send me a ticket?"

"Thanks, God! I'll send it to you right now. I'll email you."

The next day Sarah gets accompanied by the detention to the nearest airport in San Antonio, documented as a landed immigrant.

Chapter Fourteen

When Sarah arrives at Washington Dulles International Airport, her first cousin, Rosa, waits with welcome balloons and roses. As Sarah walks through the arrival area looking for her cousin, she notices Habesha working throughout the facility. Rosa sees Sarah and waves her hand frantically. Sarah runs to her cousin, and for a long while, they just hold each other. Rosa hands her the flowers and the balloons.

As Rosa drives her away from the airport, Sarah says, "I feel like I'm in Ethiopia."

"Why?"

"The airport looks like it's run by Habesha."

Rosa laughs. "There are a lot of Ethiopians here. Two hundred thousand in Washington, D.C., alone."

When they arrive at Rosa's house, Sarah asks for a phone with which to call Zahid.

The next day when Rosa arrives home from work, she shows Sarah around the city and introduces her to family Ethiopian friends in different shops.

"Where can I register in a language class?" Sarah asks Rosa.

"You just got here two days ago! Don't worry; you can start after you relax for a while."

"If you have time, I want to go out tomorrow to find a school and work."

"Don't worry; you will get them. Relax first; you'll work for the rest of your life."

"I can't waste one more day. I want to study."

"That's your choice. What do you want to study?"

"First, I want to study the language. Then I'll figure the rest out."

"Okay. In this country, if you study nursing, you'll make money and find work quickly. That's why I'm studying nursing."

"I'll see when the time comes."

Rosa is adamant. "I'm telling you what's best for you. Do you still want to be an actress and go to acting school? It's a waste of time and money."

"Thanks for your advice, Rosa. Sorry, but do you have a phone card?"

"Oh, yes. I brought it yesterday, but I forgot to tell you." Rosa hands her the card. Rosa gives her a phone to use, but Sarah shows off her own new phone. Rosa is confused.

"I went for a walk while you were at work. I saw a phone store and picked this up."

Rosa interjects. "How could you go out by yourself? You should've waited until I came home, then we could've gone and bought it together."

"Oh, it's okay. I understand you're busy. I may have traveled all those roads by myself, but I don't come from the streets in Ethiopia," She laughs.

Sarah calls Zahid, and very quickly, they are talking and laughing.

"*Amore,* this is my phone number, you can call me anytime. How are you?" They talk until the card is used up, and the phone disconnects. Then she scratches the latex ink off another phone card to reveal the password and dials her mother. She hands the phone to Rosa. "Can you please talk to her first?"

"Who?"

"It's your aunt. My mom. She doesn't have a clue I'm here."

"I know, but..." The other end of the phone comes to life. "Hey, auntie, it's me, Rosa."

Tsehay and Rosa talk for a while, then Rosa passes her phone to Sarah.

"Hey, Mom." In the background, Sarah hears her sister call out, "Thanks, God! Are you free now?"

"What are you guys talking about?" Sarah's mom asks.

Sarah explains to her mother, where she has been all this time.

"Oh God, why didn't you tell me? At least I could have prayed for you! Until when do you want to hide from me? I think if you could, you would hide your death from me! But please, daughter, stop going around the world illegally."

Sarah promises her mom; this is her last road.

As the week continues, Sarah visits and enrolls in a school recommended by Rosa and finds a job at a large, local beauty salon. She attends school in the morning and goes to work in the afternoon. Sarah learned how to read and write English in school as a child, but only speaks a form of thickly accented British pidgin English. At the salon, she has difficulty understanding the accent of her African American boss, so they develop a system where he texts directions to her, and she texts back. Or there is a Habesha grocery store next to the salon, so Sarah and her boss go to the store, and the man can help them to communicate. As she continues to work around Americans, her own American accent begins to take shape.

Sarah sits in her usual place on the stairs to talk to Zahid. They talk for hours, and Zahid shares the latest developments in the situation with his family in Ethiopia. Things have gotten much more serious, and the threats from the father more sinister. Sarah is in tears, and on the other end of the call, Zahid can't help but shed tears as well.

Sarah gathers herself. "*Amore*, it's so hard to say it, but please marry that girl. I know I love you more than anything in this world, but I won't separate you from your family."

"*Amore*, please stop saying that. It hurts me. I can't."

"Do you love me?"

"What kind of question is that? You know the answer to that."

"Do it for me. Please, I've been begging you for months. You've tried everything."

"Sari, I can't imagine you as just a sister; it's unthinkable. After all, we've had and done? And shared? That's crazy! I don't even want to imagine it, so, please, stop saying that. Please, my love, don't give up on me."

"The meaning of love is living for your partner's happiness. That's what I want to do. Your happiness comes from your family. I know you don't realize that now, but trust me, one day you will regret losing them."

"I understand that, and yes, it's very hard. But how can I marry a girl I don't even know?"

"I know it's not easy. They made a promise of engagement without you attending the ceremony, without even your permission. I understand. But, *Amore*, please do it for me. What about that poor girl?"

"How on earth can I 'do this for you?' Marry someone else, for you?? Leave you for you? How can I do that? That doesn't even make any sense!"

"I don't want to feel guilty. When you marry her, you'll be close to your family, like when you were a child. Can you please at least think about it?"

"I'll... I mean, I don't..." Zahid realizes what he has to say to close this chapter of the conversation. "Okay. I'll think about it, Sarah. But I do not promise anything."

"Thanks, my love! I'll always love you; it doesn't matter. I promise to stand next to you. Even after you marry her, if you want to come here, I'll sign for you."

"*Amore*, please don't say that; you're hurting my feelings. You're the love of my life. You KNOW that."

Rosa waits at the dinner table for Sarah. Sarah finally hangs up and comes down the stairs to the dining room. Rosa hears her footsteps approaching and chides her.

"This is crazy! You two talked forever! I've been waiting for you to..."

She sees her cousin's face, and immediately Rosa's tone changes. "Oh my gosh, are you okay? Are you crying?"

Sarah can't respond, but the tears are flowing.

"Hey, I'm talking to you," Rosa jokes sensitively. "What did he say to you? Did he cheat on you?"

"I'm okay."

"Okay!? If you're okay, why are you crying? Where have you been for the past hour?"

"Let's eat our dinner, Rosa." Sarah wipes her face with the back of her hand.

***

Several months pass. Sarah has a lot of friends at her school, and on their breaks, they hang out at a nearby coffee shop. A lot of her friends are African. There are Americans at the small college where she attends, but not in her language class. Her teacher often uses Sarah as an example because she always comes to class prepared, as though she were a full-time student.

After one particularly long day at work, she gets home and walks upstairs to talk to Zahid. After her phone conversation, she comes down the stairs crying as usual. This time Rosa refuses to take no for an answer.

"You've been acting crazy. You cry every single night after you talk to him, you don't laugh, there are no jokes, you don't want to talk to me. I've waited as long as I could. I tried to stay out of your business. And now I've been asking for more than a month for you to tell me what's going on, but you don't want to tell me. If it was me acting like this, you would pester me every single day until I told you."

Sarah looks at her cousin and makes an admission, "I lied to him."

"What do you mean? What did you say to him? I don't think you understand how worried I am about you. I don't know what to do! I feel like I don't know you. You don't even take care of yourself these days. Please, Sari, tell me."

Sarah tearfully explains that she's lied to Zahid, telling him she started dating someone else. She's shared the same made-up story with some of his friends, hoping word will get back to him second-hand. She desperately wants to help him move on and marry the woman his family has chosen. She had begged him for months, but then one of his sisters contacted her and demanded, "If you love him, please leave him alone; otherwise, he'll lose his entire family because of you. You will never be welcome in our family." After that phone call, Sarah invented the story, making sure not to mention the sister's interference.

But Zahid, knowing his fiancé, doesn't believe her. She lies and swears an oath that it's true. She's been repeating this lie for a month. Finally, he believed her and relayed to his parents over the phone his willingness to accept the arranged marriage. Now, Sarah calls him every day to give him wedding planning advice and encourage him. When Zahid asks, Sarah maintains that she's strong and has moved on. She is only his sister now. But of course, all of this is a lie. Every time she hangs up after one of these calls, she's a mess.

Rosa listens to all this with amazement. She hugs Sarah. "I'm really sorry; I didn't know any of this. It's heartbreaking, and I can't imagine. But why? Why would you do this if you love him? You should try to get him back. Get him here! Do you want me to tell him the truth?"

"He's not strong enough to handle all of this. Please, I'll be fine as time goes on. I'm strong. I can handle this. I want him to live a happy life with his family. I don't want him to lose his family because of me."

"His family will be mad for a short time, but then they'll forgive him. Sarah, think positive! You're soulmates."

"God doesn't desire him for me. Both families are unhappy. It's causing so much tension. I'll wait until the right time comes to marry somebody, but I know one thing: I can't love anyone the way I love him. I might get married one day, but I'll still be in love with Zahid. My body will be with someone, but my soul will be with him. And I know for sure he'll feel the same way about me."

"But if you know that, why on earth would you..."

"Because if God was in it, it wouldn't be making so many people unhappy. It wouldn't be tearing families apart. Why God has put me in this unsolvable situation is beyond me, Rosa. Zahid was the one who changed my life, my thinking about guys. But why did he give Zahid to me and then take him back? Why am I suffering all the time?" she cries loudly.

Rosa hugs her tight and says, "Sshhh Sari, people are sleeping upstairs. They can hear you."

"I don't care anymore. I feel empty, worthless, and weak. He was the one who lifted me up. He doesn't even know what he did for me. Because of him, I found happiness again, but not anymore. I was lucky to have him."

"Why lie about your feelings for him? If you know all of this, why act like you are so strong?" Rosa takes Sarah's head in her hands gently and looks intently into her eyes. "This lying, this sacrifice, it doesn't make you a hero, Sarah. It's foolish. Do you understand? Tell the truth about yourself. How long are you going to hide this, the rest of your life? Be miserable for the rest of your life because of a lie?"

"I'll be fine one day," Sarah protests. "Even though I can't handle it now. I think I was born to struggle. I won't tell him. Sure, he would love to hear me say I love him, but it would destroy his life. His happiness with his family will make me happy. I can live for him this way, Rosa. When you light a candle, it gives you light. But to give that light, the candle has to burn. That is it; it is a sacrifice. I can be a candle for his life."

"Please, Sarah, stop crying, you're going to hurt yourself."

"Please let me relieve what's inside of me. Then I'll feel better."

***

After two years, Sarah applies to an acting school in New York and is accepted. She excitedly tells her friends, but everyone looks at her like she's crazy. They tell her it's impossible and shower her with "better" ideas, like buying a house or building a business.

"This idea is a waste of your time and money," they say.

"I have to follow my heart. I have a dream! It's why I came here."

"You're an immigrant, Sarah," One of her friends says. "And you have an accent. Your English is broken. On top of that, you're black. Don't waste your time and your money. Be smart about this. Go to school for something else. So, you can make money and do something back home."

When she relates this conversation to her other friends, they side against her as well. "Sarah, you'd better listen to her; it's true what she says." another friend says, "Don't ignore the truth. It's clear you can't see it."

In conversation after conversation, Sarah remains firm. "Thanks for your advice, guys, but it won't happen. I can't give up now. I've gotten all this way. No one can stop me, except God, but I have faith that with God's help, I'll make it happen one day, it doesn't matter how long it takes. I'm not afraid to fail. I don't care how many times I fail in my life; I know one day I'll make it with God's help. I know because I've failed over and over already, and I'm still standing."

The responses almost become formulaic or rehearsed.

"Sarah, we thought you were smart enough to understand how the world really works. But you don't. You have to follow your head," they say.

After one such conversation with friends at a coffee shop, Rosa sought to bring a logical end to the conversation, "Leave her alone. Sometimes she acts like a child. She'll realize one day." And turning to Sarah, "How are you going to move to a new city by yourself? Here you have work and a family."

"Leaving safe places has been my life for the past eight years! This isn't my first time; I'm used to it. And I'm sorry, but I'm not following my head, I'm following my heart. My heart tells me the truth. Once again, thanks for your advice, all of you, and for your time; I know you guys are saying this because you care about me. But I heard a great saying, and I've made it my own. 'Failing isn't a failure. Giving up is a failure.' The most successful people in history spent most of their lives failing before they found success. If you want to be successful, you have to be ready to fail, fail big, and fail often."

***

Sarah moves to New York City. As she takes in the city for the first time, she smiles and says to herself, "This is America!" The city is crowded, especially in Manhattan. Tall, powerful buildings, the Brooklyn Bridge, the Twin Towers, people were selling bags and jewelry on the street who seem to vanish into thin air when police officers come into view. Sarah uses Airbnb for a week until she finds a small studio apartment in Harlem.

After two weeks of looking for work, she finally gets a job in an Ethiopian restaurant in Manhattan. Four evenings a week. She goes to acting school full time during the day.

One night while she's having her dinner break at work, she receives a phone call from Rosa.

"Hey Sari, where are you?"

"I'm at work. Just finishing my break."

"Oh, sorry. Okay. We'll talk later, or tomorrow, maybe?"

"Sure, Rosa. I'll call you."

"Okay, bye!"

"Bye. Bye."

Sarah goes to wash up and begin serving again, and about ten minutes later, two more customers walk into the restaurant. They are given menus and seated by the host.

Sarah walks to them with a friendly smile and then screams so loud the whole restaurant whips around to see what's happened. The boss runs out of the backroom. The two customers are Zahid and Rosa.

Zahid stands and hugs her tightly. Tears run down Sarah's happy face. Zahid can't help but choke back tears of his own, and he holds

Sarah for dear life. Everyone looks at them. Sarah whispers through her tears.

"This is unbelievable. Am I dreaming? I don't want to wake up."

"*Amore*, you're not dreaming. It's real."

Rosa looks at them and also tears up happily. Her voice quavers as she tries to make a joke. "Wow, Sari, I don't get a hug?"

Sarah stays locked onto Zahid, totally forgetting where she is. Her boss walks up to her. "Sarah, what's going on?"

"Sorry, he is my fiancé! And she is my sister. I didn't have any idea they were coming. Can I please get off today?"

Her boss shakes his head but grants her request.

Sarah relaxes her grip just enough to pull her head back to look in Zahid's eyes.

"Oh, my God. This is a miracle. How did this happen? How did you get here? I mean, the States. You told me you were in Ethiopia for the wedding? I'm really confused."

He looks at her with a smile that threatens to erupt right off the ends of his face and pulls her in tightly to his body.

"I don't even know what I'm talking about," she gushes.

Rosa beams as she watches them.

Zahid speaks softly into Sarah's ear. "Long story short; I went to Brazil, Peru, Ecuador, Colombia, Panama, Costa Rica, Nicaragua, Honduras, Guatemala, Mexico, and then the United States of America."

"Oh, my God! How long did it take you? Are you okay? How's the road?"

"It took me more than I expected, almost eight months." He takes deep breaths. "The road it's okay. The most important thing I'm here with you." He hugs her tightly.

"Oh, my gosh." She hugs him back. "But what about the wedding?"

"I changed the destination. I brought the wedding here."

"What?" she looks at him.

"*Amore*, my darling, my love. I'm here to marry you. Rosa told me everything. I didn't go to Ethiopia. As I told you, I was on the road, and here in the detention. Rosa hired a lawyer for me, but the case took longer than expected. I was in detention for six months."

"But what about your family? Zahid!"

"Sarah, you are my family. You're my sister, my mother, my father, and my brother. You're my world. Will you marry me?"

"Oh, yes! Yes! Yes!" She buries her head in Zahid's chest and sobs. After several moments she turns to Rosa. "I don't know what to say..."

"There's no need to say anything, Sari. You love each other! You were meant to be with each other. The old traditions aren't separating you. Zahid and I have been talking about this for more than a year and a half."

"I just don't know what to say."

"How about asking us what we want to eat?" Zahid says, playfully tugging on her waitress apron. "I'm starved."

The restaurant's patrons slowly turn back to their own meals and conversations as the three sit down and order a small feast.

***

The conflicting religious traditions make a church or mosque marriage difficult, so Zahid and Sarah marry in front of a court justice the following week. Zahid gets a job at a parking lot and begins taking classes at community college. They move into a one-bedroom apartment -- their first as a couple.

Epilogue

I n a black robe and tasseled cap, Sarah approaches the microphone. The loud applause begins to diminish as she steadies herself and looks out at the commencement audience. Behind Sarah on the stage sits a line of admiring faculty members, in black robes with colorful ornamentation. Out in the audience, several rows from the front, Zahid and Rosa sitting in suit and gown, smiling encouragingly.

"First off, I want to thank God for making my dream a reality," she starts. "Second, I want to encourage you to trust yourself and never give up. Dream big, work hard and know that your successes will only be as big as your risks and your failures. Hard work always pays off." Sarah pauses, as a lump rises to her throat. She surveys the crowd. The beautiful sky. The trees around the outer rim of the college's giant lawn. The tall, powerful buildings behind the trees.

"Twelve years ago, I left my country to come here. To be here, doing this. Twelve years of work just to get to the starting line. This is the beginning of my sunrise."

THE END.

ABOUT THE AUTHOR

Elsabet Ademe was born in Ethiopia, and as a teenager, she embarked on the most dangerous journey of her life – traveling the treacherous smugglers' route toward the West. She traveled as an illegal immigrant, lived in several countries, and worked in each one to save money. She was working toward a life goal – making it to the United States to pursue a career in film. Elsabet was persistent and made that dream come true. She became a U.S. citizen, and after graduating from the New York Film Academy, Elsabet became an actor, writer, and producer with an active career in Los Angeles.

"*Behind Sunrise*" is her first book, and she hopes to continue writing. To contact Elsabet for public appearances, book signings, or interviews, contact her at Haymielsa@gmail.com.

Dear Readers:

Thank you so much for purchasing my novel. It really means a lot to me that you did. May I ask you one more favor? Please leave me an honest review on Amazon and Goodreads. I read all reviews and appreciate your feedback.

I remain sincerely,

Elsabet Ademe

BEHIND SUNRISE

Made in the USA
Middletown, DE
19 December 2020